Volcanoes: IN HISTORY, IN THEORY, IN ERUPTION

THIS BOOK IS PUBLISHED WITH THE
ASSISTANCE OF THE *Dan Danciger* PUBLICATION FUND

Volcanoes

IN HISTORY, IN THEORY, IN ERUPTION

by Fred M. Bullard

UNIVERSITY OF TEXAS PRESS

UNIVERSITY OF TEXAS PRESS
Austin 12

THOMAS NELSON AND SONS LTD
Parkside Works Edinburgh 9
36 Park Street London W1
312 Flinders Street Melbourne C1

302–304 Barclays Bank Buildings
Commissioner and Kruis Streets
Johannesburg

Thomas Nelson and Sons (Canada) Ltd
91–93 Wellington Street West Toronto 1

Société Française d'Éditions Nelson
97 rue Monge Paris 5

Library of Congress Catalog Card No. 61–10043
Copyright © 1962 by Fred M. Bullard
All rights reserved

Third Printing, 1963

Manufactured in the United States of America
by the University of Texas Printing Division

7.50

TO BESS

For encouragement and never-failing enthusiasm for
   the project,

For help on the research and in the preparation of the
   manuscript, and

For companionship on trips to volcanoes in many parts
   of the world where living conditions often were
   difficult.

ACKNOWLEDGMENTS

The material on which this book is based was assembled from studies carried on in volcanic regions in many parts of the world for more than a decade. For the opportunity to visit the various volcanic regions, for time from my regular duties to make the investigations and to do the research necessary to assemble this material, I am indebted to many organizations, foundations, and individuals. Space does not permit a complete listing but I would like to acknowledge to the following my appreciation for material aid in various phases of the work: The Geological Society of America and the Instituto de Geología of the Universidad Nacional de Mexico for aid in the study of Parícutin Volcano; the University of Texas Research Institute and the Geology Foundation of the University of Texas for research time, travel funds, and aid in the preparation of the manuscript; the U.S. State Department for two Fulbright grants which enabled me to study the volcanoes of Italy and Peru; the United Fruit Company for assistance in the work in Central America; the Compañía Minera de Guatemala (through Mr. Alan Probert, Manager) for aid in the work in Guatemala; the Instituto Tropical de Investigaciones Científicas of the

Universidad de El Salvador, and the Servicio Geológico Nacional de El Salvador for assistance in the work in El Salvador; Mr. Donald Spencer and associates of the Compañía Minera La India for help in the work in Nicaragua; and the Instituto Geográfico de Costa Rica for aid in Costa Rica. The Pan American Institute of Geography and History and the Inter-American Geodetic Survey also assisted in the work in all of the Central American countries.

I am particularly indebted to Professor Arthur Holmes, University of Edinburgh, Edinburgh, Scotland, who read the galleys and offered many constructive suggestions and helpful criticisms.

To my many friends in each of the countries where I have worked, who contributed generously of their time and provided transportation, guides, and other services, I wish to express my deep appreciation; unfortunately the list is too long to print.

All of the photographs not otherwise credited are my own. Those obtained from other sources are acknowledged in each case and I want to express my thanks to the individuals who have made such contributions.

I have drawn freely on published material both in the preparation of the text and for illustrations. In each case, however, the source is acknowledged and I wish to express my thanks for the use of this material. I am particularly grateful to the authors and publishers who have granted me permission to reproduce illustrations and to quote directly from their publications.

I wish, also, to express my thanks to the staff of the University of Texas Press for their exceptional cooperation in all aspects of the production of this book.

Finally, I wish to thank my wife, Bess Mills Bullard, for aid in every phase of the work from the preparation of the manuscript to the reading of the proof.

CONTENTS

Prologue 3

PART ONE: *Facts and Fiction about Volcanoes*

1. What Is a Volcano? 7

2. Mythology and Early Speculation on Volcanoes . 10

3. Volcanology Becomes a Science 15

4. Classification of Volcanoes 31

5. What Comes Out of a Volcano 37

6. Cones, Craters, and Calderas 70

PART TWO: *Types of Volcanic Eruptions*

7. The Peléan Type of Volcanic Eruption . . 95

8. The Vulcanian Type of Volcanic Eruption . . 128

9. The Strombolian Type of Volcanic Eruption . 191

10. The Hawaiian Type of Volcanic Eruption . . 207

11. The Icelandic Type of Volcanic Eruption . . 243

PART THREE: *Theory, Cycles, and Utilization of Volcanoes*

12. Volcanic Cycles 257

13. Birth of New Volcanoes 271

14. Man's Use of Geothermal Energy . . . 323

15. Volcanoes in Geologic Perspective . . . 366

Retrospect 404

Appendix: Geologic Time Scale 407

Glossary 409

Bibliography 415

Index 425

LIST OF PLATES

Parícutin Volcano, July, 1945 . . . . . Frontispiece

1. Dr. Thomas Jaggar 29
2. Pumice Layers in Road Cut near Antigua, Guatemala . 46
3. Crater Lake Caldera, Oregon 74
4. Caldera of Coseguina Volcano, Nicaragua 89
5. Ruins of St. Pierre after Its Destruction by a *Nuée Ardente* on May 8, 1902 111
6. *Nuée Ardente* Eruption at Mount Pelée, December 16, 1902 115
7. Lake Avernus, Phlegraean Fields, Italy 132
8. Excavations in Progress at Pompeii, Italy, in 1952 . . 145
9. Excavations at Herculaneum 151
10. Lava Flows of Mount Vesuvius . . . . facing 160
11. Mount Vesuvius and the Bay of Naples 165
12. Mount Vesuvius and the Harbor of Naples 167
13. Vulcano from Quattr'ochi on Lipari Island . . . 177
14. Obsidian Flow from Crater of Campo Bianco, Lipari Island 179
15. Crater of Vulcano with Island of Lipari in the Distance . 187
16. Stromboli Volcano 193
17. Stromboli and Sciara del Fuoco 195
18. Mauna Loa (Shield Volcano) in Profile with Kilauea Caldera in Foreground 218
19. Summit Caldera (Mokuaweoweo) of Mauna Loa . . 219
20. Detail of the Floor of Mokuaweoweo 220
21. Map of the Island of Hawaii Showing the Principal Volcanic Mountains and the General Pattern of Lava Flows 221
22. The 1940 Eruption (Curtain of Fire) within the Caldera of Mauna Loa 222
23. The 1940 Eruption of Mauna Loa from Hawaiian Volcano Observatory, Twenty-five Miles Away 223
24. Mount Etna, Sicily, from Taormina 262
25. The 1805 Eruption of Mount Vesuvius 269
26. Parícutin Volcano, Michoacán, Mexico 277
27. Parícutin Volcano, October 9, 1944 279

28. Towers of the Church above the Lava Flow from Parícutin
 Volcano, June, 1944 280
29. *Boca* of Parícutin Lava Flow of September, 1944 . . 281
30. Close View of *Boca* Shown in Plate 29 283
31. Volcán Jorullo, Mexico 295
32. Eruption of Myozin-syo Volcano 320
33. Larderello Steam Area, Italy 333
34. Condensing Towers of Chemical Plant at Larderello, Italy 334
35. Steam Well at Hveragerdi, Iceland 355
36. Natural Steam Development at The Geysers, Sonoma
 County, California, 1960 361
37. Geothermal Power Plant at The Geysers, Sonoma County,
 California 363

LIST OF FIGURES

1. Types of Volcanic Bombs 45
2. Diagrams Illustrating the Origin of "Shards" by the Explosive Disruption of Pumice 47
3. Andesite Line in Western Pacific Area 61
4. Stages in the Development of a Caldera 73
5. Restoration of Mount Mazama, Ancestral Cone of Crater
 Lake 77
6. The Caldera of Krakatoa 79
7. Stages in the History of Krakatoa 81
8. Limits of the Volcanic Ash and the Noise of the Explosions
 in the 1883 Eruption of Krakatoa 82
9. Active Volcanoes of Costa Rica and Nicaragua . . 86
10. The Lesser Antilles, West Indies 98
11. Island of Martinique, Lesser Antilles 101
12. Devastated Areas in the May 8 and the August 30, 1902,
 Eruptions of Mount Pelée 112
13. Lava Dome in the Crater of Mount Pelée, April 30, 1934 119
14. Spine of Mount Pelée with Ruins of St. Pierre . . 121
15. Spine of Mount Pelée on March 15, 1903 . . . 122
16. Area Devastated (shaded) by Eruption of May 7, 1902,
 on Island of St. Vincent 124

17. Bay of Naples and Surrounding Area 131
18A. Vesuvius Prior to the Eruption of A.D. 79
18B. Vesuvius Today 136
19. Profiles of the Crater of Vesuvius since the 1906 Eruption 166
20. Structure Section of the Bay of Naples 169
21. Depth of Magma Chamber at Vesuvius 171
22. Map Showing Location of Larderello Steam Area, Italian
    Volcanoes, and Major Structural Trends . . . 172
23. Aeolian Islands 174
24. Lipari and Vulcano, Aeolian Islands 176
25. Sequence of Eruptions at Vulcano 186
26. Relative Sizes of Vesuvius, Stromboli, and Etna . . 192
27. Crater of Stromboli on June 21, 1952 197
28. Hawaiian Archipelago 208
29. Stages in the Development of Oahu Island, Hawaii . . 210
30. Map of Hawaii, Including the Submerged Area . . 212
31. Stages in the History of a Volcanic Island in the Central
    Pacific 216
32. The 1949 Summit Eruption of Mauna Loa . . . 224
33. Map of a Portion of the Southwest Rift of Mauna Loa
    Showing the 1949 and the 1950 Lava Flows . . 227
34. Map of Kilauea Caldera (Crater) Area 230
35. Diagrammatic Illustration of the Significance of Tilt . 233
36. Map of the Southeastern Part of the Island of Hawaii,
    Showing the Lava Flows of the 1955 and the 1960
    Eruptions of Kilauea 238
37. Columbia River and Snake River Lava Plateaus . . 244
38. Icelandic Type of Eruption 245
39. Iceland and the Mid-Atlantic Ridge 246
40. Map of Iceland Showing Glaciers and Major Volcanic
    Features 248
41. Map of Mount Etna Showing Principal Lava Flows and
    Parasitic Cones 263
42. Eruptive Cycle of Mount Vesuvius 266
43. Map Showing Location of Parícutin and Jorullo Volcanoes 274
44. Lava Flow of Parícutin Volcano during First Two Years 285

45. Lava Fields of Parícutin Volcano at the End of the
    Eruption 287
46. Sketch Map of Volcán Jorullo and Subsidiary Cones . 293
47. Section of Volcán Jorullo and Malpais 300
48. The Azores 311
49. Fayal Island, Azores 312
50. Aleutian Islands, Alaska 315
51. Successive Events in the History of Bogoslof Island .   . 317
52. Map Showing Location of Myozin-syo Volcano .   .   . 321
53. Map Showing Relation of Volcanic Areas to Larderello . 331
54. *Soffioni* Areas in the Vicinity of Larderello 332
55. Map of North Island, New Zealand 341
56. Structural Trends in the New Zealand Region .   .   . 343
57. Cross Section at Wairakei Based on Exploratory Drill
    Holes 345
58. Major Structural Features of North Island, New Zealand 346
59. Map of The Geysers Area, Sonoma County, California . 359
60. Active Volcanoes of the World .   .   .   .   . facing 368
61. Spacing of the Volcanoes in the Galapagos Islands .   . 373
62. Section of the Earth Showing the Various Zones .   . 378
63. Section of Continental Area and Ocean Basin Showing
    Relationship of Sial and Sima 380
64. Distribution of Alpine-Cascade and Circum-Pacific Oro-
    genic Belts 383
65. Polar Projection Showing Ring of Mountain Chains (Oro-
    genic Belts) Bordering the Pacific Ocean .   .   . 385
66. A Simplified System of Convection Currents .   .   . 388
67. Possible Correlation between the Stages of an Orogenic
    Cycle and Those of a Hypothetical Convection-Current
    Cycle 389
68. Diagrammatic Illustration of How Convection Currents
    Build Mountains 390
69. Diagram of a Simple (single) Island Arc 394
70. Map of Indonesia Showing Gravity Anomalies .   . 397
71. Gravity Profile of Guam Island and Nero Deep .   .   . 398

Volcanoes: IN HISTORY, IN THEORY, IN ERUPTION

PROLOGUE

Volcanoes are unquestionably one of the most spectacular and awe-inspiring features of the physical world, and they have
contributed to man some of his most exquisite pleasure and some of his
most devastating misfortune. The most lofty mountains on the face of
the earth, affording majestic scenery enjoyed by millions, are volcanic
cones. On the other hand, great volcanic eruptions in historic times
have wrought death and destruction to many areas. In ancient times
volcanoes were surrounded by mystery and superstition, and even today,
notwithstanding the tremendous advances in all sciences, people still
ask many unanswered questions about volcanoes. But it is highly probable that when man has learned more about them their terrific power
may be harnessed for the benefit of mankind.

This book is an effort to summarize in nontechnical language our
present knowledge of volcanoes. Some of the important volcanoes and
volcanic regions of the earth are described as examples of the various
types of volcanoes. Volcanoes are found in those regions of the earth
where mountains are growing. But since they are but one manifestation
of active mountain-building processes, it is understandable why the
geologic setting must be presented in the description of a volcanic region.

My own interest in volcanoes began while I was a member of a
United States Geological Survey expedition to Alaska in 1929. On this

trip I first saw an active volcano and I was tremendously impressed. Only the year before I had received a Ph.D. degree in geology from the University of Michigan and had taken courses with Professor W. H. Hobbs, a distinguished scholar in the field of volcanoes, earthquakes, and mountain building. Nevertheless, when I actually saw the active volcano I realized that I knew very little about it, notwithstanding my college degrees and the fact that I had been teaching geology in a major university for several years. Voicing my thoughts to Dr. S. R. Capps, director of our party, he remarked that if I was really interested in volcanoes I should go to Hawaii and work with Dr. Thomas A. Jaggar, director of the Hawaiian Volcano Observatory and a world-famous authority on volcanoes. He further stated that he thought such a program could be arranged. It was arranged. But a severe economic depression (during the mid-thirties) intervened before I was able to go to Hawaii as an assistant to Dr. Jaggar.

Here I learned the technique of modern volcanic research and acquired some of Dr. Jaggar's enthusiasm for research on volcanoes. Back in Texas in the early forties I saw little opportunity to apply my newly acquired knowledge, except insofar as it was useful in teaching. However, on February 20, 1943, the situation suddenly changed. On that date a new volcano, Parícutin, was born in Mexico. By a fortunate combination of circumstances I was scheduled to teach a course on the volcanoes of Mexico in the 1943 summer school of the National University of Mexico. Naturally, I lost no time in visiting Parícutin and adopting it as a laboratory for my classes. Circumstances also worked out so that I spent a part of each year for the next seven years at Parícutin and was thus able to follow from personal observations almost its entire life history. Another milestone in my quest for knowledge of volcanoes was the opportunity to spend a year as a Fulbright scholar studying the classic volcanoes of the Mediterranean area. With headquarters at the University of Naples and the Vesuvian Volcano Observatory, I studied Vesuvius, Etna, Stromboli, and other volcanoes in Italy, where the science of volcanology actually developed. Later an opportunity to investigate the active volcanoes of Central and South America arose, and that work, which has been under way for several years, is still in progress.

PART ONE: *Facts and Fiction About Volcanoes*

By turns hot embers from her entrails fly,
And flakes of mountain flame that arch the
sky.   VIRGIL'S *Aeneid*

I. WHAT IS A VOLCANO?

"WHAT IS A VOLCANO?" is a familiar question. An oft-given answer is that "a volcano is a burning mountain from the top of which issue smoke and fire." Such a statement, although it does express the popular idea of a volcano, held even today, contains few elements of truth. In the first place, no "burning" in the sense of combustion, such as the burning of wood, occurs in a volcano; moreover, volcanoes are not necessarily mountains; furthermore, the activity takes place not always at the summit but more commonly on the sides or flanks; and finally the "smoke" is not smoke but condensed steam, mixed, frequently, with dust particles until it is dark in color, and the "fire" is the reflection of the red-hot material on the vapor clouds above the volcano.

The great cloud of gases, vapor, and ash particles is the most conspicuous feature of the explosive eruption of a volcano. The eruption cloud may be luminous or dark depending on whether the material is incandescent and whether it contains a small or large amount of ash particles. The "fiery" and "smoky" appearances, together with the red glow reflected from the lava in the crater beneath, are responsible for the popular idea that volcanoes are "burning mountains." Apparently supporting this fallacy, the material that falls from the eruption cloud (known to the geologist as "pyroclastics" from the Greek *pyro,* meaning "fire," plus *clastic,* meaning "broken") often resembles ash and cinders, by which names they are still known. Although there is intense heat in a volcano, actual burning plays only a minor role in volcanic activity and is confined to almost imperceptible flames from certain combustible gases such as hydrogen.

To describe what a volcano is *not* is much easier than to give a concise definition of what it *is*. A volcano is a vent or chimney which connects a reservoir of molten matter known as "magma," in the depths of the crust of the earth, with the surface of the earth. The material ejected through the vent frequently accumulates around the opening, building up a cone, called the "volcanic edifice." The loftiest mountains on earth are volcanic edifices. The material ejected consists of liquid lava and broken fragments of partially or completely solidified rock (pyroclastic debris), as well as great quantities of gases. The gases are the motivating force and the most important factor in volcanic action. Some authors have maintained that the only feature common to all volcanoes is the channel through which the molten or gaseous material reaches the surface, and therefore a volcano should be defined as "the vent through which this material is erupted." This, however, leaves us in the difficult position of trying to explain that Vesuvius is not really a volcano but merely a mountain built around one! As now used, the term *volcano* includes both the vent and the accumulation (cone) around it.

Volcanic eruptions vary between two extremes. In one the lava rises more or less quietly to the surface and overflows the lip of the crater.

The gases bubble through the lava and escape undramatically, or, in some instances, rush out with sufficient force to form lava fountains hundreds of feet in height. Nevertheless, the lava is not disrupted but flows away as a river of lava, with little resulting damage except to objects in the path of its flow. On the other extreme, tremendous explosions occur in the chimney, and as the lava rises into zones of less pressure it "froths," because of admixture with the rapidly expanding gases, and is ejected in the form of ash and pumice (pyroclastics). Thus in these volcanoes the magma never reaches the surface as a liquid (lava) but is disrupted and ejected as pyroclastic material (ash). It was this type of material that buried Pompeii in the classic eruption of Vesuvius in A.D. 79. The explosions are sometimes so severe as to disrupt the cone, frequently blowing away large sections of it, spreading the debris over the countryside. Needless to say, such volcanoes cause extensive property damage as well as loss of life. The essential difference in the two types is the gas content and the manner in which the gas is released when the magma reaches the surface. This is largely a function of the composition of the magma, which is discussed in Chapter 5.

The great majority of the volcanoes of the world are intermediate between the two extremes described, yielding both lavas and fragmental products.

Since it is not possible to examine the magma reservoir which feeds a volcano, our information must be obtained by studying the material ejected from the reservoir. The material, as already indicated, consists of three kinds of products: liquid (lava), fragmental (pyroclastics), and gaseous. A special problem is encountered in studying the gases, both in collecting them under hazardous—and in many instances near-impossible—conditions and also in ascertaining that the gases collected are true volcanic gases and are not contaminated with atmospheric gases.

*Science moves, but slowly, creeping on
from point to point.*   TENNYSON

2. MYTHOLOGY AND EARLY SPECULATION ON VOLCANOES

PERHAPS NO OTHER PHENOMENON of the physical world has been surrounded by as much mystery and as little truth as have volcanoes. Indeed, in ancient times volcanoes were regarded with suspicion and awe, and it would have been considered wicked and dangerous to attempt to investigate them. We are told by the poet Virgil that Mount Etna in Sicily, one of the large active volcanoes of the world, is the spot where the gods in their anger buried the giant Enceladus, and that the frequent earthquakes which shake the mountain are the struggles of the giant to free himself. Under such circumstances it would have been rash indeed for mere humans to meddle in the affairs of the gods.

Classic Myths

Some of the world's most active volcanoes are near the centers of ancient civilization in the Mediterranean region, Mount Etna in Sicily and Vesuvius on the shore of the Bay of Naples. Thus it is not strange that classic literature contains many references to volcanoes, and that many myths and legends are associated with them. This wealth of folk-lore is an important source of information on the activity of volcanoes in ancient times.

In Greek mythology Hephaestus is the god of fire, and the name, meaning "burning," "shining," or "flaming," probably originally referred to the brilliance of lightning. In Roman mythology Vulcan, one of the three children of Jupiter and Juno, was god of fire, especially terrestrial fire, volcanic eruptions, and the glow of the hearth and forge. Vulcan was the blacksmith of the gods. His forge at Olympus was equipped with anvils and all the implements of the trade. Vulcan made the arrows for Apollo and Diana, the shield of Achilles, and the invincible breast-plate of Hercules. He was toolmaker to the gods, utilizing the power of his forge for their welfare. His wife, according to the *Odyssey*, was Venus.

Poets have identified Vulcan's workshop with various active volcanoes in the belief that the smoking mountain was the chimney of Vulcan's forge. The explosions in the eruption of a volcano were believed to be Vulcan pounding on his anvil, while the fire and smoke came from the forge. It was here that Vulcan made the thunderbolts which Jove threw about so recklessly. Most frequently in ancient writings Vulcan's forge was located on the island of Vulcano,[1] one of the Lipari or Aeolian Islands in the Tyrrhenian Sea, off the coast of Sicily. In fact, the name *volcano* is derived from the Latin name *Vulcanus* or *Volcanus*, applied to the island in ancient times because it was believed to be the location of the forge of Vulcan. From this association, the name *volcano* has been applied to all mountains which give off "smoke and fire" throughout the world.

[1] A description of Vulcano is given in Chapter 8.

Primitive Myths

Since many of the primitive peoples of the earth were fire-worshipers it would seem reasonable that volcanoes, as a source of fire, might be a part of their mythology. In support of this idea is the fact that the earliest pyramids in Mexico, such as Cuicuilco in Mexico City, are round and similar in shape to a volcanic cone. That the people were familiar with volcanoes is obvious, since this particular pyramid was partially buried by a lava flow about the beginning of the Christian era. The lava flow, known as the "Pedregal," covers a large area in the southern part of Mexico City. Later pyramids are the conventional four-sided structures. Nevertheless, Frazer (1930) indicates that few myths allude to volcanoes as a source of fire. An exception is the Polynesian myths, which do ascribe fire to volcanoes. The Tongan people tell of the hero Maui, who "stole fire in the nether world" and ran out of a passage and set the bushes on fire, since which time all people have had fire. A Samoan version relates that one of their ancestors struggled with the god Mafuie, and, after breaking off one of the god's hands, permitted him to go free in exchange for fire, which Mafuie had concealed in a vertical rock. The superstition today is that Mafuie is somewhere below Samoa, occasionally shaking the island with his one good hand; and the Samoans thank their gods that he has only one good hand, for with two hands he would surely shake their island into ruins.

Fire Deities

In contrast to the Polynesians who regarded volcanoes as a source of beneficial fire, the Romans thought of their god of fire, Vulcan, as a spirit of destructive fire. During the reign of Romulus a temple to Vulcan was erected in Rome, and a festival called Vulcanalia was held on August 23 of each year, the ceremony consisting of a sacrifice to Vulcan for the purpose of averting all mishaps that might arise from the use of fire or light. The Aztecs of Mexico, like the Polynesians, had a fire god, but he was a benign god who kept the home warm, cooked the meals, and in other ways benefited man. He was not, in their mythology, connected with volcanoes.

The legend of Pele, fire goddess of Hawaiian volcanoes, has many variations, as well as adherents, even today. The most common account relates how "Madam" Pele (so called by the natives in a mixture of respect and familiarity) in search of a home, visited first one island and then another looking for a suitable abode. Koko Head and Koko Crater, prominent landmarks at the eastern end of the island of Oahu, are evidences of Pele's last visit to Oahu. Pele built these craters while trying to find a home on Oahu. Finally coming to Kilauea, active crater on the island of Hawaii, she found a place to her liking and made this her home. In every case, the beginning of an eruption of the volcano is preceded by the appearance of Madam Pele and many residents of the Big Island will testify that they have seen her in the form of an old woman just before an eruption! In most accounts Madam Pele is described as a revengeful goddess, taking care of her friends and destroying her enemies.

Influence of Volcanoes

Volcanic eruptions have exerted a marked influence upon all peoples who live in a region frequented by disastrous eruptions. For example, in Japan divine interference has often been sought to prevent eruptions or to stop an eruption. Some Japanese practice a form of worship of mountain deities which may have had its origin through the fear created by volcanic eruptions. The famous volcano of Japan, Fujiyama ("never-dying mountain"), is sacred to many of the Japanese, and fifty thousand inhabitants make pilgrimages to its crater each year. Not infrequently the Japanese commit suicide by leaping into the crater, believing that therein they will find eternal rest.

Volcanology among the Ancients

A very indistinct line separates the mythologies of the early Greeks and Romans and their more scientific ideas concerning volcanoes. Although the Greeks were among the first to formulate explanations of the various physical features of the earth, including volcanoes, it should be recalled that they did not employ deductive reasoning, that is, the collection of the facts followed by the development of an explanation to interpret the facts. It was centuries later, in fact not until the time of Charles

Darwin, only about one hundred years ago, that this type of reasoning came into general use.

Despite shrewd guesses of Plato, Aristotle, and Strabo, and observations of Pliny the Younger, none of the early Greeks or Romans had any real concept of the true nature of volcanic activity. Aristotle (384–322 B.C.), following Plato (427–347 B.C.), refers vaguely to "pent-up" winds imprisoned in subterranean channels as being the cause of earthquakes and also of such winds' striking fire from seams of sulphur and coal as being the cause of volcanoes. Strabo (63 B.C.–A.D. 21), a learned geographer of his time, in allusion to the tradition that Sicily had been separated from Italy by a convulsion, remarked that at present the land near the sea was rarely shaken by earthquakes since there were "now open orifices whereby fire, and ignited matter, and water escape," but formerly, when the volcanoes Etna, the Lipari Islands, Ischia, and others had been closed up, the imprisoned fire and wind might have produced more violent movements. Thus, while holding to the old Aristotelian idea of "pent-up" winds, Strabo seems to infer that volcanoes act as safety valves, a somewhat modern concept.

Shakespeare (1564–1616), reflecting the general idea of his time, has Hotspur reply to Glendower in *Henry IV* as follows:

> Diseased nature often times breaks forth
> In strange eruptions; oft the teeming earth
> Is with a kind of colic pinched and vex'd
> By the imprisoning of unruly winds
> Within her womb: which for enlargement striving
> Shakes the old bedlam earth, and topples down
> Steeples and moss-grown towers.

Volcanoes, first regarded with superstition and fear, sometimes even as the abode of the gods, finally became the subject of scientific inquiry. Then investigators learned to identify the causes producing volcanoes. This knowledge made possible speculations on the prediction and control of volcanic eruptions and the development of ways and means of harnessing volcanic energy for the benefit of mankind.

Advance in science comes by laying brick
upon brick, not by sudden erection of fairy
palaces.   J. S. Huxley

3. VOLCANOLOGY BECOMES A SCIENCE

Since volcanology is intimately connected with geology, it seems impossible to separate the two in tracing
the development of knowledge in this field. As early as
the Middle Ages thinkers, such as Dante, recorded their
speculations on the origin of the earth, and the ancients
possessed considerable knowledge of minerals and
metal-mining. But it was not until the Italian Renaissance that geologic inquiry on modern lines was begun.

Early Geologic Inquiry

Such practical engineers as Leonardo da Vinci (1452–
1519) recognized the true meaning of sea shells found

in the rocks, and the interpretation of these fossils soon came into conflict with theology. Later, when all fossils were considered relics of the flood of Noah's time, the study of geology was pursued mainly for its bearing on the Mosaic account of the Creation. As a result, the early attempts at geology, such as Bishop Burnett's *Sacred History of the Earth* (1681–1689), since they were concerned with the creation of the world were cosmogonies. About one hundred years later methods of geologic inquiry developed facts which were inconsistent with the Mosaic account of the Creation, and a bitter controversy between geology and theology then developed. Geology deals with the earth as a whole, whereas up to this time the interest had been in the origin of the earth rather than in the later stages of its history. These thinkers were, therefore, cosmogonists rather than geologists. We have not, even to this day, developed an entirely satisfactory theory of the origin of the earth; yet geology has continued to progress. But as the modern cosmogonist, Harlow Shapley, has warned:

. . . we should remember that the hardest problems of cosmogony would not necessarily be disposed of even if we should get a satisfactory theory of the origin of the earth. For we would ask at once concerning the origin of the sun and galaxies and eventually be driven back to deeper puzzles of the origin of matter, origin of space, of time, and of origins. Planetary genesis is therefore only a decoy, leading to universal processes.

The Beginnings of Volcanology

Volcanology may be defined as that branch of science which deals with the eruption of magma (molten material plus its gaseous content) upon the surface of the earth or its rise into levels near the surface. It is closely related to geology and in fact may well be considered a phase of geology, but it is also intimately related to seismology, geochemistry, and geophysics. Like all other sciences, its limits are difficult to define, since all sciences are interrelated.

The beginnings of modern volcanology, that is, an objective account of volcanic phenomena divorced from superstition and mythology, was the description of the eruption of Vesuvius in A.D. 79 by Pliny the Younger. It was in this eruption that his uncle, Pliny the Elder, lost his life. The description of the eruption was contained in two letters to the

Roman historian, Tacitus, at the latter's request, giving the details regarding his uncle's death. Pliny's letters are full of accurate observations and may well be regarded as the earliest contributions to the science of volcanology. These letters and a description of the A.D. 79 eruption of Vesuvius are given in a later chapter.

For the next seventeen hundred years, or during the Dark Ages and well into the Renaissance, scientific subjects were completely neglected. The first noteworthy contribution after this period was a work entitled *Observations on Mt. Vesuvius, Mt. Etna, and Other Volcanoes,* by Sir William Hamilton, English ambassador to the Court of Naples, which was published in 1774. Hamilton was an enthusiastic student of volcanoes, and his firsthand accounts of the eruptions of the volcanoes of Italy still provide a valuable source of information.

The Italian naturalist, Lazzaro Spallanzani (1729–1799), was one of the first to apply experimental methods to volcanic rocks. He attempted to find out whether gases would escape when lava was melted and to determine the composition of these gases. His results were not conclusive, but he was obviously on the right track. Spallanzani is best known for descriptions of his travels through the volcanic regions of Italy, which far surpass in scientific accuracy and completeness all previous contributions of a similar nature.

At about the same time the French geologist, Gratet de Dolomieu (1750–1809), showed how much could be learned regarding volcanic actions by a study of the material ejected. Instead of confining his study, as his predecessors had done, to the volcanic cone and to the eruptive action, Dolomieu studied the products of eruption—the lavas and fragmental ejecta—and compared these with other rocks. He arrived at the correct conclusion that there is a complete series of transition stages between the coarsely crystalline lavas and the glassy obsidians. Dolomieu confirmed the igneous origin of basalt and recognized the similarity between the lava stream of Mount Etna and some of the so-called traprocks[1] of southern France, thus confirming their volcanic origin. Dolomieu also called attention to the unusual composition of some of the limestones in the Alps, which he showed contained a high percentage

[1] A general name for dark, fine-grained igneous rocks, particularly lavas or dikes.

of magnesium carbonate in addition to the usual calcium carbonate. Today such rock is known as "dolomite." The name *Dolomieu* is also perpetuated in the name "Dolomites" given to the beautiful Tyrol section of the Alps of northern Italy.

The Neptunist-Plutonist Controversy

Unfortunately, at about this time the progress of volcanology, as well as geology in general, was delayed certainly for two or three decades, because of the dispute which arose between the so-called Neptunists and the Plutonists, or Vulcanists. The Neptunists, led by the renowned teacher, Abraham Gottlob Werner, advocated the theory of deposition of all rocks, including lava and granite, from a universal ocean, and for this reason they were termed Neptunists.

Werner had a profound influence on geology. In 1775 he was named professor of mineralogy at the Freiberg School of Mines in Saxony. Mining had long been taught in France, Germany, and Hungary, and mineralogy was recognized as an important branch of mining. Werner, however, did not limit his attention to the composition and character of minerals but considered also the grouping of the rocks, their geographical position, and other relations, all of which he termed "geognosy." When Werner pointed out the application of these topics to mining, they were quickly regarded as an essential part of a professional education. In his lectures he treated all aspects of minerals, including their influence on rocks, the soil, and even the language and migration of tribes of people, which he held has been determined by the direction of specific strata. His charm of manner and his eloquence attracted many students and inspired many to become ardent disciples. The school at Freiberg soon became famous, and many came from distant countries to study under the great master.

Werner had not traveled far, and he had explored only a small portion of Germany, but he was able to convince his students that the whole surface of the earth, and all the mountain chains, were made after the model of his own small area. It became a passion with his students to travel to distant parts of the globe to discover his "universal formations," which he taught had been precipitated over the entire earth from a "chaotic fluid." The basalts of Saxony, to which his observations were confined, consisted of tabular masses capping hills and were not connected with the existing valleys, as is the case in many regions of recent volcanic activity. Strange as it may seem to us today, Werner held that basalt and all other related rocks, wherever found, were precipitated from water.

As early as 1768, before Werner began his mineralogical studies, the true igneous nature of basalt had been established by several workers. Notable among them was the Italian scholar Arduino (1759), who in a study of the rocks of the region around Padua and Verona in northern Italy, divided the rocks into primary, secondary, and tertiary groups, and recognized the resemblance of numerous varieties of basalt, interbedded with the rocks, to present-day lavas of Italian volcanoes.

One of the most careful studies was made by Desmarest in the Auvergne district of southern France. He showed that the most recent craters are still intact and that their streams of lava conform in level to the present rivers. He observed that in others the craters are nearly destroyed, and that the lavas from these are less closely associated with the present stream levels. He also noted that some volcanic rocks, still more ancient, without any visible craters, resemble in all details the rocks of Saxony, which had been attributed by Werner to precipitation from a universal ocean. Nevertheless, the dogma as expounded by Werner was accepted, and the advocates of the igneous origin of basalt were subjected to ridicule.

Hutton and Uniformitarianism

James Hutton of Edinburgh, Scotland, a contemporary of Werner, was to have a leading role in the development of geology. Hutton was educated as a physician, but instead of practicing his profession, he was content with a small inheritance from his father and gave his full time to scientific pursuits. He made frequent trips through England and Scotland and acquired considerable competence as a mineralogist, constantly striving to understand the broader concepts of geology. He finally published his observations in the *Transactions* of the Royal Society of Edinburgh in 1788 under the title, "Theory of the Earth." In 1795 a more elaborate work was published. Hutton was the first to maintain that geology was not primarily concerned with "the origin of things." He explained the former changes of the earth's crust as due to natural processes and refuted the idea that they were the result of great cataclysms, as was the prevailing view at the time:

The ruins of an older world are visible in the present structure of our planet; and the strata which now compose our continents have been once beneath the sea and were formed out of the waste of pre-existing continents. The same forces are still destroying, by chemical decomposition or mechanical violence, even the hardest rocks and transporting the materials to the sea, where they are spread out and form strata analogous to those of more ancient date. Although loosely deposited along the bottom of the ocean, they become afterwards altered and consolidated by volcanic heat and then heaved up, fractured, and contorted.

This concept of Hutton's, for which he is perhaps best known, has come down to us today as the "doctrine of uniformitarianism," or the uniformity of present processes in producing changes in the surface of the earth. The processes assumed in this theory required an immensity of time for the destruction of whole mountain ranges, and when one range was found resting on another, and another, Hutton (1788, p. 216) could find "no trace of a beginning" into such a remote past. Such a statement, made at a time when the date of the Creation was placed at about 4000 b.c., was sensational.

Although Hutton had never visited a region of active volcanoes, he convinced himself that basalt and other similar rocks were of igneous origin and that some of them had been injected in a molten state into fissures in older strata. The absence of stratification in granite and its similarity of mineral character to that of rocks which he considered igneous led Hutton to conclude that granite was formed by solidification from a molten state. He could not fully confirm this theory unless he could find a contact of granite with other strata to see if there was any evidence of alteration by heat at the boundary, such as was common in the case of the traprocks with which he was familiar. In 1785 he resolved to test his theory. In Perthshire (Scotland) there is a large granite mass, and Hutton surveyed the contact between the granite and the overlying strata until finally at Glen Tilt he found clear proof of his theory. Here he found not only the adjacent limestone profoundly altered but veins of red granite branching from the main mass and traversing the limestone. On finding verification of his theory in this exposure he was filled with so much delight that the guides who accompanied him, says his biographer, were convinced that he must have discovered a vein of gold or silver (Playfair's works, [1822] Vol. 4, p. 75). Hutton was the leader of the Plutonists (or Vulcanists), who maintained that many rocks (even some of those now known to be of sedimentary origin) had cooled from a molten state and were either poured out as lavas on the surface of the earth through volcanoes, or had solidified in great masses below the surface, such as granites.

The Neptunists used some arguments which were very plausible from the mineralogical standpoint against the theory of the origin of granite from a molten state. They held, of course, that all rocks, including granite, were deposits from a universal ocean. Granite is composed essentially of three common minerals: quartz, feldspar, and mica. It is obvious from the relationship of the crystals of these minerals in a granite that quartz was the last to crystallize, and since it has the highest melting point it would be expected to crystallize first; therefore, they reasoned, granite could not have cooled from a molten state. It was many years later before it was discovered that the constituents of the granite magma form a complex solution in which the components are mutually dissolved and that the order of crystallization is governed by solubility rather than fusibility. This means that the most soluble constituents, such as quartz, crystallize last, while the least soluble crystallize first. The Plutonists were as much in error in assigning to all rocks an igneous origin as the Neptunists were wrong in contending that all rocks were precipitated from water.

A New Tool for Geologists

No discussion of the development of geology, however cursory, can omit the contribution of William Smith, popularly known as "Strata" Smith. An English surveyor by trade who collected fossils from the areas in which he worked, he soon came to realize that he always found the same kinds of fossils associated with the same types of rocks. This led him to conclude that he could identify the "formation" by the fossils. In 1815 he completed a map of the whole of England, based on his new-found tool, the fossil content of the various formations. The publication of his paper entitled *Strata Identified by Organized Fossils* in 1816 is one of the most important accomplishments in the development of geology. With this new tool the geologists were now ready to arrange the rocks of the earth's crust in the order in which they were deposited, even in widely separated areas, and to interpret the sequence of events of which they are the record. When geologic events could be assigned a time sequence geology had become a historical science, an earth history.

Lyell and Modern Geology

The development of geology is the result of the efforts of many individuals, but one man stands out so prominently that he may well be considered the "founder of modern geology." This man is Charles Lyell, later knighted by the Queen of England for his work in this field. Lyell was able to appreciate that many great forces had been at work in modifying the crust of the earth. He was not beset with the narrow provincialism of many of his predecessors and contemporaries who applied to the whole world the processes at work in their own regions, neglecting or even denying the effectiveness of forces which were either dormant or had never been active in their regions. Thus Lyell, while a strong advocate of the Huttonian doctrine of uniformitarianism, was fully aware of the importance of cataclysms, such as volcanic eruptions and earthquakes, as earth processes. Lyell accomplished the monumental task of formulating an explanation of geologic processes. His *Principles of Geology,* published in 1830, was the first textbook on the subject and marked the beginning of modern geology.

The Controversy over Volcanic Craters

Another controversy which effectively delayed the development of geology was the dispute between the adherents of the craters-of-elevation theory and the craters-of-accumulation theory. Leopold von Buch, one of Werner's disciples, was the leading advocate of the craters-of-elevation theory, which held that volcanic cones are caused by molten material rising from below and arching the crust of the earth into a great blister or dome. They denied that the cone is formed by the cumulative fall of material ejected by the volcano.

The craters-of-elevation theory

Leopold von Buch (1774–1853) entered the Academy at Freiberg when he was sixteen years of age. He stayed three years, living with Werner most of the time. A man of independent means, von Buch traveled widely, always seeking to confirm Werner's teachings. However, he received a rude shock when he witnessed in Italy a volcanic eruption. He observed the streams of lava, the rocks hurled into the air by explosive eruptions, and the ash spread for miles around the vent. He noted the conical shape of the volcanic peak, and reasoned—incorrectly —that it could not be due to outpouring of lava, because the streams of lava were not continuous over its surface. Since many of the volcanic cones rise from the sea, he further reasoned that such a cone could not be formed from a vent on the sea floor, because the lava would immediately solidify on coming in contact with the sea water.

When von Buch reached the Auvergne district in southern France and studied the Puy de Dome and realized that here was a smooth dome-shaped mountain with no crater, he conceived his craters-of-elevation theory. He reasoned that if the intruded mass retained its form, a mountain of the Puy de Dome type would result, but if the blister burst at the summit the collapse and infalling material would form a crater such as is typical of many volcanoes. He did not realize that the Puy de Dome is a lava plug which formed in the crater of the volcano in its last stage of activity, and that the surrounding cone has since been removed by erosion. Plugs of this type, known as "tholoids," are common throughout the world. Tholoids are now growing at Santa María (Santiaguito) Volcano, Guatemala, Mount Pelée in the Lesser Antilles, and in several of the volcanoes of Japan, notably Tarumai and Usu volcanoes.[2] In later

---

[2] The development of a tholoid is described in Chapter 7 on Mount Pelée.

years, von Buch, with great regret, relinquished the Neptunian teachings of his great master and from the accumulating evidence adopted the views of the Plutonists.

Another of Werner's students, who was to exert a profound influence, was Alexander von Humboldt. He entered the Freiberg School of Mines two years later than von Buch, and he, too, lived with Werner. He and von Buch were lifelong friends. Like von Buch, he traveled widely, devoting his life to the physical sciences. His travels took him to Central and South America, Russia, and Siberia, as well as over Europe. His life's work culminated in the publication of *The Cosmos* (1841–1858), a work aimed at presenting the whole world of nature. His main contributions were the study of volcanoes and earthquakes, and, like von Buch, he in time came to accept the truth of the Plutonists.

The crater-accumulation theory

The crater-accumulation theory, supported by Lyell, Hutton, and others, is of course, the modern concept that the volcanic edifice is a result of the accumulation of ejected debris. It should be acknowledged that modern volcanology recognizes that a certain amount of swelling (or uplift of the crust) of the earth precedes the eruption of a volcano; tilt meters and other instruments have been developed to measure the swelling. Yet this feature is far different from that envisaged by the proponents of the crater-elevation theory. In the early editions of Lyell's *Principles of Geology* many pages of the section on volcanoes are devoted to citing evidence to disprove the crater-elevation theory.

Finally even the disciples of Werner were convinced that lava was molten rock which had risen to the suface from beneath the crust of the earth. Then was developed a theory that volcanoes were vents which connected the surface of the earth with a still molten interior. This was the first explanation to be offered by modern science, and it was readily accepted for nearly a hundred years, being in vogue as recently as the beginning of the twentieth century. However, as the study of earthquakes progressed, it was found that earthquake waves are transmitted freely through the greater part of the earth, and since some of these waves do not travel through a liquid, it followed that no considerable portion of the earth could be liquid. Accordingly, new explanations were required in order to conform with the newly discovered facts. These new explanations are in fact a description of currently held concepts.[3]

Beginnings of Modern Volcanology

The earliest attempt at a systematic and all-inclusive treatise on volcanoes was that by G. Paulett Scrope, entitled, *Considerations on Volcanoes*, published in 1825. This work is dedicated to Lyell and was undertaken "in order to help dispel that signal delusion as to the mode of action of subtelluric forces with which the crater-elevation theory has mystified the geological world." Scrope was the first (1825) to suggest that decreased atmospheric pressure accompanying stormy weather may be responsible for an increase in volcanic activity. The activity of Stromboli Volcano, in the Tyrrhenian Sea off the coast of Sicily, has long been used by the local inhabitants as a "weatherglass" to forecast the weather. Lyell was "dubious" of the connection, but the idea has adherents even today.

A contemporary of Scrope was Charles Daubeny, who in 1827 published a volume on *A Description of Active and Extinct Volcanoes, of Earthquakes and Thermal Springs*. Dr. Daubeny was trained in chemistry, and he advocated a "chemical theory of volcanic action." The second edition of his treatise, an eight-hundred-page volume published in 1848, gave information on most of the volcanic regions of the earth.

John W. Judd, a professor in the Royal School of Mines in London and an ardent student of volcanoes, made extensive studies in southern Europe, especially in the Lipari Islands in the Tyrrhenian Sea. His book on *Volcanoes: What They Are and What They Teach*, published in 1881, is a complete manual on the general characteristics of volcanoes, presenting many individual volcanoes in descriptions based on personal observations. It is really a continuation of Scrope's work, since the latter's woodcuts were turned over to Judd, and many are included in his book.

An English physician who was also an enthusiastic student of volcanoes, Dr. Tempest Anderson, contributed many valuable observations during the last quarter of the nineteenth century. His major con-

[3] They are presented in the chapters which follow.

tribution, *Volcanic Studies in Many Lands,* published in 1903, is still a storehouse of information. In the preface of the above work, Dr. Anderson says:

Very few branches of science still remain available for the amateur of limited leisure. Electricity, chemistry, bacteriology, most branches of geology and mineralogy have all led to results of highest economic value, and they are cultivated by a large body of professional men subsidized by colleges or by the government. They are in a position to give their whole time to their work, and their results are so voluminous that to keep abreast of the literature of any single branch would occupy more than the entire leisure of most men, yet this is a necessary preliminary to any attempt at original work. I was consequently led to seek some branch of science which gave no prospect of pecuniary return, and I determined on volcanology, which had the additional advantage of offering exercise in the open air and in districts often remote and picturesque.

Dr. Anderson says further "that for the last 18 years [this was in 1903] I spent the greater part of my holidays in exploring volcanic regions."

Twentieth-Century American Volcanologists

To trace adequately the development of volcanology in the twentieth century alone would require a volume. Two men in the United States, however, stand out so significantly that it seems necessary to acquaint the reader with them here. They are Frank A. Perret and Thomas A. Jaggar, who are important not only because of their actual contributions but also because of the inspiration they have afforded to other workers.

Perret

Frank A Perret, trained in physics and chemistry, became interested in volcanology during a visit to Italy in 1903 for his health. There he became acquainted with Professor Matteucci, director of the Vesuvian Volcano Observatory, who inspired in him an intense interest in volcanoes. He was given an honorary appointment to the Observatory staff as assistant to Professor Matteucci and was a witness to the great Vesuvian eruption of 1906. Perret was an expert photographer, and his training in physics and electrical engineering provided an excellent scientific background for his studies. During the next twenty years he made Naples his home and was a constant student of Vesuvius, but he also extended his studies to volcanic eruptions in other parts of the world—to Stromboli in the Lipari Islands, to Etna in Sicily, to Tenerife in the Canary Islands, to Kilauea in Hawaii, and to Sakurashima in Japan.

In 1930 Perret established an observatory at Mount Pelée on the island of Martinique in the Lesser Antilles (West Indies). This volcano had become world famous because of the eruption of 1902, in which the entire population of the city of St. Pierre, something over thirty thousand, were killed. A renewal of eruptive activity at Mount Pelée in 1929 convinced Perret that an observatory was needed. He maintained the observatory, which was supported largely from private gifts, until his death on January 12, 1943.

Jaggar

Thomas A. Jaggar, educated at Harvard University, and in Germany, taught geology at Harvard from 1895 to 1906 and also worked for the U.S. Geological Survey in the Black Hills and the Yellowstone regions. In 1906 he was appointed head of the Department of Geology at Massachusetts Institute of Technology, a position which he held until 1912, when he went to Hawaii to establish and direct the Hawaiian Volcano Observatory. He was one of the geologists sent in 1902 to study the results of the catastrophic eruption of Mount Pelée in the West Indies. It was this experience which guided him into volcanology as a lifetime career.

Dr. Jaggar traveled widely in his quest for knowledge of volcanoes. He visited Italy in 1906 to study the eruption of Vesuvius; in 1907 he led an expedition to the Aleutian Islands; in 1909 he visited the volcanic areas of Japan; and in 1910 he was sent to Costa Rica to study the effects of the great Cartago earthquake. Later his travels took him back to Alaska and Japan, to New Zealand, and to many of the Pacific islands.

In 1909 the trustees of the Whitney Estate gave Massachusetts Institute of Technology $25,000 to be used for research in geophysics and seismology, with a view to protecting human life and property. It was decided to use these funds to establish a laboratory at Kilauea Crater,

Hawaii. The first problem selected for study was measurement of the temperature of the lava lake, and for this work special resistance thermometers were designed by Dr. A. L. Day and Dr. E. S. Shepard of the Geophysical Laboratory of the Carnegie Institution of Washington. Dr. Shepard and Dr. Jaggar were to make the measurements in the summer of 1911, but since Dr. Jaggar could not leave his work at the Massachusetts Institute of Technology at that time it was arranged for Dr. Frank Perret to accompany Dr. Shepard.

The people of Hawaii were eager to have the laboratory at Kilauea Crater become a permanent observatory, and through Dr. Jaggar's efforts funds were subscribed to provide for its operating expenses. In 1912 Dr. Jaggar gave up his professorship at Massachusetts Institute of Technology and became the director of the Hawaiian Volcano Observatory, a position he filled until he retired in 1940. The first few years were trying times in the operation of the Observatory. Everything was new— new instruments had to be designed and built, new methods worked out, and the entire program organized. Funds were never adequate, and at times the outlook was most discouraging. However, Dr. Jaggar persisted, and in 1919 the U.S. government assumed the responsibility for the operation of the Observatory, an arrangement which continues today. In the expansion of the work at the Observatory no phase of the activity of Kilauea or Mauna Loa was neglected if means could be found to include it in the program.

Dr. Jaggar was a pioneer in volcanology, and many of his methods and techniques have become standard the world over. Aside from his great contribution to the science of volcanology, he will be long remembered for his ideas on the protection of harbors and cities from lava flows. He was the first to employ aerial bombing as a means of deflecting or stopping a lava flow.[4] He also developed detailed plans for protecting the harbor of Hilo, Hawaii, from lava flows by a system of barriers or dikes. He was an ardent advocate of the idea that many volcanic eruptions were the result of steam-blast explosions, an idea he developed during his study of the 1924 eruption of Kilauea in Hawaii. He believed that the steam explosions resulted from ground water entering the zone of highly heated rocks as the magma column receded, an idea

[4] A description of this significant experiment is given in Chapter 5.

PLATE 1. Dr. Thomas A. Jaggar.
Photo by author, 1939.

that is now generally accepted, although there is some difference of opinion as to the immediate source of the ground water. One of his last major contributions was a special report on "Steam Blast Volcanic Eruptions" (Jaggar, 1949) in which he presented convincing evidence that many volcanic eruptions throughout the world were steam-blast explosions. After retiring as director of the Hawaiian Volcano Observatory at the age of seventy, Dr. Jaggar became research associate in geophysics at the University of Hawaii, and in this capacity continued his work on volcanoes until his death on January 17, 1953.

Modern European Volcanologists

Several European workers made outstanding contributions during the early part of the twentieth century. Professor G. Mercalli's book, *I Vulcani attivi della Terra* (1907), is a survey of the volcanoes of the world. Mercalli was Director of the Vesuvian Volcano Observatory at Naples, Italy, for many years, and he made many important contributions to volcanology from his studies of Vesuvius. Two German workers, Dr. Karl Sapper and Dr. F. von Wolff, stand out prominently. Sapper spent many years in the study of Central American volcanoes, and his work in that region is the basis, even today, for all future studies. His most important book, *Vulkankunde* (1927) is still in use. Von Wolff, in a series of publications entitled *Der Vulkanismus* (1914–1931) describes the various volcanic areas of the world.

More recent works in the field of vocanology are mentioned throughout the text. These publications are included in the bibliography.

From superstition and myth, through early objective descriptions of actual volcanic phenomena, finally to scientific attempts to understand the nature of volcanoes, volcanologists have traveled a long road and are now arrived at a point where significant knowledge indicates significant goals for man's future attainment—points further along the route to complete understanding of volcanoes and of what they can mean to the welfare of humanity.

*The purpose of classification is not to set
forth final and indisputable truths but
rather to afford stepping stones towards
better understanding.*

L. C. GRATON

4. CLASSIFICATION OF VOLCANOES

CLASSIFICATION, in a scientific sense, is the systematic
arrangement of all the representatives of a group, such
as plants, animals, or volcanoes, based on natural relationships. It is an effort to simplify a complex subject
by grouping together those elements which have similar characteristics. In the case of volcanoes a classification based on the type of eruption would be useful.
Although many attempts have been made to classify
volcanoes, no entirely satisfactory scheme has yet been
devised. A review of the classifications which have been
proposed will acquaint the reader with the problems involved in the classification of volcanoes.

Nineteenth-Century Classifications

The earliest systematic treatise on volcanology was Scrope's *Considerations on Volcanoes,* published in 1825. In this work Scrope made a distinction between (1) permanent, (2) moderate, and (3) paroxysmal eruptions. The permanent type included those in which the eruptions were of a more quiet and regular nature, such as Stromboli; while the paroxysmal eruptions were violent and irregular, such as those exhibited at times by Vesuvius. Moderate eruptions were those similar to paroxysmal eruptions except less violent. This general distinction was adopted by French geologists, and the terms "Strombolian stage" and "Vesuvian stage" were used to describe the state of activity of a volcano.

Late in the nineteenth century volcanoes were commonly classified as (1) explosive, (2) intermediate, and (3) quiet. The explosive type, such as Krakatoa, ejects almost entirely fragmental material, which accumulates around the vent, forming a cone with steep slopes. In the quiet type, such as the Hawaiian volcanoes, the material is chiefly lava, which rises to the surface without disruptive explosions and accumulates in huge, flat domes. The great majority of volcanic eruptions belong to the intermediate type. They begin with strong explosions accompanied by abundant fragmental material, followed by the outpouring of lava, thus displaying the characteristics of both the explosive and the quiet types. To this intermediate type the name strata-volcano is often applied, since the cone consists of layers of ash alternating with lava flows. This classification, although useful, is too general; its inadequacy makes necessary further divisions for a correct grouping of the various types of volcanic eruptions. Furthermore, the choice of at least one of its terms, *quiet,* seems misleading as applied to volcanoes. With all its disadvantages, however, this classification has been widely used and is still found in some texts.

Lacroix's Classification

Professor A. Stoppanni in 1900 made an effort to devise a classification of volcanoes which would be more exact yet still based on the type of eruption. He used as type names in a general classification of volcanoes the names of Italian volcanoes which display different types of eruptions, such as Ischia, Stromboli, and Solfatara. A few years later, Professor Mercalli (1907) modified and amplified Stoppanni's classification but retained the general plan. Meanwhile, the French geologist, Professor A. Lacroix (1908), who had made extensive studies at Mount Pelée following the tragic eruption in 1902, proposed a classification which, making use of terms introduced by others, recognized four types of eruptions: (1) Hawaiian, (2) Strombolian, (3) Vulcanian, and (4) Peléan. Lacroix's classification was adopted by Sapper (1927) and was later used (Sapper, 1931, pp. 1–34) in the National Research Council volume on volcanology. It was then widely introduced into many of the textbooks of geology. It will be of interest, at this point, to review Lacroix's types.

Hawaiian type

This type, represented by the volcanoes of the Hawaiian Islands, has abundant outpourings of basaltic lava in which the gases are liberated more or less quietly. Explosive eruptions are rare, but fountains of lava, projected by jets of escaping gas, may play at heights up to 1,000 feet or more. The product is basic lava with only minor amounts of cinders and ash. The outpourings of lava develop flat lava domes, forming, as in the case of Mauna Loa,[1] some of the largest mountains on earth.

Strombolian type

This term, introduced by the Italians in the early part of the twentieth century to indicate an eruptive type, had been used by the French to designate a type of activity at least fifty years earlier. Stromboli,[2] a volcano in the Aeolian Islands off the coast of Sicily in the Tyrrhenian sea, is in a constant state of activity and since ancient times has been known as the "Lighthouse of the Mediterranean." The eruptions of Stromboli consist of more or less regular explosions of moderate intensity which throw out pasty, incandescent lava (scoria), accompanied by a white vapor cloud. The lava in the crater crusts over lightly, and at intervals of about one-half hour the pent-up gases escape with mild ex-

---

[1] Mauna Loa is described in some detail in Chapter 10.
[2] Stromboli is described in some detail in Chapter 9.

plosions, hurling out clots of lava and fragments of the crust. Many of the fragments fall back into the crater to be blown out again, but others fall on the slope of the cone and roll into the sea.

Vulcanian type

This term, first used by Mercalli (1891), is named from the Island of Vulcano, near Lipari in the Aeolian group north of Sicily. The lava from Vulcano[3] is more pasty and viscous than Strombolian lava, and it forms a thick, solid crust over the crater between the infrequent eruptions. Gases accumulate beneath the congealed crust, and in time the upper part of the magma column becomes thoroughly gas-saturated. Finally, with strong explosions, sometimes sufficient to partially disrupt the cone, the obstructions are blown out; and the broken fragments of the crater plug, together with some new lava in the form of "breadcrust bombs" and scoria, are ejected. Such eruptions are accompanied by a great "cauliflower-shaped" eruption cloud containing an abundance of ash. When the plug is suddenly blown out, the gas-saturated magma is disrupted into pumice and ash by the explosively expanding gases. After the clearing of the obstruction, lava flows may issue either from the crater or from fissures on the sides of the cone. Indeed, the initial explosion may split the cone from top to bottom, and lava flows may issue along these fractures.

In view of the fact that Vulcano has been inactive for the past seventy years, the latest eruption having occurred in 1889–1890, it is more appropriate to use Vesuvius as the example of the Vulcanian type of eruption. Stoppanni (1900) applied the term *Plinian* (a name which had already been in use for some time) to describe an eruption of extreme violence, such as the A.D. 79 eruption of Vesuvius. The name is from Pliny, who described the A.D. 79 eruption of Vesuvius in letters to the Roman historian, Tacitus (Chapter 3). Pliny described the eruption cloud as resembling the Italian stone pine tree. It was shot upward as a column by the tremendous force of the explosion and then, on reaching the height of its course, began to spread out. The Italian word *pino* ("pine") has been adopted by volcanologists to describe explosions of unusual vigor which develop eruption clouds similar in shape to that

[3] Vulcano is described in Chapter 8.

described by Pliny. It seems useful to retain the term *Plinian* to designate a phase of the most violent Vulcanian eruptions in which pino clouds are developed. Most eruptions where obstructed vents must be cleared begin with Vulcanian characteristics.

Peléan type

This is the only new term introduced by Lacroix, all the other terms in his classification having been used previously by other writers. It is derived from Mount Pelée, on the Island of Martinique in the West Indies, which erupted in 1902, destroying the City of St. Pierre with the loss of more than 30,000 lives. The Peléan type produces magma of the highest viscosity and is characterized by extreme explosiveness. The distinguishing feature of the Peléan eruption is the *nuée ardente,* or "glowing cloud." It is a highly heated gas so charged with incandescent ash particles that it resembles a mobile emulsion, yet dense enough to maintain contact with the surface as it rushes down the slopes of the mountain with hurricane force. It was such a cloud that overwhelmed St. Pierre and resulted in the destruction of everything and everyone in its path. In Peléan eruptions the upward escape is frequently blocked by a plug of lava in the crater and the explosions break out as horizontal blasts from beneath the plug. The magma is expelled as a highly ash-charged gas, and no lava issues except that pushed up as a viscous plug in the crater. The characteristics of this type are described in connection with the 1902 eruption of Mount Pelée.[4]

Although Lacroix's classification has some apparent defects, as was early recognized, it is widely used and has become firmly entrenched in the literature of geology. The real difficulty, which is inherent in any classification of this kind, is that any one volcano selected as a "type" has various kinds of eruptions, so that to designate a volcano as "Strombolian" is misleading when the activity at Stromboli is variable in type. Recently Rittmann (1944) has recommended, as De Fiore did nearly fifty years ago, that a new nomenclature of descriptive terms be adopted to replace Lacroix's terms based on specific volcanoes. It does not seem desirable to abandon Lacroix's classification at this time, but some modifications are introduced in this work.

[4] Described in Chapter 7.

Additional Categories

In order to make Lacroix's classification more complete one new type is added, the Icelandic; and a "stage," the Solfataric, is recognized. Both of these terms have been in use for many years and inclusion of them in the classification makes possible a more comprehensive view of volcanic activity.

Icelandic type

In this type great volumes of lava issue from fissures, often many miles in length, and spread in sheets over the adjacent countryside. The basaltic lava is quite fluid and able to flow for long distances, building up great lava plateaus consisting of hundreds of superimposed flows covering thousands of square miles. The Columbia River lava plateau, covering parts of Washington, Oregon, and Idaho, is an example of areas formed by such eruptions. The composition of the lavas in the Icelandic and the Hawaiian types is similar, but the Icelandic lavas, unlike the Hawaiian type, in which the lavas form great domelike masses, cover large areas with relatively flat-lying beds.

Historic eruptions of the Icelandic type are known only in Iceland, the most famous being the Laki Fissure eruption[5] in 1781.

Solfataric stage

This term is applied to the final phase of a volcanic eruption, in which only gases are given off. The name is from the Volcano Solfatara (Italian for "sulphur") in the Phlegraean Fields near Naples, Italy. Since its latest eruption in 1198 it has emitted only gases. A volcano may remain in the Solfataric stage for many hundreds of years after its activity has ended.

The Lacroix classification of volcanoes, as modified, is the basis for the grouping of the volcanic eruptions described in Part Two. The identification of a volcanic eruption with one of Lacroix's types, even though the classification is not entirely consistent, will enable the reader to anticipate the kind of material to be ejected as well as the general character of the eruption.

[5] The Laki Fissure eruption is described in Chapter 11.

Volcanism everywhere has unity; gas is the prime mover. T. A. JAGGAR

Gas is the active agent and the magma is its vehicle. F. A. PERRET

5. WHAT COMES OUT OF A VOLCANO

Volcanic Gases

Water vapor

IT HAS LONG BEEN RECOGNIZED that gas is the primary force in producing volcanic explosions. When water changes its state from a liquid to a solid (i.e., to ice) a slight expansion, equal to about one-ninth of its volume, occurs, but when water changes to the gaseous state the volume increases instantly one thousand times! Here is the force necessary to produce a volcanic eruption. It was early recognized that the chief gas given off in a volcanic eruption was water vapor, or steam; so Scrope, Lyell, and others developed the concept that the arching (folding) of the earth's crust caused a sufficient release of pressure to permit the water in the magma to vaporize and cause an explosive eruption.

Although this is essentially the current idea, the debate as to the source of the water in the magma is still vigorously pursued. Lyell (1875, p. 226) explained the concentration of volcanoes around the ocean margin on the assumption that the sea was the source of the water. Daubeny (1827, p. 368) depended on the percolation of sea water into the deep interior, where reaction with the alkaline metals provided the heat for the "chemical theories." Others relied on meteoric (rain) water as the chief source, pointing out that while volcanoes are concentrated on the margins of the continents, they are frequently fifty to a hundred miles from the coast and the percolation of sea water to depth beneath such volcanoes was highly improbable.

In the last century the proponents of seepage water, either sea water or meteoric water, have lost ground, and evidence is accumulating in favor of the theory that the water is an original constituent of the magma, that is, "juvenile" water in geologic terminology. It would appear that this problem might be resolved by simply collecting and analyzing gases from an active volcano. However, the collecting of gases from an active volcano involves some serious problems in securing the collector's safety and in protecting the samples from contamination by atmospheric gases. Early in the twentieth century several workers showed that when recent lavas were heated in a vacuum the gases given off were similar to those obtained at volcanic vents, and it was correctly concluded that the juvenile gases were entrapped in the lava at the time of solidification. This opened up an unexpected and fruitful method of studying volcanic gases.

In 1911 Dr. A. Brun of Geneva advanced a startling theory in which he maintained that water vapor is not an abundant constituent in volcanic gases. He cited as evidence the facts that the white clouds emanating from a volcano do not dissipate in the air, as is true for steam, but drift in a streamer for many miles; that rainbows and other optical effects are absent; and finally that volcanic ash falling from such a cloud is quite dry. According to Brun, the clouds of vapor accompanying volcanic eruptions consist mainly of volatilized chlorides mixed with dust from the explosions.

Study of composition of gases

This theory by a reputable scientist, challenging the long-accepted idea, proved a great stimulus to the study of volcanic gases in an effort to refute it. As is often the case, an incorrect theory does much to advance the science because it inspires other workers to pursue the subject with zeal in order to prove the theory wrong and thus to uncover entirely new evidence. The obvious way to test Brun's theory was by direct observation of gases being emitted by active volcanoes, and it was not long before such results were forthcoming.

Two capable scientists, Dr. Arthur L. Day and Dr. E. S. Shepard, both of the Geophysical Laboratory of the Carnegie Institution of Washington, were able to collect primary volcanic (juvenile) gases at Kilauea Crater in Hawaii in 1912. Kilauea Crater, at that time, had a permanent lake of molten lava, which provided an ideal laboratory for the study. Furthermore, the Hawaiian Volcano Observatory was at that time just being established and the long-time director, Dr. T. A. Jaggar, was to repeat the experiment many times in later years and confirm the results. The problem, of course, was to collect the gases directly from the molten lake of lava without introducing atmospheric gases. Descending to the floor of the crater, equipped with gas masks, Day and Shepard (1913) were able to thrust an iron pipe into the large gas bubbles which developed over active gas vents in the lava pool and to conduct these gases to their collecting chambers. In the course of one collection it was noticed that air coming in near the base of the bubble behaved like an air blast in a furnace, causing the gases collected at the top of the bubble to be partially burned (i.e., oxidized). Hence free hydrogen had combined with atmospheric oxygen to form water, and in a like manner sulphur had oxidized to sulphur dioxide, carbon monoxide to carbon dioxide, etc. The interaction of these gases with the air and with each other provided an effective source of heat which actually brought the surface layers of the lava in the pool to a higher temperature than it had reached at some depth below the surface. This interesting topic is developed in a following section on the temperature of lavas.

Of twenty-four samples collected by Day and Shepard, steam averaged 68.2 percent by volume. Next in abundance were carbon dioxide, nitrogen, and sulphur gases, with smaller amounts of carbon monoxide, hydrogen, and chlorine. The nitrogen contained argon to the extent of 3 percent, whereas the percentage of argon in air is about 5½ percent. If, as is probable, these gases are due to atmospheric contamination, some of the nitrogen must have been used up in the "magmatic" furnace to form ammonia and other nitrogen-bearing compounds. Only small amounts of fluorine were noted.

The proof that granitic magmas can contain water in solution was furnished by Goranson (1931) in a series of notable experiments on artificial silicate melts. These experimental studies, which unfortunately were limited to granitic rocks, are of the utmost importance in the study of volcanism as well as other aspects of geology. Geologic studies have shown that most granitic magmas have crystallized at depths of from 4,000 to 12,000 feet and a temperature not exceeding 870° C. Under such conditions of depth and temperature Goranson showed that a granitic magma was capable of holding from 6 percent to 9 percent of water in solution. Further experiments by Goranson (1936) using water systems containing albite or orthoclase, the most abundant minerals in granitic rocks, provided information on the tremendous pressures developed in a magma chamber by the "boiling off" of the water due to crystallization. The albite-water system at 1,100° C. and a pressure of 606 bars[1] (equal to 2.25 km. in depth) can hold up to 4.2 percent of water. When the system cooled albite began to crystallize at 960° C. and when the temperature had dropped to 819° C. more than half of the albite had crystallized, leaving a liquid that contained 9.5 percent of water, and the pressure had increased to 3,000 bars. Continued crystallization must raise the pressure from 5,000 to 6,000 bars, and here, Goranson writes, "is a mechanism for developing all the pressure a volcanologist may desire."

The composition of the gases varies considerably from one volcanic region to another, although a high percentage of water is present in all cases. The so-called oceanic volcanoes, such as the Hawaiian volcanoes, are low in chlorine and relatively high in sulphur, while the continental volcanoes (those situated on the continent) show higher chlorine and

[1] A *bar* is the pressure of one atmosphere (14.7 pounds per square inch) and is equal to about twelve feet of rock load.

lower sulphur. Fluorine was brought forcibly to the attention of the author, when, during close observation of active fumaroles at Parícutin Volcano, Mexico, a camera lens was etched by hydrofluoric acid gas condensing on it.

At most volcanic vents the gases react with the lava on the walls surrounding the gas vents to form deposits of brightly colored sublimates. The most common is sulphur, of sufficient importance to provide commercial deposits in some regions, with yellow ferrous chloride and white ammonium chloride being also common. Many of the metallic oxides, such as iron, lead, zinc, tin, etc., also have been identified in volcanic sublimates. Although these have never been found in sufficient quantity to be of commercial importance, they do provide important clues to the way in which metals are transported through the rocks of the earth's crust and eventually concentrated in ore deposits.

Volume

The total volume of gases evolved during an eruption of a volcano is stupendous. Alfano and Friedlander (1928) calculated the volume of gas in the 1906 eruption of Vesuvius from the size of the conduit and the velocity of emission, and "it appears that not only the volume but also the weight of the gases must be many times greater than the total mass of ash and lava."

Geologic significance

A growing mass of evidence indicates that the earth's atmosphere and the waters of the ocean may have been derived from volcanic or plutonic gases throughout geologic time rather than from a dense, primitive atmosphere which was believed to have enveloped the earth. Rubey (1951) in a study of the geologic history of the sea, points out that the more volatile materials, such as H_2O (water), CO_2 (carbon dioxide), Cl (chlorine), N (nitrogen), and S (sulphur), are much too abundant in our present atmosphere, hydrosphere (ocean), and in ancient sediments to be accounted for as the products of rock weathering alone. From a consideration of geologic evidence he also rules out the possibility of these "excess" volatiles being residual from a primitive atmosphere. He points out that the relative abundance of the different "excess" volatiles is similar to the relative amounts of the same materials in gases escaping from volcanoes, fumaroles, and hot springs and in gases occluded in igneous rocks. It is possible, therefore, that the atmosphere and the waters of the oceans may have come almost entirely from plutonic gases. Volcanic eruptions and lava flows have brought large quantities of these gases to the surface throughout the geologic past. However, Rubey believes that intrusive magmas are probably a more adequate source of the constituents of the atmosphere and hydrosphere and that hot springs may have been the principal channels by which the "excess" volatiles reached the surface. Igneous rocks now contain about 1 percent of water. On the assumption that the original magma contained 4 percent of water, this would mean that the magmas have given off 3 percent of water during crystallization. On this basis Rubey concludes that the crystallization of a shell of igneous rocks forty kilometers thick would be sufficient to account for all of the water in the oceans.

Hot springs

The presence of a preponderance of water in volcanic gases might naturally lead one to infer that "magmatic" springs should occur in regions of recent igneous activity or recent vulcanism. Perhaps the surprising thing is the rarity of such features, but the fact that they do exist is in itself of great interest. Yellowstone National Park, with its many hot springs and geysers, immediately comes to mind as an outstanding example. The problem is to prove that the water issuing as a boiling spring or a geyser and heated by a magma still buried below the surface is not simply surface (meteoric) water which has become heated by contact with the cooling magma. The proof in such cases lies in the unusual constituents which are derived from a magma in contrast to the usual constituents found in normal springs.

In springs of meteoric origin the principal constituents are those of the surrounding sediments through which the water has percolated. These commonly include calcium-magnesium carbonates from limestones and dolomites, calcium sulphate from gypsum-bearing beds, sodium sulphate from some types of shales, hydrogen sulphide from the reduction of sulphates by organic matter, and carbon dioxide from

reactions between calcium carbonate and other compounds. Occasionally, sodium chloride and related compounds are derived from saline
formations, or from original sea water (connate water) which was
entrapped in the sediments.

Hot springs in regions of recent volcanic activity carry a high percentage of sodium carbonate and considerable quantities of sodium chloride.
Silica is frequently an abundant constituent of these waters. Outstanding examples are the great geyser areas of Yellowstone, Iceland, and
New Zealand, where extensive deposits of siliceous sinter (geyserite)
are being formed. Springs in volcanic regions also frequently contain
boron, fluorine, nitrogen, and carbon dioxide in notable amounts, as
well as traces of arsenic, antimony, quicksilver, cobalt, copper, nickel,
and other elements. Studies at Vesuvius, Etna, and elsewhere indicate
that carbon dioxide is usually associated with the declining stage of
volcanic activity. The possibility that it may continue to be emitted long
after volcanic activity has ceased and even after erosion has destroyed
the cone is suggested by the exhalations of carbon dioxide encountered
in the famous gold mines at Cripple Creek, Colorado, located in the core
of a Tertiary volcano (Daly, 1933, p. 510).

It is obvious that the distinction between magmatic and meteoric
springs is not clear-cut. This is especially true where magmatic water
passes through a thick layer of rock formations in reaching the surface
with resulting modification of its composition. In many cases water of
magmatic origin mixes with ground water and the two issue together.
In a study of the hot springs and geysers in Yellowstone, Fenner (1936)
concluded that from 10 to 15 percent of the water was of magmatic
origin, the remainder being meteoric water. Other examples of magmatic springs include Karlsbad, Czechoslovakia, Ems and Weisbaden,
Germany, and Steamboat Springs, Nevada. Magmatic water in the
form of natural steam is now being utilized as a source of electric power
and chemicals. Italy has been the leader in this development[2], but New
Zealand, California, and other areas are now operating such projects

[2] This topic is discussed in some detail in Chapter 14.

Volcanic Solids

Pyroclastic material

The ejection of solid fragments (projectiles) is one of the most spectacular phases of a volcanic eruption. The writer was privileged to watch at close range the eruption of Parícutin Volcano, Mexico, during its most active period. At night the spectacle was awesome. With each explosion literally thousands of red-hot fragments were blown to a height of several thousand feet above the crater rim and then, showering the cone like a giant skyrocket, they left a trail of fire as they cascaded down the sides. So abundant were these red-hot fragments that frequently the entire cone was covered with interlacing fiery trails. The fragments of solid material ejected by a volcano range in size from huge blocks of the crustal layers, which are blown out in the initial break-through of the vent, to fine dustlike particles which are so light that they may drift completely around the earth several times. The accumulation of this debris around the vent, together with any lava which may be poured out, builds the volcanic cone. All the fragmental material ejected by a volcano is described as "pyroclastic" (pyro "fire" + clastic "broken") material.

Classification of pyroclastics

A simple classification of pyroclastic material, based on size and shape, is useful. The larger fragments, consisting of pieces of the crustal layers beneath the volcano or of older lavas broken from the walls of the conduit or from the surface of the crater, are called "blocks." Volcanic "bombs" are masses of new lava blown from the crater and solidified during flight, becoming rounded or spindle-shaped as they are hurled through the air. In size they range from small pellets up to huge masses weighing many tons. Sometimes they are still plastic when they strike the surface and are flattened or distorted as they roll down the side of the cone. Occasionally one may strike a tree and be molded around a limb. I observed a splendid example of such a tree-limb-molded bomb at Parícutin Volcano, Mexico, during the early stage of its activity. Thinking it would make an excellent museum specimen, I returned to camp to get a saw, in order to collect it undisturbed. However, when

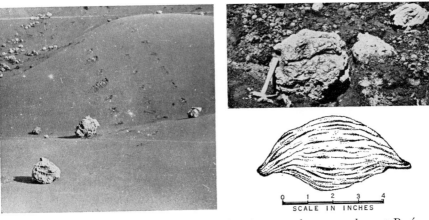

SCALE IN INCHES

FIGURE 1. Types of Volcanic bombs. The photographs were taken at Parí-cutin Volcano, Mexico. Note the impact trails of the bombs in the photo-graph on the left.

I returned some tourist had already broken off the limb as a souvenir! Another type, known as a "bread-crust bomb," resembles a loaf of French bread with large gaping cracks in the crust. This cracking of the crust results from the continued expansion of the internal gases. In contrast to bombs, smaller broken fragments are lapilli (from Italian meaning "little stones"), about the size of walnuts, then in decreasing size, cinders, ash, and dust. Frequently no distinction is made between ash and dust, but cinders are sand-size particles, intermediate in size between lapilli and ash. Originally the terms *cinders* and *ash* were applied because the material resembled the cinders and ashes from grates of the fires in the home, and since volcanoes were then believed to be due to the burning of underground coal seams, the names seemed appropriate. The cinders and ash are, of course, pulverized lava, broken up by the force of the rapidly expanding gases contained in it or by the grinding together of the fragments in the crater, like a huge mill, as they are repeatedly blown out and fall back into the crater after each explosion.

Pumice is a type of pyroclastic produced by acidic lavas in which the gas content is so great as to cause the magma to "froth" as it rises in the chimney of the volcano and, with approach to the surface, into zones of decreasing pressure. When the explosion occurs the rock froth

PLATE 2. Pumice layers in road cut near Antigua, Guatemala. Each layer represents an eruption. Note earlier topography (sloping surface in lower right) buried by pumice from later eruptions.

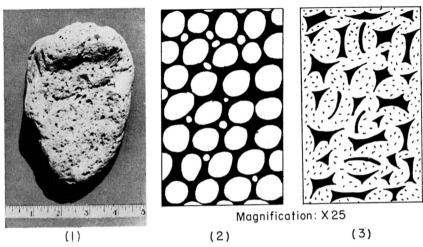

Magnification: X 25

(1)   (2)   (3)

FIGURE 2. Diagrams illustrating the origin of "shards" by the explosive disruption of pumice. In diagram (2) the open cavities (gas vesicles) are shown in cross section. The "shards" (3) are fragments of the walls of the gas vesicules.

is expelled as pumice. Much of the material is shattered into dust-size particles, but pieces varying from the size of marbles up to a foot or more in diameter are abundant. Pumice will float in water because of the many air spaces formed by the expanding gases. It should be remembered that this material is as truly magma as any lava flow, but because of its high gas content, it is expelled as pumice and ash rather than as a liquid. The debris which buried Pompeii in A.D. 79 was pumice from the eruption of Vesuvius. It was nearly one thousand years later before any liquid lava issued from Vesuvius. Volcanoes which eject chiefly pumice are the most highly explosive volcanoes known. The volcanoes of Central America, in general, eject chiefly pumiceous material which, over the ages, has blanketed most of the country to a thickness of hundreds or even thousands of feet (Pl. 2). Volcanic eruptions on the floor of the sea often discharge huge quantities of pumice. It was reported that in 1878 masses of floating pumice covered the sea in the vicinity of the Solomon Islands to such an extent that it took ships three days to force their way through it. Other times the pumice may drift with the currents and accumulate in such quantity in favorable bays that one can walk on the floating raft of pumice, unable to tell the exact position of the shoreline. Pieces of pumice can be found on most of the beaches of the world, having drifted throughout all the oceans. ·

Volcanic ash results when the rapidly expanding gases (explosions) shatter the rock froth. The fragments consist of sharply angular glass particles, which under the microscope are easily identified by their "shard" structure (Fig. 2). Such material is widely used as a scouring powder, just as it is found, as in Old Dutch Cleanser, or mixed with soap powder to form the "new improved foaming" type.

Lava fountains in which steam jets blow the lava into the air sometimes produce a material resembling spun glass, known as "Pele's Hair," after the Hawaiian goddess of volcanoes. Pele's Hair is identical with varieties of "rock wool" which are manufactured by blowing a jet of steam into a stream of molten rock. Rock wool is widely used for all types of insulation.

The coarse angular fragments (blocks) which fill the crater of a volcano become cemented to form a rock known as "volcanic breccia." Indeed the presence of such material is frequently the only evidence to show the location of the actual throat of the volcano after erosion has completely destroyed the cone. The finer material, such as cinders and ash, forms thick deposits, even many miles removed from the volcano. Such material becomes consolidated through the percolation of ground water and is know as "tuff." The common building stone in the volcanic regions of Italy is tuff. Soft enough to be easily quarried and shaped by hand, it has sufficient strength to be set into walls with mortar. The outer surface, as well as the inner, is plastered to keep water out of the porous material. In Italy the tuff which is removed in digging a basement or foundation for a building is chopped (with an ax) into blocks and used for the walls!

Distribution of pyroclastic material

The eruption of Krakatoa in 1883 provided an opportunity to study the distribution of volcanic ash in an eruption. Krakatoa is located on a small island between Java and Sumatra in Indonesia. Being one

of the great volcanic eruptions of historic time, perhaps the greatest
of all, the distribution of its ash was more extensive than is usually the
case. It is estimated that in the eruption one cubic mile of material was
blown to a height of seventeen miles and that the dust was carried completely around the earth several times by air currents. Dust fell in quantity on the deck of vessels 1,600 miles away three days after the eruption.
Measurements of the sun's rays reaching the earth's surface for the year
following the eruption were only 87 percent normal, attesting to the
effect of the dust in the atmosphere. The brilliant glow of the skies before
sunrise and after sunset due to the reflection of the sunlight from the
dust particles in the upper atmosphere attracted world-wide attention.
The phenomenon suddenly appeared in a belt fifteen degrees on either
side of the equator in the week following the eruption. It then gradually
spread until it covered the entire earth.

In England, particularly, it was the subject of a heated controversy
which was debated in the daily newspapers as well as in the scientific
journals. One group held it to be due to the "volcanic ashes" ejected
into the atmosphere by the eruption of Krakatoa; others held that it was
due to the earth's passing through a cosmic cloud, the tail of a comet,
a shower of meteors, or to gases foreign to our atmosphere, possibly
derived from the eruption of Krakatoa or from outer space. In the
United States scientists soon took sides in the controversy and articles
on the subject appeared in the leading scientific journals. The facts, as
set forth in these articles on the "Sun Glows" (Hazen, 1884, p. 201),
as well as the basis for objections to the "volcanic-ashes" theory, will be
of interest. The glows were first seen in the United States at Yuma,
Arizona, on October 19 (the eruption of Krakatoa was August 26),
and in the eastern United States on October 30. On this night the
spectacle was unusually brilliant and "fire engines were summoned at
Poughkeepsie [New York] and New Haven [Connecticut] to quench the
burning skies." The phenomenon continued, with varying degrees of
brilliance, for months. It was noticeably more marked during dry
periods. Some of the objections to the volcanic-ashes theory were:

1) The situation required the ejection of sufficient material to cover
more than 135,000,000 square miles (45° on either side of the equator).

The attempt to account for this from an isolated volcano thousands of miles away "can only be regarded as an endeavor to support a weak cause."

2) Such distribution of volcanic ash would have required upper-air currents of sufficient velocity to carry ashes a distance of 12,000 miles in 150 hours, a velocity of eighty miles per hour to the west. "We know little of velocities of air currents at great height but they are probably slight."

The advocates of the "volcanic-ashes" theory, notably Mr. Norman Locker in the December 10 issue of the London *Daily Mail,* pointed out that ash had fallen in Spain and in Holland and that analysis of this material showed that it was identical with the Krakatoa ash. Yet this was not convincing to the opponents of the theory.

The world-wide distribution of ash in the eruption of Krakatoa in 1883 provided important information on the circulation of matter in the upper layers of the atmosphere.

Although the eruption of Parícutin Volcano, Mexico, from 1943 to 1952 must be recognized as a minor eruption as compared to that of Krakatoa in 1883, the fact that it was studied in detail makes it important for purposes of comparison. The greater part of the ash from Parícutin was ejected during the first year of its activity, its more violent outbursts ejecting enough ash to cause considerable inconvenience in the streets of Uruapan, 30 miles away, with slight ash falls on Mexico City, 200 miles distant. The east-west elongate shape of the area covered by ash from Parícutin reflects the influence of the prevailing winds. It extends a greater distance to the west of the cone, indicating that the east winds of the rainy season are the stronger. Segerstrom (1950), in connection with erosion studies at Parícutin, prepared a map showing the thickness of ash deposits around Parícutin Volcano. The one-meter line, representing the limit of a thickness of one meter or more, extends 3.8 kilometers to the east and 6.6 kilometers to the west of the cone. The one-fourth–meter (about 10-inches) line extends 7 kilometers to the east and 11.5 kilometers to the west of the cone. The one-millimeter line passes through Guadalajara, 190 kilometers to the west, and includes an area of 60,000 square kilometers.

Lava

Meaning of the term

The molten rock material, before reaching the surface, is one component of magma. Magma differs essentially from molten rock in being charged with varying amounts of gases. While the magma is confined under sufficient pressure, the gaseous constituents remain in solution, but as the magma rises toward the surface and the overlying pressure is reduced, the gases escape, sometimes with explosive violence. Indeed, it is the expansive force of the pent-up gases which supplies most of the energy released in a volcanic eruption. The expansive force of a gas-charged liquid is familiar to anyone who has opened a bottle of soda-water or, on a more elegant level, uncorked a bottle of champagne. The frothing of the liquid and the overflowing of the bottle are analogous, on a small scale, to the flashing of the magma into pumice (rock froth) when the pressure is suddenly relieved by the blowing out (uncorking) of the plug filling the crater of the volcano.

The term *lava*, from the Italian *lavare* meaning "to wash," was used to denote anything which "washes away." Samuel Johnson's dictionary defines it as an Italian term meaning "a running gullet, streame or gutter, södainly caused by raine." In early Italian usage it was applied to a flood of water or mud; so they speak of "water lava" or "mud lava," or even "lava di gente" meaning a hurrying crowd of people. It was first applied in Neapolitan dialect to lava streams from Vesuvius, and then adopted into Italian literature, from which it has developed its present meaning. The verb *lavare*, common to Latin, French, and Italian, is found in the English language in such words as "lavatory" or a place for washing. Many current misconceptions have been introduced through the misinterpretation of the meaning attached to the term *lava* in accounts of early volcanic eruptions in the Italian region. Indeed, the mud flow which buried the city of Herculaneum in A.D. 79 following the eruption of Vesuvius was described as a lava flow. *Lava*, as now used, however, refers to the liquid product, or molten rock, which issues from a volcano.

Composition of lavas

Lavas in their chemical composition are a mixture of several oxides, with SiO_2 (silicon dioxide) greatly in excess over the others. The ingredients are virtually the same in all types of lavas but vary considerably in their relative proportions. The range in SiO_2 content, which varies from as little as 35 percent up to 75 percent by weight in typical volcanic rocks, is the basis for grouping the lavas (and, in fact, all igneous rocks) into three categories. Those which contain 66 percent or more of SiO_2 are the "acid" rocks, because SiO_2 acts as an acid, combining with the remaining oxides to form silicate compounds. The lavas with SiO_2 content between 52 percent and 66 percent are "intermediate," and those with SiO_2 content under 52 percent are termed "basic" lavas. The composition affects the viscosity, thereby influencing the ease with which the gases are liberated, and as a consequence determines the type of eruption, the rate of flow, and other characteristics. In general, the acid lavas, more stiff and viscous, even at high temperatures, thus causing the gases to escape with difficulty, result in explosive types of eruptions. Such lavas, known as "rhyolites," are generally light in color, frequently grey or pink. The basic lavas are dark-colored, and, being quite fluid, flow readily, thus allowing the gases to escape with ease. Their eruptions are of the quiet type, and they yield a lava known as "basalt." Between the two extremes described above are the intermediate lavas, known as "andesites," from the Andes Mountains of South America. They occur abundantly throughout the western United States.

A typical acid lava may contain 70 percent or more SiO_2, 12 to 15 percent Al_2O_3 (aluminum oxide), 6 to 8 percent alkalies—Na_2O (sodium oxide) and K_2O (potassium oxide)—and relatively small amounts, 3 percent or less, of the oxides of iron, magnesium, and calcium. An average of many analyses of basalt, a typical basic lava, with percentages rounded off to the nearest whole number, shows 49 percent SiO_2, 16 percent Al_2O_3, 12 percent iron oxides, 9 percent CaO (calcium oxide), 6 percent MgO (magnesium oxide), and relatively small amounts, 3 percent or less, of the oxides of sodium and potassium. It will be noted that in addition to the marked difference in SiO_2 content, the chief distinction between acid and basic lavas is the relatively high percentages of alkalies and the low percentages of iron, magnesium, and calcium in the acid lavas, with reverse proportions in the basic lavas. The great majority of lavas, the andesites, are intermediate between acid and basic lavas. An average of twenty analyses, with percentages rounded off to the nearest whole number, shows 59 percent SiO_2, 16 percent Al_2O_3, 7 percent iron oxides, 6 percent CaO, 4 percent Na_2O, 3 percent MgO, and 2 percent K_2O. While all lavas have a similarity in composition, no two volcanoes erupt lavas of exactly the same composition, and in fact the composition may vary from one eruption to another in the same volcano.

Temperature observations

The color of a heated body depends on the temperature, not the nature of the material. By observing the color with which a body glows one can make an accurate estimate of the temperature.

APPROXIMATE COLOR SCALE OF TEMPERATURE

Color	Degrees Centigrade	Degrees Fahrenheit
Incipient-red heat	540	1,000
Dark-red heat	650	1,200
Bright-red heat	870	1,600
Yellowish-red heat	1,100	2,000
Incipient-white heat	1,260	2,300
White heat	1,480	2,700

Temperature of the lava as it emerges from the volcano has been measured by various devices. One of the most useful, because of its portability, is the optical pyrometer. This instrument, based on the fact that color is a true index to temperature, is designed to measure the temperature by matching the color of the glowing lava with the same color from an electrically activated cell. Thus red-hot and white-hot are colors associated with definite temperatures, and these, along with many intermediate shades, can be determined with the optical pyrometer in terms of temperature. Such instruments are widely used to measure temperature in brick kilns, steel furnaces, and similar industrial plants. In measuring the temperature of a lava flow, an operator focuses this instrument, which resembles a hand telescope, on an incandescent surface of the lava and rotates a dial in the instrument until the color appearing on the gauge matches that of the lava. He then reads the temperature in degrees on a scale in the instrument. Another instrument, successfully used when it is possible to approach the lava at close range, is a thermoelectric pyrometer. In this type the "fire end" is thrust into the lava or gas vent and a cable connection with the cold end, where a thermometer is provided, gives the correction to a heat-generated electric current which is read directly in degrees of heat.

Basic lavas, which are the only ones on which good temperature measurements have been made thus far, have a temperature of around 1,100° C. The highest temperature measured by the author at Parícutin Volcano, Mexico, was 1,135° C., and in this case a slaglike crust began to develop on the incandescent lava when the temperature dropped to around 950° C. Perret records temperatures for the lava of the 1910 eruption of Mount Etna in Sicily of between 900° C. and 1,000° C., and from 1,015° C. to 1,040° C. on Vesuvian lavas in 1916–1918. The hottest lavas known, with temperatures in excess of 1,200° C., are the Hawaiian lavas at Kilauea Crater. One of the most unusual temperature observations ever recorded was made by Dr. T. A. Jaggar at Kilauea Volcano, Hawaii, in 1917. He inserted Seger cones (ceramic cones constructed to melt at definite temperatures) in an iron pipe which he then thrust into the lava pool at Halemaumau within Kilauea Crater. Although he was able to penetrate only twenty feet or so below the surface, his test showed conclusively that temperatures at this depth were on the order of 100° C. lower than at the surface. This somewhat anomalous situation, at first perplexing, now seems simply explained when one realizes that the greater heat at the surface is generated by the reaction of the evolving gases with one another and especially with atmospheric oxygen. Minimum temperatures observed on lavas are around 750° C.

Solidification of lava

After being poured onto the surface, the lava spreads out as tongues or sheets which flow over the countryside, often finding their way into stream valleys along which they may extend for many miles. Some sheets of lava, such as those forming the great lava plateaus, cover thousands of square miles and extend tens or even hundreds of miles from their source. The thickness of an individual flow may vary from a few inches to many hundreds of feet. The average person may think that lavas are something rather rare on the earth's surface. To dispel this idea he needs only to consider, in addition to the lava flows from individual volcanoes, the great plateau basalts such as those which make up the Columbia River Plateau of the Pacific northwest of the United States. Here, covering most of Oregon and parts of Idaho and Washington with an area of 200,000 square miles, are basaltic lavas reaching a thickness of 3,000 feet and representing hundreds of flows superimposed one upon another. When one realizes also that this is but one of many such areas of the earth he obtains some appreciation of the tremendous quantity of lava on the earth's surface.

The mobility of molten lava depends on its composition and temperature. The stiff, viscous acid lavas usually congeal before they have traveled far, whereas the basic lavas, being more fluid, tend to flow freely for long distances before they come to rest. The speed of a lava flow depends on its viscosity (which depends on temperature and composition) as well as upon the slope of the surface on which it is flowing. In unusual cases, some of the basic lavas on Mauna Loa, Hawaii, have attained velocities up to ten to twenty-five miles per hour, but this is highly exceptional. At Parícutin Volcano, Mexico, velocities up to fifty feet per minute were observed near the source, but at a distance of one mile, where the lava spread out on a more gentle slope, the velocity decreased to fifty feet per hour. At Parícutin a tongue of lava might continue to move for months, finally decreasing its forward advance to only a few feet per day in its final stage.

The upper part of a lava flow is usually made up of a porous, spongelike mass of lava known as "scoria." The porous character is due to the escape of the contained gases or to the expansion of the gases to form bubbles just prior to the freezing of the flow. These bubbles, or voids which were occupied by gas, may become elongated or drawn out into tubelike forms, as the stiff, viscous material in which the bubbles are entrapped continues to move slowly forward. The surfaces of lava flows commonly develop into one of two contrasting types for which the Hawaiian names of *aa* and *pahoehoe* are used. In the pahoehoe type (known as "corded" in Italy) the surface is smooth and billowy and frequently molded into forms which resemble huge coils of rope. Such lava surfaces commonly develop in the basic lava, in which a skinlike surface covers the still liquid lava below and as the flow continues to move the smooth skin is wrinkled into ropy or billowy surfaces which are preserved when the mass finally congeals. Occasionally the solidified crust may become attached to the sides of the channel and as the molten lava beneath drains away, the crust is left suspended. Lava tunnels are thus formed, and such features are common in many basaltic lavas. The liquid lava, dripping from the ceiling and congealing into stalactites and other curious shapes are common features of lava tunnels, such as the Thurston Lava Tube in Hawaii National Park at Kilauea Volcano. In the aa type, the surface of the lava is covered with a confused mass of angular, jagged blocks which render the flow practically impassable. In this type no continuous surface forms over the flow and the confused mass of angular blocks which are being carried on the surface are preserved when the flow freezes.

Crystallization of lava

The magma is a melt in which the various constituents are, in effect, mutually dissolved. Thus the temperature may drop well below the melting point of all the constituents; yet the magma will remain liquid. Salt dissolved in water produces a similar result in that it lowers the freezing point of the water. From this it follows that the order of crystallization of the minerals from a magma is based on solubility rather than fusibility. That is, the least soluble in the magma are the ones that begin to crystallize out first. The minerals which crystallize first will have well-developed crystal outlines, because they encountered no interference in development, while the last mineral to form must necessarily fill the spaces left and its shape is determined, not by its own crystal structure but by the surrounding minerals.

The early stage of crystallization of a magma doubtless begins in the magma chamber, long before the actual eruption takes place. Thus olivine, the first mineral to crystallize, may have developed into fairly large crystals which were floating in the magma at the time of the eruption. When the lava is poured out on the surface the cooling is greatly accelerated, and the olivine crystals are entrapped in a groundmass of small crystals which result from the rapid cooling. If cooling is extremely rapid there may not be time for crystallization, and a glassy groundmass will form. Hence, nearly all lavas, when examined with a hand lens, will show some large, evident crystals (phenocrysts) embedded in a much finer-grained or even glassy groundmass. Such a texture is known as "porphyritic," and the rock is called a "porphyry." The lavas of Hawaii are mostly olivine basalt porphyries and the green olivine phenocrysts are readily discernible without the aid of a hand lens. On weathering, the olivine crystals are freed from the rock and accumulate on the weathered surface of the lava flow or along the stream beds where they have been carried by water. These crystals are known locally as "Pele diamonds" and are used as a semiprecious gemstone.

Obsidian is a volcanic glass which results when viscosity is too high to permit crystallization during the period of cooling. Small amounts of obsidian are usual associates of most volcanic regions, but extensive flows of obsidian, although not common, are known in many parts of the world. Perhaps the most famous is on the Island of Lipari, off the coast of Sicily, but numerous examples are also to be found in the western United States. Flow structures are an alignment of the elongate crystals in the rock, similar to that observed in a mass of logs being floated in a river to the mill. Usually such structures are best observed in thin slices of the rock viewed under a microscope.

Causes of variation in composition of lavas

An interesting query in relation to lava flows is why there are so many different kinds of lavas, or for that matter, of igneous rocks in general. It was pointed out earlier in this section that different volcanoes erupt different kinds of lava and, in fact, that the same volcano may erupt lavas of different compositions in succeeding eruptions. Does this imply that separate reservoirs are tapped in different eruptions, or at different times? The answer is certainly no. The full explanation, however, would involve a topic known as "magmatic differentiation," or the splitting of a parent magma into various components, and this subject would involve a knowledge of advanced geology and physical chemistry beyond the scope of this work. Nevertheless, it is felt that the reader is entitled to at least a general idea of the types of explanations which have been proposed to account for magmatic differentiation, rather than complete avoidance of the topic. We must hasten to admit that it is a highly controversial subject and that perhaps generations of scientific investigations will be needed before the ultimate truth is known. An explanation which has been popular with many geologists, largely the work of Bowen (1928), will be briefly sketched.

According to this explanation the many rock types are believed to have been derived from a parent magma through a process known as "fractional crystallization." The minerals that crystallize first from a magma are the heavier and more basic ones (olivine, pyroxene, etc.) and, as they settle, the remaining mass becomes more acidic because of the removal of the basic fraction. It is a process known to geologists as crystal differentiation by gravity and was suggested by the olivine-rich ledge in the Palisade Sill. The Palisade Sill of New Jersey, in places over one thousand feet thick, outcrops continuously for a distance of fifty miles along the west bank of the Hudson River facing the city of New York. It was intruded into the surrounding rocks as a great molten sheet. The name refers to the huge columnlike appearance of the outcrop, resulting from the joints which formed as the mass cooled. As olivine began to crystallize, it settled to the lower part of the mass, forming a layer about fifteen feet thick. The olivine-rich bed is at the top of the lower chilled border layer about fifty feet from the base of the sill. Thus the composition of the mass was altered by the removal of the constituents making up olivine. Since the process of crystal settling, conceivably, could be halted at any point by freezing of the magma or its expulsion to the surface in a volcanic eruption, an infinite variety of rock types is possible. The process may be compared to "fractional distillation," in which crude oil is split into gasoline, kerosene, and other components by heating it to different temperatures.

While many geologists regard fractional crystallization as the main factor in controlling igneous rock differentiation, a growing number hold divergent views. Other processes held to be effective in producing differentiation are: assimilation of the wall rock of the magma chamber or of portions of the already crystallized magma, mingling of magmas, gaseous transfer, thermal diffusion-convection, etc. After reviewing the problem of magmatic differentiation, Barth (1950, p. 161) concluded: "Petrologists agree that differentiation cannot be attributed to any one mechanism, and for most of the igneous bodies actually studied no complete or satisfactory explanation has been proposed. Crystallization differentiation, assimilation, mingling of magmas, etc., may each have played its part, and there may be still other important processes of which we know nothing today."

The parent magma or primary magma which has given rise, by magmatic differentiation due to crystal settling or by other processes, to the various types of igneous rocks is believed to be a world-encircling layer of basaltic composition. There is, however, a marked difference between the continental areas and the oceanic areas in crustal composition. Apart from a thin veneer of sedimentary rocks on the surface, the continents are believed to be composed to a depth of ten to thirty-five kilometers of material known as "sial," with much greater thicknesses (up to sixty kilometers) under mountain ranges. This material, sometimes known as "granitic," is composed of rocks rich in the oxides of silica (Si) and aluminum (Al), hence the name *sial*. It corresponds more or less in composition with granitic-type rocks and with the acid lavas, previously mentioned.

Under the continents a basaltic layer, conforming in composition to the basic lavas and known as "sima," underlies the sial. However, beneath the oceans the crust is sima with little or no sial present. Hence, the Hawaiian volcanoes, coming from the floor of the Pacific ocean, erupt a primary basaltic magma, whereas, in volcanoes which occur on the continents the primary basaltic magma must rise through the sialic crust to reach the surface. The contamination by assimilation of the sialic crust results in a more acid type of material, yielding the andesites. The contamination (or lack of contamination) of the primary basaltic magma by assimilation as it passes through the surface layers of the earth's crust had led to the recognition of three major types of lavas:

1) The Atlantic-type lavas are the primary olivine basaltic magma, believed to be world-wide in distribution, which reaches the surface

without contamination. This type is necessarily found in those areas in which the sialic crust is missing. It was designated the "Atlantic" type because examples first cited were from islands in the Atlantic Ocean. However, without exception, the lavas within the Pacific Ocean basin proper are Atlantic-type lavas.

2) Pacific-type lavas are those resulting from the contamination of an originally Atlantic type by assimilation of sialic material. The lavas erupted by volcanoes along the continental margins of the Pacific Ocean are of this type. These lavas are andesites for the most part, and the line separating Pacific- and Atlantic-type lavas is known as the "Andesite Line." It is not exactly at the edge of the existing continents but some distance offshore (Fig. 3) and may properly be considered as the limit of the Pacific Ocean basin.

3) Mediterranean-type lavas, which are produced by Italian volcanoes, do not fit into either of the other two classes, although they might be considered as a special variation of the Pacific type. In the Mediterranean region the high limestone content of the crust and the shallow depth of the magma had resulted in marked changes in the composition of the lavas because of the assimilation of large quantities of limestone by the magma in reaching the surface. Mediterranean-type lavas may also be produced by the interaction of carbonate-rich basic magmas and sial, and hence can occur in areas in which there is no limestone to be assimilated (Holmes, 1950).

Thus, the statement made earlier that volcanoes tend to erupt basic lavas in the early stages of their history and more acid lavas in the declining stage can now be rationalized. In the initial stage, the primary basaltic magma reaches the surface uncontaminated, but as the magma rises in the crust and has time to assimilate sialic material it becomes more and more acidic, and the lavas ejected reflect this progressive change. The preceding statement is an oversimplification of an extremely complex and inadequately understood process. It appears that no amount of assimilation by basic magma would yield material of the composition of rhyolite, which is the end product of the eruptive cycle in many volcanic regions. The answer probably lies in the assimilation of sial by high-pressure gases but this problem is awaiting solution.

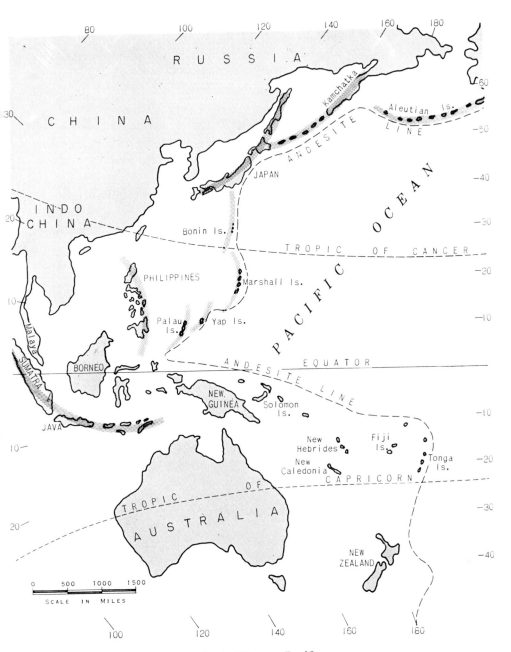

FIGURE 3. Andesite Line in Western Pacific area.

Rate of Cooling of a lava flow

Lava, like all rock, is a poor conductor of heat, and it cools very slowly. The scoriaceous nature of the surface layer, with its many cavities and entrapped air spaces, provides a splendid insulation to prevent the heat of the lava from escaping. It is possible to walk over a lava stream in which only a few inches below the surface the rock is still red-hot. In the author's experience the gases rising from the cooling lava, particularly from fissures, are more of a hazard than the heat of the lava surface.

How long will a lava flow remain hot? Naturally, this will depend on the size of the flow, for it will take a large mass longer to cool than a small one. The hot springs and geysers of Yellowstone National Park attest the fact than an acid lava buried only a short distance below the surface will remain hot for thousands, even hundreds of thousands, of years. Hence, the material failed to reach the surface but did come close enough to heat the ground water issuing as hot springs and geysers. Old Faithful geyser was active before and during the Ice Age, as is indicated by geyser deposits interbedded with glacial deposits. So we have a means of estimating, with some degree of accuracy, the approximate age in years. Cooling at the surface, of course, would be much more rapid, but nevertheless it is a slow process in terms of our everyday concept of time. Daly (1933, p. 63) estimates that a magma at a temperature of 1,100° C., if exposed to the air on top (as a lava flow), would cool to 750° C. in accordance with this schedule:

3 feet thick	12 days
30 feet thick	3 years
300 feet thick	30 years

This, however, is down to only 750° C., and the cooling will become progressively slower as the mass approaches air temperature; so the time required for further cooling would be greatly, and disproportionately, lengthened. Many lava deposits are between thirty and three hundred feet in thickness, and were formed by flows in which the temperature of the lava was around 1,100° C. when it reached the surface. It is not surprising, therefore, that a lava flow will remain hot and steaming internally for years. Once a crust has formed, it serves as an insulation to prevent radiation of heat and the cooling is a very slow process indeed.

At Parícutin Volcano the San Juan flow of 1944, with a thickness of about thirty feet, was still steaming in 1956. The last flow to issue from Parícutin Volcano was in March, 1952. In September, 1956, it still contained some fumaroles at various points on the flow, and even small pieces of lava broken from the surface of larger blocks were too hot to hold in the hand; yet it had been cooling for four and one-half years. Judd recorded that during the 1872 eruption of Vesuvius masses of snow which were covered with a thick layer of scoria and afterwards by a lava flow, were found three years later consolidated into ice but not melted. This attests the insulating properties of scoria. "Eleven months after an eruption of Mt. Etna, Spallanzani records that 'red hot lava could still be seen at the bottom of fissures, and a stick thrust into one instantly took fire.' The Vesuvian lava of 1785 was found by Breislak to be still hot and steaming internally after seven years, although lichens had already taken root on the surface. Hoffman records that the lava which flowed from Etna in 1787 was still steaming in 1830. But more remarkable is the case of Jorullo Volcano, in Mexico, which erupted lava in 1759. Twenty-one years later, it is said, a cigar could be lighted at its fissures; after forty-four years it was still visibly steaming, and even in 1846, after eighty-seven years of cooling, two vapor columns were still rising from it." (*Encyclopedia Britannica*).

Stopping a lava flow

In most regions the towns, either because of the accessibility of water or because of the fertility of the soil, are located in the valleys. Since lava flows seek the lowest course, the valleys are the first areas to be invaded. As a result, many towns and even cities have been destroyed by lava flows. On the thickly populated slopes of Vesuvius it would be practically impossible for a lava flow to miss all of the towns, and many of them have been destroyed repeatedly. Torre Annunziata, in the path of the 1906 lava flow from Vesuvius, had been destroyed on three previous occasions in the past nine hundred years, but each time had been rebuilt. Torre del Greco, another important town on the slope of Vesuvius, has had a similar history, and the number could be multiplied many times over. It is reported that in the 1669 eruption of Mount Etna in Sicily fourteen villages, with a total population of three to four thousand, were destroyed, and that eventually the flow swept through Catania and extended into the sea. In the recent eruption of Parícutin Volcano in Mexico, which, compared to Italy, is sparsely populated, two towns, San Juan de Parangaricutiro, with a population of about three thousand, and Parícutin, with a population of five hundred, were buried by lava flows. It is only natural, then, that the problem of stopping or diverting a lava flow should have been considered since earliest times. An understanding of the structure of a lava flow is essential to the solution of this problem.

When a lava flow pours out on the surface, the edges, as well as the top, crust over, while the interior remains liquid and moves forward, carrying the surface crust along with it in the aa type flow, or flowing beneath the crust in the pahoehoe type. The cooled edges form a natural levee, or wall, which confines the lava flow in a channel. The thickness of the flow will, of course, determine the height of the levees, which in many flows will range from ten to fifty feet.

Perhaps the first attempt, or at least the first attempt on record, to alter the course of a lava flow occurred during the 1669 eruption of Etna in Sicily. The flow, which originated about ten miles above the city of Catania, was advancing toward the city and threatening to destroy it. In an effort to save the city, several dozen men covered themselves with wet cowhides for protection against the heat, and with iron bars dug an opening through the side wall of the flow, in effect breaking through the natural levee. The operation was initially successful. A stream of lava escaped through the gap thus created and moved away at a high angle from the direction of the original flow, partly relieving the pressure on the tongue moving toward Catania. Unfortunately the new flow moved in the direction of Paterno, and some five hundred irate citizens of that town descended upon the men from Catania and drove them away from the newly dug lava channel. Left unattended, the gap in the wall soon clogged with cooled lava, and the main branch of the flow continued toward Catania, destroying a large section of the city as it passed on and into the sea (Rittmann, 1929, pp. 95–96). Even to this day large masses of the 1669 flow block streets and cover portions of the city of Catania. Although this early effort to divert a lava flow ended in failure, it demonstrated the possibility of changing the course of a flow by artificially breaking down the retaining natural levee of the flow.

The first serious consideration given to the control of a lava flow was in Hawaii, where the city of Hilo and its harbor were in a position to be threatened from the ever active Mauna Loa Volcano.[3] Hilo, now a city of around fifty thousand inhabitants which possesses the only harbor on Hawaii Island, was spared when the 1881 flow from Mauna Loa stopped after reaching the outskirts of the city. The harbor of Hilo is in a depression between ancient lava flows from Mauna Loa and Mauna Kea. This depression, or lowland, extending far up the mountain side, is also the course of the Wailuku River, Hilo's water supply. Being a depression (with respect to the terrain on either side), it is the natural course of the lava flows originating on the north flank of Mauna Loa. The volcanoes of Hawaii are described elsewhere in this work, but it will be useful in relation to the stoppage of lava flows to review briefly the activity of Mauna Loa at this time.

Mauna Loa is a huge "shield-shaped" mass, rising over thirteen thousand feet above sea level and consisting of innumerable lava flows, one superimposed upon another. At the summit is a huge crater (caldera) from which lava flows frequently issue. However, most of the flows issue from a prominent fissure, or fracture zone, the Great Rift zone, which extends in a northeasterly direction through the summit crater. Dr. Jaggar, long-time director of the Hawaiian Volcano Observatory, had worked out the pattern for the lava flows on Mauna Loa. He noted that from 1868 to 1926 the lava flows had been moving progressively up the mountain along the southwest Rift zone (Pl. 21). Each flow, on cooling, sealed the fissure at that point, and the next outbreak shifted to a higher point along the Rift zone. In the 1933 outbreak lava occurred in the summit crater. Summit-crater eruptions had always been followed by flank outbreaks, and Dr. Jaggar reasoned that because of the sealing of the fissure on the south flank by successive eruptions from 1868 to 1926, the next outbreak would be on the northeast Rift zone.

Firmly convinced, he issued a prediction in March, 1934, that a lava

[3] Mauna Loa, one of the world's largest volcanoes, is one of five volcanoes making up the Island of Hawaii. Mauna Loa and Kilauea, the only two active volcanoes in the Hawaiian Islands, are both located on the Island of Hawaii.

flow was to be expected within two years and that it would come from the north flank and would probably endanger Hilo. As predicted, the lava outbreak occurred on the north flank on November 21, 1935, first from a point near the summit and a week later from a point along the Rift zone, four thousand feet lower and ten miles from the summit. On December 22 this flow, which had pooled in the saddle between Mauna Loa and Mauna Kea, turned toward Hilo. Prior to that date a possibility had existed that it might drain westward into waste lands. When it turned eastward into the drainage of the Wailuku River it was headed for Hilo, and by December 26 it had covered five of the twenty miles that would put it in Hilo. Dr. Jaggar had proposed, in 1931, the possibility of controlling a lava flow by bombing. In theory the bombing could bring about the diversion of the flow by breaking the retaining walls, thereby diverting the supply of lava from the flow below the point of rupture and causing stagnation of the lower end of the flow. This could be most easily accomplished, providing the terrain was suitable, through breaking the natural levees by bombing, thus permitting the lava to feed out into other channels. This is a modern approach to the method employed by the cowhide-protected men of Catania in 1669. The new flow might move off at a high angle, as in the 1669 flow at Catania, or more likely it might simply follow the edge of the older flow, and in time reach the same destination. This, however, would be a delaying tactic, and if necessary the breaching could be repeated as many times as necessary. Further, bombs dropped directly into the flow might break the surface crust and clog the channel with solid fragments, or it might stir up the liquid lava, causing it to solidify and clog the channel, thus forcing the lava to seek a new outlet and delaying the forward advance of the lava front.

On December 23, after consultation with the military authorities, Dr. Jaggar decided that the time had come to test the bombing hypothesis. The bombing operation was carried out by a U.S. Air Corps Bombing Squadron from Honolulu. Two targets areas were selected, one at an elevation of 8,500 feet, near the source of the flow, and the other about one mile below. On December 27 twenty 600-pound bombs were dropped on these two target areas from an altitude of about 3,500 feet above the lava surface. The direct hits were sufficient in number to blast open the roofed channel of the flow and also to break the levees, permitting at least one lateral flow to develop. The movement of the lava front at noon on December 27, the day of the bombing, was eight hundred feet per hour; by noon of the following day, it was forty-four feet per hour, and by 6:00 P.M., or thirty hours after the bombing, it had stopped altogether! Such remarkable results were entirely unexpected, and the skeptics maintained that the lava stream would have stopped anyway, and that the relationship to the bombing was purely coincidental. This view is also maintained by Stearns and Macdonald (1946, p. 94), both experienced observers who have had many years' acquaintance with Mauna Loa and whose opinion must be respected. Dr. Jaggar, in his investigation of the effect of the bombing, concluded that the rupture of the roof of the lava channel and the resulting cooling had solidified the lava back to the source and that the remainder of the eruptive energy was expended in lava fountains at the upper end of the rift.

Another test of the bombing hypothesis was made in the same area on Mauna Loa in 1942, with comparable results. These tests show that a lava flow is in a much more delicate state of equilibrium and more sensitive to disturbance than anyone had dreamed. Dr. Jaggar had long believed that a properly designed wall would deflect a lava stream. In 1938, in conjunction with the U.S. Engineers, he prepared plans for a lava-diversion channel to protect Hilo. The plan was not to block the passage of the lava but to deflect it by means of an artificial barrier. This would force the lava stream along natural downhill grades, forcing it diagonally away from the business district, harbor, and airport of Hilo. The length of the barrier required was seven miles. Although the plan was sound from an engineering standpoint and was approved by a review board in Washington, it became involved in harbor improvements which called for a new breakwater, and in the end it was not authorized.

History records several instances where walls have deflected lava flows. Lyell (1875, p. 23) in describing the 1669 eruption of Mount Etna in Sicily says: ". . . the lava current, after overflowing 14 towns, some with a population of 3,000 to 4,000 arrived at length at the walls of Catania. These had been purposely raised to protect the city; but the burning flood accumulated till it rose to the top of the rampart, which was 60 feet in height, and then it fell in a fiery cascade and overwhelmed part of the city. The wall, however, was not thrown down, but was discovered long afterwards, by excavations made in the rock by Prince Biscardi; so that the traveler of today may now see the solid lava curling over the top of the rampart as if still in the very act of falling."

In 1952 the writer attempted to verify this statement and to see if any fragments of the 1669 wall remained. However, it seems probable that the severe earthquakes during the 1669 eruption or in subsequent eruptions destroyed the wall, for no part of it could be located, and even the "arcade" of lava seems to have disappeared.

De Lorenzo (1906, p. 476), in reporting on the eruption of Vesuvius in 1906 says: ". . . it [the lava] reached within a few hours the cemetery of Torre Annunziata, against the walls of which it stopped, breaking into two branches." Today a suitable plaque and shrine set in the cemetery wall commemorate the stopping of the lava at that point. The author observed many actively advancing lava flows at Parícutin Volcano, Mexico. Frequently a tree or large boulder would suffice to temporarily halt the advance of the flow at some point by causing large blocks to lodge and in turn block others, until finally a considerable buttress was formed. The lava might then move ahead on other fronts, leaving the tree at the head of an indentation, or as an island. It seems entirely probable that a properly placed barrier might have diverted the lava from the major part of the town of San Juan de Parangaricutiro, which was destroyed by a lava flow from Parícutin Volcano in 1944 (Fig. 44).

An example of the diversion of a lava flow at O'Shima Volcano, Japan, has recently been reported by Mason and Foster (1953). Miharayama is the active, central cone of O'Shima Volcano on O'Shima Island, 110 kilometers south of Tokyo. Active repeatedly in historic times, it experienced a major eruption in 1950–1951. In this eruption the crater filled with lava, which overflowed the rim at several points. On the northwest side of the crater rim was Kako Jay (Crater Teahouse), a rectangular building about twenty-five by thirty-six feet on a concrete foundation with concrete walls about four feet thick and ten feet high. A gabled roof was supported by wood rafters. There were doors and windows on all sides of the building. On March 9, 1951, as the lava began to overflow the rim of the crater, it reached the building, whose roof and wood parts burned. The lava entered the building through the windows and doors, filled the interior and flowed out in small amounts through the windows and doors on the opposite side. The lava also flowed on either side of the building and continued down the slope. The building thus served as a buttress. In this case it was subjected to only the hydrostatic pressure of the lava, which was equal to the vertical height up to the point of overflow and not to the full momentum pressure. The Teahouse on Miharayama thus confirms the observations made elsewhere that properly placed structures will divert a lava flow.

Although we have discussed the products of volcanoes under the separate headings of gases, liquids, and solids, it must be remembered that this separation does not exist until the material approaches the surface. It may be appropriate to recall the quotation at the beginning of this Chapter: "Gas is the active agent and the magma is its vehicle." In the magma chamber the gases are dissolved in the magma. When the magma reaches the surface the gases may escape more or less quietly and the material will flow out as lava or they may escape with explosive violence disrupting the magma into fragmental material such as ash and cinders. Thus a study of the products ejected by a volcano will reveal the type of eruption, even though it may have occurred thousands of years ago.

Who hath . . . comprehended the dust of the earth in a measure, and weighed the mountains in scales, and the hills in a balance?   ISAIAH 40:12

6. CONES, CRATERS, AND CALDERAS

Cones

A VOLCANIC CONE is the result of the accumulation of ejected material around the vent, and its shape is determined by the proportions of lava and pyroclastic elements in the material composing it. Typically a cup-shaped depression, the crater occupies the apex of the cone. This is the surface connection of the volcanic conduit through which the ejected material reaches the surface. As the ash, cinders, and other fragmental material shower down around the vent, a cone is formed, the slopes of which are determined by the angle of repose of the debris. Fine ash and cinders come to rest on slopes of 30° to 35°, while nearer the summit coarser material may stand at 40° or more. Simple cinder-and-ash cones, with slopes of 30° to 35° and a truncated summit occupied by the crater, are common features throughout all volcanic regions. Hundreds of examples are to be found in the western United States, and they are readily identified, even from a considerable distance, by the characteristic profile. Parícutin Volcano, Mexico, is an example of a cinder cone which was formed in recent years. Parícutin attained a height of 450 feet by the end of the first week and 1,000 feet by the end of the second month (Chapter 13).

Most of the larger volcanoes of the world are composite cones consisting of layers of ash and cinders, alternating irregularly with tongue-like lava flows. The lava flows issue through breaches in the crater wall or through cracks on the flank or at the base of the cone. When the lava (or magma) solidifies in the fissures which serve as feeder channels for the lava flows, it forms dikes, which greatly strengthen the volcanic edifice. Mount Etna has more than two hundred secondary vents dotting its surface. A volcanic cone of the composite type is known also as a "strato-volcano."

Calderas

Distinction between a crater and a caldera

Where the ejected material consists predominantly of lava, as in the Hawaiian volcanoes, a lava cone is formed. The successive flows of lava usually spread out in thin sheets to form a wide-spreading dome with gentle slopes, rarely more than 5° to 10°. In some cases a particularly violent eruption may blow away the top of the cone, leaving a great depression, known as a "caldera," much larger than the actual crater. If the caldera did originate in this way, fragments of the missing part of the cone would form the greater part of the debris produced by the eruption. When, as is often the case, such fragments are rare, the only alternative explanation is that the vanished material must have collapsed into the magma chamber. Some of the greatest volcanic eruptions of historic time, such as that at Krakatoa in 1883,[1] have produced calderas. There is considerable difference of opinion as to the origin of many calderas, even of some of those which have been formed in his-

[1] Described on pp. 80–84.

toric time. A working definition of a caldera is useful at this point, since the term has been applied to a variety of features.

The term *caldera*, as now used, was defined by Williams (1941) as a large depression, more or less circular in form, the diameter of which is many times greater than that of the included vent or vents. The problem then arises as to the distinction between a crater and a caldera. The crater is the vent through which cinders, ash, lava, and other ejecta are erupted to form cones. Craters may be enlarged somewhat by the force of the explosions, but rarely, if ever, do they exceed three-fourths to one mile in diameter. By contrast, many calderas with diameters of five to ten miles, and even more, are known. Obviously, such tremendous depressions cannot be normal craters.

In the Portuguese language the term *caldera* signifies a "kettle" or "cauldron," and it was originally used by the natives of the Canary Islands for all natural depressions of that shape without reference to their size or origin. The term was introduced into geological literature by Leopold von Buch early in the nineteenth century when he applied it to the summit depression of La Palma Volcano in the Canary Islands, which he considered to be a fine example of a crater of elevation. The caldera, according to von Buch, resulted from the collapse of the "blister" which had pushed up from below to form the volcanic cone. Lyell, Scrope, and others disproved the crater-of-elevation hypothesis and proposed that calderas result from unusually violent explosions.

Fouqué (1879), from a study of Santorin Volcano, Greece, in 1866, and Verbeek (1886), from a study of the 1883 eruption of Krakatoa, were impressed by the scarcity of fragmental debris around these calderas and concluded that they must have been formed by engulfment. Since that time many workers throughout the world have confirmed the engulfment theory of the origin of calderas. The rapid draining of magma chambers, either by flank eruptions of lava, as in the Hawaiian type volcanoes, or by the ejection of tremendous quantities of pumice and ash in the Peléan and Vulcanian types, leaves the upper part of the cone without support, and its summit collapses.

Williams' (1941) conclusion, that "almost all volcanic depressions more than a mile in diameter are produced for the most part by collapse," may be taken as a basis for separating calderas and craters. Al-

1. Mild explosions of pumice. Magma stands high in conduit.

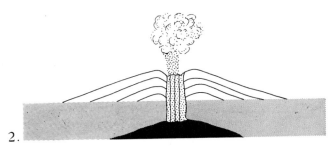

2. Explosions increase in violence. Magma level recedes into main chamber.

3. Culminating explosions. Part of the ejecta is hurled high into the air but most of it rushes down the flanks of the cone as *nuées arden-tes*. Magma level is deep in chamber. Roof begins to crack.

4. Lacking support, the top of the cone collapses into the magma chamber.

5. After an interval of quiescence and erosion, new cones appear on the caldera floor, especially near the rim.

FIGURE 4. Stages in the development of a caldera. From van Bemmelen (1929) and Williams (1941).

PLATE 3. Crater Lake caldera, Oregon, with Wizard Island, a cinder cone, in the foreground. Courtesy U.S. National Park Service.

though such a distinction is quite arbitrary, it does work out satisfactorily in practice. Reck (1936) clearly stated the fundamental distinction between craters and calderas when he pointed out that a crater is related to cone building and is thus a positive volcanic form, while a caldera is the collapse area above an exhausted magma chamber and is thus a negative, passive form. Calderas are commonly the result of a combination of explosion and collapse. Calderas formed by explosion only are rare and relatively small. The explosion-collapse theory, although devised originally to explain the 1883 eruption of Krakatoa, has been found applicable in general to caldera-making eruptions. According to this theory, the initial stages of the eruption discharge tremendous quantities of primary magmatic material in the form of pumice. This creates an empty space in the magma chamber into which the upper part of the cone collapses. The various stages, as visualized by Williams (1941), are shown in Figure 4. In many volcanic districts, especially among the Tertiary volcanics of Scotland, there are areas marked by a series of concentric dikes, which due to their circular plan are known as "ring dikes." They dip steeply outward and are believed to result from the intrusion of magma along fractures formed by the subsidence of the roof of the magma chamber. Thus they may mark the site of ancient calderas in which the ring dikes and associated features (cone sheets, etc.) are exposed after erosion has removed all traces of the surface caldera. In a recent study of the mechanism of caldera formation, based on the relationships of ring dikes and related features, Reynolds (1956) concluded that rising gas streams play an important role as agents of heat transfer, magma formation, transportation, and geomorphic development in the evolution of calderas. If her conclusions are correct, caldera formation may help explain some of the funnel-shaped intrusive masses, the origin of which has long been in question. A description of one ancient and two modern caldera-making eruptions will acquaint the reader with the caldera problem. The two modern caldera-making eruptions were, perhaps, the greatest volcanic eruptions of historic time, and from this standpoint alone are worthy of our attention.

Crater Lake, Oregon

One of the best-known examples of a caldera, and perhaps the most perfect, is that occupied by Crater Lake in southern Oregon. It has been exhaustively studied by experienced investigators and has been the source of much of the controversy concerning the origin of calderas. Crater Lake, one of the scenic wonders of the United States, and now a national park, is visited by thousands yearly. It is on the crest of the Cascade Range, which throughout its entire extent is surmounted by lofty volcanic cones, beginning at the north with Mount Rainier (14,-405 ft.) and Mount Adams, (12,307 ft.) in Washington, Mount Hood (11,253 ft.) in northern Oregon, and Mount Shasta (14,161 ft.) in northern California, these being only a few of the better-known volcanoes.

Crater Lake is nearly circular, stretching across its diameter about six miles, and extending in depth 2,000 feet. It is encircled by cliffs from 500 to 2,000 feet high. The deep blue waters of Crater Lake, broken only by the 780-foot symmetrical cinder cone known as Wizard Island, is an impressive sight, and few who see it fail to speculate concerning its origin. Diller (1902) was the first to study the problem, and he concluded that the caldera had been formed by subsidence. He realized that if it had been produced by tremendous explosions the slopes should be covered by a vast accumulation of debris from the former top of the cone. Not finding this material, he reasoned that engulfment was the only alternative and that this implied the removal of support from beneath the summit of the cone. In Hawaii large outpourings of lava on the outer flanks of the cone frequently result in collapse at the summit caldera. Diller believed that similar flank flows had occurred at Crater Lake, and, although he was unable to locate these flows, he believed that someday they would be found.

The ancestral cone, the summit of which disappeared to form the Crater Lake caldera, has been named Mount Mazama. Like other large volcanoes in the Cascades, Mount Mazama was active during and following the Pleistocene (Ice) Age and much glacial debris is found interbedded with volcanic ejecta. Some of the last glaciers to occupy Mount Mazama were more than ten miles long and a thousand feet

FIGURE 5. Restoration of Mount Mazama, ancestral cone of Crater Lake.   After Atwood (1935).

thick, and when the top of the cone collapsed the lower ends of the glaciers were left stranded on the slopes. Today the wide U-shaped cross sections of these glacial valleys are preserved as notches in the caldera rim. It is apparent that to support such large glaciers Mount Mazama must have risen far above its present height, probably reaching approximately twelve thousand feet, or roughly the height of Mount Hood.

The first explosions of the caldera-forming eruption were probably not catastrophic, but, as at Krakatoa, they increased gradually to a climax and then diminished rapidly. After the initial activity the vents must have enlarged, and the pressure on the magma was reduced so that the gases "boiled" off with increasing rapidity. Finally, the frothy magma was expelled in such volume that it not only rose above the cone, but fell back on the cone and rushed down the slope in a succession of *nuées ardentes,* spreading out on the surrounding plains for a distance of thirty-five miles. The temperature of the *nuées ardentes* must have been quite high, for large tree trunks embedded in the pumice as far as thirty miles from the caldera are carbonized.

Williams calculated that the total volume of material blown out of Mount Mazama was between ten and twelve cubic miles. The pumiceous material, which was obviously new magma, contained relatively small quantities of fragments from the demolished mountain. Assuming that Mount Mazama was twelve thousand feet high, some seventeen cubic miles disappeared when the caldera was formed, but not more than two cubic miles of the demolished material is mixed with the pumice. Thus, it is necessary to account for fifteen cubic miles of material which disappeared from the top of the cone. The ten to twelve cubic miles of inflated pumice which was blown out in the eruptions would be equivalent to only five cubic miles of space in the magma chamber. Assuming that the cone collapsed into this space, there would still remain about ten cubic miles to be accounted for, and this Williams does by postulating that "collapse of the peak into the magma chamber was brought about not only by drainage resulting from the eruption but also by the drainage consequent on some form of deep seated intrusions" (1941, p. 275). As a rule the space made available by pumice eruptions and the total volume of rock which has disappeared in forming a caldera should be equal. The discrepancy which exists at Crater Lake may be due in part to the difficulties involved in estimating volume of rock, which at best can be only an approximation.

Krakatoa Volcano, Indonesia

LOCATION AND HISTORY. A historic caldera-forming eruption and one of the greatest volcanic eruptions of all times occurred at Krakatoa in 1883. Krakatoa is an island in the Strait of Sunda, between Java and Sumatra, and had long been recognized as only the stump of an old volcanic cone which had been blown to pieces by an ancient eruption. There are, at present, three main islands in the Krakatoa group (Fig. 6), of which Rakata, the largest, rises to a height of about 2,700 feet

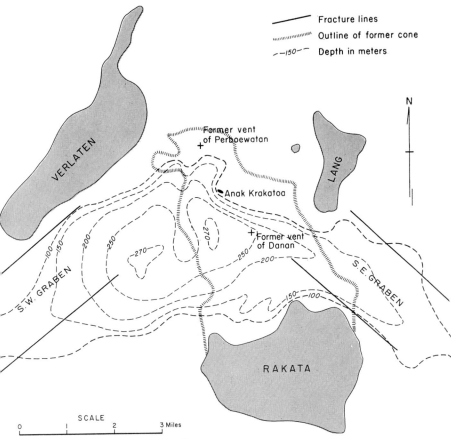

Fracture lines
Outline of former cone
−150− Depth in meters

FIGURE 6. The Caldera of Krakatoa.
Compiled from Escher, Stehn, and Verbeek. By Williams (1941).

above sea level, while Lang and Verlaten do not exceed 600 feet in height. These three islands are on the rim of a caldera nearly four miles in diameter, from the floor of which rise the rocky islet of Bootsmansrots and the cinder cone of Anak Krakatoa (literally, "child of Krakatoa"), which first appeared in 1927 and has been intermittently active since that time.

The history of Krakatoa prior to the eruption of 1883, as reconstructed by Escher (1919), Stehn (1929), Williams (1941), and others, is shown by a series of diagrams in Figure 7. The prehistoric cone which occupied the site of the present caldera is believed to have had a height of 6,000 feet (Stage 1). Following a great eruption, probably similar to that of 1883, the central part of the cone callapsed, leaving several small islands on the rim of the ancient caldera (Stage 2). A new cone, Rakata, then developed on the southeast margin of the prehistoric caldera, erupting lava and fragmental material until it reached a height of about 2,700 feet (Stage 3). Later the smaller andesitic cones, Danan and Perboewatan, 1,460 and 400 feet respectively, rose within the caldera and ultimately united with Rakata to form one large central island, which was commonly known as Krakatoa Volcano (Stage 4). The last activity, prior to the eruption of 1883, was a flow of andesitic obsidian from the vent of Perboewatan in 1680.

THE ERUPTION OF 1883. The initial activity began with explosions from the vent on Perboewatan on May 20. The explosions were not particularly violent, and no one was alarmed; in fact the people of Batavia thought the display such an attraction that on May 27 a steamer was chartered to visit the island. Some of the more venturesome of the excursion party climbed to the rim of the crater, where they beheld a vast column of steam issuing with a terrific noise from an opening estimated to be about thirty yards in width. However, it was observed that Rakata and Verlaten islands were covered with fine ash and that the vegetation, although not burned, had been killed. Following the preliminary explosions the activity subsided, only to be resumed on June 19. A few days later a second vent opened on Danan. There is no record of activity in July, but it must be presumed that the mild explosive activity continued. When the islands were visited on August 11, the last time before the catastrophic eruption, there were three main vents, all in a state of mild activity.

At 1:00 P.M. on August 26 the first of a series of tremendous explosions occurred. At 2:00 P.M. a black cloud rose above Krakatoa to a height of 17 miles, followed by sharp explosions which increased in intensity until 5:00 P.M., when the first collapse and tidal wave occurred. The explosions continued through the night, accompanied by severe air shocks, but there were no earthquakes. The noise was heard all over Java, and at Batavia, 100 miles distant, all through the night the houses trembled and windows rattled as if heavy artillery were being fired in

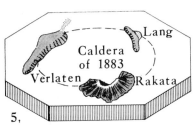

5. After the 1883 eruptions. Later eruptions have since built up the island of Anak Krakatoa within the caldera.

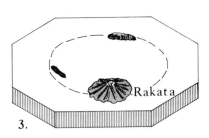

4. Krakatoa before 1883, after two later andesitic cones had coalesced with Rakata.

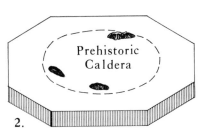

3. Growth of Rakata, a basaltic cone.

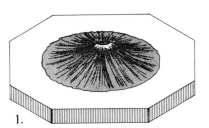

2. After explosive evisceration, probably accompanied by collapse of the superstructure, a great caldera was formed, rimmed by three small islands.

1. Original andesitic cone of Krakatoa.

FIGURE 7. Stages in the history of Krakatoa. Modified from B. G. Escher (1919).

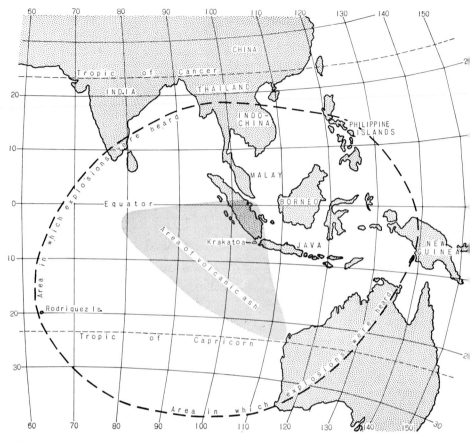

FIGURE 8. Limits of the volcanic ash and the noise of the explosions in the 1883 eruption of Krakatoa.

the streets. Because of the inccessant noise, no one in all of western Java was able to sleep. Between 4:40 A.M. and 6:41 A.M. of the next day, August 27, several large tidal waves spread outward from Krakatoa, probably due to further collapse of the northern part of the main island. By 10:00 A.M. the rehearsal was over, and the real performance was to begin. The climax of the eruption was reached at this time, when the ash cloud rose to a height of 50 miles, and the noise of the detonation was heard nearly 3,000 miles away.

Westward, across the Indian Ocean, is the Island of Rodriquez,

2,968 miles from Krakatoa, where an alert coast guard observer carefully noted the character of the sound and the time, just four hours after the explosions, which leaves no doubt that the noise was from Krakatoa. The noise was also heard 2,250 miles to the southeast in central Australia. The intensity of the sound is better appreciated if one assumes that were Pikes Peak to erupt as Krakatoa did, the noise would be heard all over the United States. About one-half hour after the cataclysmic explosion a tidal wave which reached a height of 120 feet in some bays swept the neighboring coasts of Java and Sumatra, wholly or partially destroying 295 towns and killing 36,000 people, mostly by drowning. A Dutch warship was washed ashore and left stranded 30 feet above water level and one-half mile inland. At 10:52 A.M. a second explosion rocked the area, but it was not attended by a tidal wave. At 4:35 P.M. there was still another loud explosion, followed by a small tidal wave, and throughout the night of the twenty-seventh and the early morning hours of the next day the explosions continued, although with decreasing intensity, and then virtually ceased.

The tremendous amount of ash blown into the air plunged the surrounding region into darkness which affected areas as much as 275 miles away. At a distance of 130 miles the darkness lasted for twenty-two hours, and at a distance of 50 miles for fifty-seven hours. Dust fell in quantity over a wide area (Fig. 8). Ships 1,600 miles away reported that dust began to fall on the decks three days after the eruption. The fine dust in the upper atmosphere traveled around the earth many times and remained in the atmosphere for months, causing sky glows, which were widely observed all over Europe and the United States, and which became a controversial issue, particularly in England. Tennyson records the event in verse as follows:

> Had the fierce ashes of some fiery Peak
> Been hurled so high they ranged round the World,
> For day by day through many a blood-red eve
> The wrathful sunset glared.[2]

This topic is discussed in more detail in the section dealing with Volcanic Solids (Chapter 5, pp. 48–50).

[2] Tennyson's "St. Telemachus."

After the eruption, two-thirds of the main island had disappeared, and where the land, before the explosion, had stood from 400 to 1,400 feet above sea level, was now a great cavity some 900 feet below sea level. The present caldera of Krakatoa has a diameter of approximately seven kilometers and consists of two basins, between which is a northwest-trending ridge where Bootsmansrots and the cinder cone of Anak Krakatoa are located (Fig. 6). Extending to the southwest and southeast from the caldera are elongate grabens. The southwest-trending graben is essentially parallel to the main volcanic chain of Sumatra, and the southeast-trending graben is on a tectonic line which passes through a series of volcanoes and intersects the main volcanic chain at a high angle. It seems apparent that the location of Krakatoa is determined by the intersection of these two fissure systems (Williams, 1941, p. 260).

Verbeck calculated that about five cubic miles of material was blown out of Krakatoa in the eruption, the greater part of which fell within a radius of eight to nine miles of the volcano. The well-bedded pumice deposits of the earlier phases of the eruption were the product of a Vulcanian-type eruption in which the ash was blown high into the air and drifted with the wind, while in the culminating explosions of August 27 the ash and pumice deposits were formed by *nuées ardentes* in which no sorting was possible. More significant, however, is that 95 percent of the ejecta consists of new material in the form of pumice and only 5 percent of old rock fragments from the former cones of Danan, Perboewatan, and Rakata. It follows, therefore, that these cones were not blown away but must have disappeared by collapse or engulfment into the magma chamber. Powerful support for the collapse theory comes from calculations which show that the volume of pumice erupted in 1883, when recalculated as magma, approximates closely the volume of material which disappeared. The close correlation between the volume of the erupted material and the volume of material which disappeared makes Krakatoa a splendid example of the "collapse-type" of caldera, and in some classifications of calderas this type is designated the "Krakatoa type."

After forty-four years of quiescence, Krakatoa renewed its activity in 1927, when eruptions began at the vent Anak Krakatoa on the floor of the caldera. From the beginning of its existence until October, 1952, the eruptive center was submarine, but during a vigorous eruption on October 10–11, 1952, a cinder cone emerged, rising 72 meters above sea level. There was more activity reported in March, 1953, and again in September of the same year, when eruptions destroyed vegetation over a considerable portion of the island. At this time the cone had attained a height of 116 meters and its crater had been enlarged by a displacement of the eruptive center. Decker (1959) reported that in 1959 eruptions were continuing at Anak Krakatoa and that a new cinder cone was forming in the center of the older crater.

Coseguina Volcano, Nicaragua

The eruption of Coseguina Volcano in 1835 has been regarded as the most violent historic eruption in the Western Hemisphere and one of the great caldera-forming eruptions of all time.

MEASUREMENT OF VOLCANIC EXPLOSIVENESS. Coseguina is a part of a belt of active volcanoes which extends along the Pacific coast from Guatemala to the Panamanian border, one segment in the "fire girdle of the Pacific" (Chapter 15).

One of the greatest concentrations of volcanoes in the entire belt is in Nicaragua, where there are six volcanoes currently in various states of activity: Concepción, Santiago, Momotombo, Las Pilas, Cerro Negro, and Telica. The activity ranges from brisk solfataric emissions to explosive discharges of ash with minor lava flows. In addition to being the center of the greatest concentration of volcanic vents, it is one of the most highly explosive volcanic regions on earth. Sapper (1927, p. 348), in an effort to compare the intensity of activity of various regions, devised an index of explosiveness:

$$\text{Index of explosiveness (E)} = \frac{\text{Quantity of fragmental material ejected}}{\text{Total ejected material}}$$

It has been shown in preceding chapters that in the most highly explosive volcanoes only ash, pumice, and other fragmental material are ejected. This is because the stiff, viscous, acid magma is so highly charged with gases that when the pressure is released the explosive expansion of the gases shatters the magma, and it is expelled as pumice and ash, and

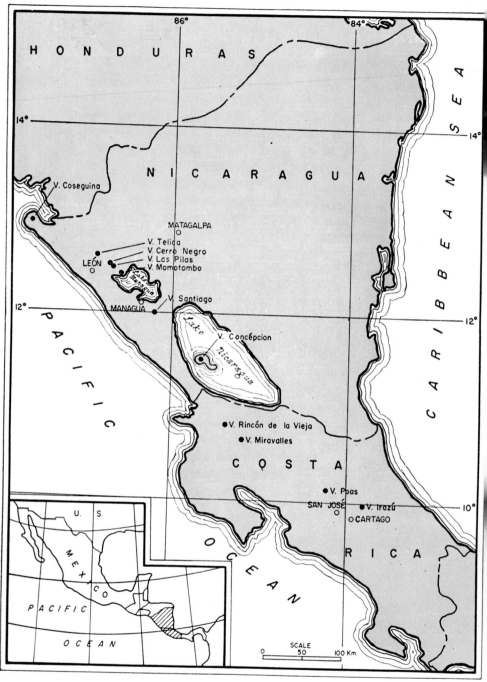

FIGURE 9. Active volcanoes of Costa Rica and Nicaragua.
From Bullard (1954).

no liquid (lava) material is ejected. This is the typical Peléan type of eruption. In the least explosive type (Hawaiian) the magma is more fluid, and the gases escape without disrupting the mass so that the material is ejected as lava. Thus the ratio of fragmental material to the total ejected material is a measure of the explosiveness. If all the erupted material is fragmental the volcano is 100 percent explosive; if all the ejected material is lava the volcano is 0 percent explosive.

Sapper calculated the emission of volcanic material throughout the world in the interval from 1500 to 1914. His estimate, notwithstanding the uncertainty of the figures for some areas, does give the order of magnitude and an over-all view of recent active volcanoes. According to Sapper's calculations the two areas tying for first place with $E = 99$ percent are the Malayan Archipelago and Central America. Within a given region the distribution of volcanoes is often very irregular. In order to determine the most explosive areas, Sapper compared the ratio between quantity of fluid lava and fragmental material per one hundred kilometers of distance along the volcanic belt and concluded that the most explosive zone on earth is the belt in Nicaragua, extending from Coseguina southeastward to Concepción Volcano in Lake Nicaragua. The 1835 eruption of Coseguina is the only historic example of the type of eruption which must have occurred thousands of times throughout the area in recent geologic time.

THE ERUPTION OF 1835. Coseguina is a great decapitated cone with an oval-shaped crater (caldera) from one to one and a half miles in diameter, occupying its summit. The crater, which is 1,500 to 2,000 feet deep and occupied by a clear blue lake, has precipitous walls, which reach a maximum elevation on the rim of 2,850 feet. Coseguina has an old "somma" ring[3] on the northern and western flanks approximately two-thirds of the way from the base, indicating that it had been disrupted and rebuilt at least once prior to the 1835 eruption.

There are no reliable accounts of eruptions of Coseguina prior to 1835, and it was generally regarded as extinct. The details of the great eruption are based largely on the eye-witness account of Vicente Romero, then commandant of the port of La Unión in El Salvador,

---

[3] *Somma* is the name applied to a remnant of an earlier crater rim.

thirty miles away across the Bay of Fonseca. Reports from more distant points tell little about the eruption other than the fall of ash, the duration of darkness, and the noise accompanying the eruption. Colonel Juan Galindo, who at the time was traveling along the Polochic River in Guatemala, has reported the most reliable information on the acoustical phenomena of the eruption. A recent description of this eruption by Williams (1952) reviews and evaluates the early accounts and adds much new information from field studies.

The inhabitants of La Unión, El Salvador, reported that about 8:00 A.M. on the morning of January 20 a white cloud, like an immense plume of feathers, rose from the top of Coseguina. It soon turned gray, then yellow, and finally crimson. Noteworthy was the absence of any preliminary earthquakes, although some rather severe shocks were felt around 4:00 P.M., about eight hours after the initial outbreak. By 11:00 A.M. the ash had so obscured the sky that lamps were lighted at La Unión. By midafternoon heavy showers of flourlike pumice were falling, and the darkness became complete, spreading terror and confusion among the inhabitants. At Nacaome, Honduras, 40 miles north of the volcano, the ash was three inches deep by 5:00 P.M., and at San Miguel, El Salvador, 50 miles to the northeast, there was complete darkness by 4:00 P.M., and the people "could not see their hands in front of their eyes." By nightfall the ash spread as far north as Tegucigalpa, 80 miles away, and San Salvador, 110 miles to the northeast.

On the morning of the second day conditions improved a little at San Miguel, but complete darkness, accompanied by strong earthquakes and subterranean noises, prevailed at La Unión. On Tigre Island, in the Gulf of Fonseca, 20 miles from the volcano, pumice fragments as large as hen eggs fell. Throughout the day the whole of Honduras was in darkness and some effects were observed in Guatemala City.

On the third day, January 22, the winds shifted to the southeast, and the section which had been relatively free of ash was now enveloped in it. At Chinandega, 50 miles south of the volcano, the ash fall was so thick that complete darkness prevailed. "The terror of the inhabitants at Alancho, anticipating the approach of the Judgment Day, was so great that three hundred of those living out of wedlock were married at once." The climax of the eruption, at least according to the distance at

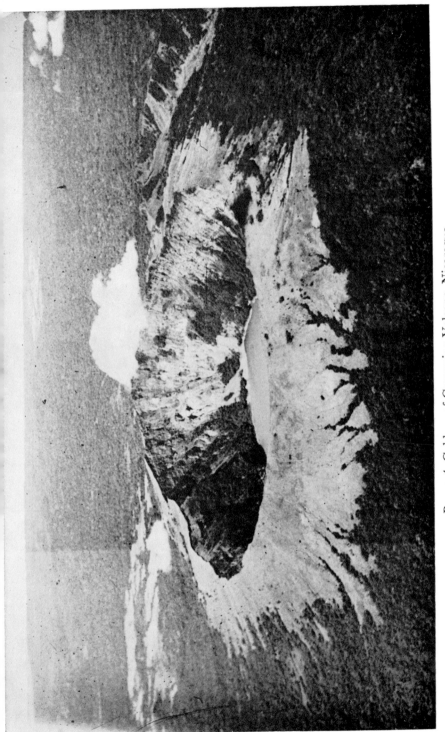

PLATE 4. Caldera of Coseguina Volcano, Nicaragua.

which the noise could be heard, appears to have come on the night of the twenty-second. Colonel Galindo, who was camped on the banks of the Polochic River in eastern Guatemala, heard sounds like artillery fire, which he thought were coming from Port Izabal. To the north, in British Honduras, "the superintendent at Belize, 400 miles distant, mustered the troops of his garrison, manned the fort, under the belief that there was a naval action off the harbor." (Squier, 1859, p. 756). The sounds were alarming as far away as Kingston, Jamaica, and Bogotá, Colombia. In Guatemala City the noises were so loud that the local barracks, thinking it was cannon fire of an approaching enemy, hastily prepared to defend themselves. In places the roar was practically continuous for seven hours, during which time the ash fall increased and complete darkness enveloped an area with a radius of about 50 miles. Most of El Salvador was obscured and ash fell as far north as Chiapas, Mexico, and on localities near the Costa Rican border.

On the following day, January 23, the activity began to decline, although fine ash continued to fall over El Salvador and Guatemala, and even at Jamaica, more than 800 miles to the east. At La Unión and León it started to clear, and conditions continued to improve on the twenty-fifth and twenty-sixth, although Guatemala City remained in darkness during this period. By the twenty-seventh the fall of ash had ceased, although some noises were heard in Guatemala City until the end of January. The main eruption, however, actually ceased on January 23, having lasted only four days.

For the next thirty-five or forty years, visitors who climbed to the rim of the crater reported some fumes and vapor columns issuing from cracks on the crater walls, but when visited by Sapper in 1879, no fumaroles were present.

VOLUME OF EJECTA. The tremendous quantity of material ejected was one of the remarkable features of the eruption. Squier (1859, p. 576) states that "the sea for 50 leagues was covered with floating masses of pumice, resembling the floe-ice of the Northern Atlantic." Estimates of the volume of ash ejected in the eruption of Coseguina vary from 150 cubic kilometers to as little as 10 cubic kilometers. The estimate by Reclus (1891) of 50 cubic kilometers is the figure most often quoted and was the figure used by Sapper in his computation of the index of explosiveness. Williams (1952, p. 36), from investigations of earlier reports and from field studies, concluded that the volume of ash erupted by Coseguina "may not have been greater than 10 cubic kilometers, and possibly was even less." How much of the mountain was destroyed in the eruption is not known, since there were no accurate descriptions of the cone before the eruption. The volume of the present crater approximates 4 cubic kilometers, and doubtless the diameter was considerably enlarged by the eruption. Williams (1952) concludes that perhaps about 5 cubic kilometers of material vanished. In his study of the ash and pumice deposits from the eruption, he calculated that not more than 7 percent of the total consisted of fragments of the old mountain top, the remainder being primary magmatic material. These figures indicate that only a small fraction of the part of the old cone which disappeared in the eruption could have been demolished by explosions. The alternative, of course, is engulfment. Thus, Coseguina has followed the same pattern in developing a caldera by collapse as was the case at Krakatoa and Crater Lake. The eruption is exceptional in its violence, its brief duration, the noise, and the quantity and fineness of the ash.

Thus we have seen how prolonged volcanic eruptions from a vent may construct a magnificent cone, some of which are among the most lofty mountains on earth. On the other hand, prolonged eruptions may also result in the destruction of the cone by so emptying the magma chamber that the cone, left unsupported, collapses into it (caldera formation).

PART TWO: *Types of Volcanic Eruptions*

Volcanic eruptions are one of the most awe-inspiring and ter-rifying phenomena of nature, having resulted in many of the great disasters of modern times. Their awesome grandeur is even more impressive when the processes of their behavior are well understood.

Volcanoes behave in varying ways and have been classified (Chapter 4) according to the nature of their eruptions. In Part Two these various types of eruptions will be explained, with a detailed description of a representative volcano for each type. A description of these types will give the reader a comprehensive view of the entire range of volcanic eruptions.

This section begins with the most explosive, or Peléan, type, and follows in succeeding chapters through the classification ending with the least explosive, or Icelandic, type. In each case a description is given of the geologic features of the region in which the type of volcano is included. A volcano is simply one manifestation of certain geologic conditions and by neces-sity the two cannot be separated. In most cases several vol-canoes in each region could serve equally well as types, and in a few instances additional examples are described in order to present a more complete account of the type of eruption.

Then the Lord rained ... fire and brim-stone ... and, lo, the smoke of the country went up as the smoke of a furnace.

GENESIS 19:24–28

7. PELÉAN TYPE OF VOLCANIC ERUPTION

THE PELÉAN TYPE OF ERUPTION, which is the extreme in explosiveness, is represented by many volcanoes in Central America and the West Indies. The type was first recognized in the eruption of Mount Pelée in 1902.

Stimulus to Volcanology

On May 9, 1902, the world was shocked at the news that St. Pierre, the largest and most beautiful city of the Lesser Antilles, had been annihilated by a tremendous eruption of the nearby volcano Mount Pelée. It seemed likely that the reports were grossly exaggerated. However, when the report was confirmed on the following day it brought the further news that La Soufrière on the island of St. Vincent had also erupted with much loss of life and property on the day preceding the St. Pierre catastrophe. Thus there were two disasters in the same area. The United States government immediately dispatched the cruiser *Dixie* with supplies for the stricken islands. It sailed from New York on May 14 carrying scientists representing various organizations to study the eruption. Among those making the trip were: Professor I. C. Russell from the University of Michigan, Dr. T. A. Jaggar from Harvard University, Dr. R. T. Hill and Mr. G. C. Curtis from the United States Geological Survey, and Dr. E. O. Hovey of the American Museum of Natural History. Others soon joined them, including Dr. A. Heilprin from the Geographical Society of Philadelphia and representatives from the scientific societies of England, France, and elsewhere. With such a distinguished group of scientists working in the field of volcanology, the hitherto obscure branch of science immediately became of first-order importance. In fact the stimulus which the eruption of Mount Pelée gave to the study of volcanoes was largely responsible for the rapid development of the science. Since the eruption of Mount Pelée did not conform to the then known types of volcanic eruptions a new classification and new theories were required to explain its activity. A brief review of the geography and geology of the region will be helpful in understanding the eruption of Mount Pelée and that of its neighbor, La Soufrière.

The Lesser Antilles

The Lesser Antilles, a group of islands which stretch "like piers of a bridge" across the entrance to the Caribbean Sea, form a part of the West Indies. In the shape of an arc, bowed out towards the Atlantic Ocean, they extend for 450 miles from the Anegada Passage just east of the Virgin Islands southward almost to the coast of South America. The northern islands are sometimes referred to as the Leeward Islands while the southern part is known as the Windward Islands because of their position with respect to the Trade Winds.

Geologically, the Lesser Antilles can be separated into two groups: (1) On the outer part of the arc to the northeast is an older, low-standing and long extinct series of submerged volcanoes capped by limestone deposits. This section is often called the Limestone Caribbees (Fig. 10).

(2) A younger, western and southern series of high-standing, more or less active volcanic islands are designated as the Volcanic Caribbees. This latter group constitutes a unique and peculiar geologic province similar to the island arcs in the Pacific Ocean. It is one of only two such features occurring in the Atlantic and has given rise to much speculation that geologically it belongs to the Pacific region.

All of the Lesser Antilles are oceanic islands; that is, they have been built up by volcanic action from the floor of the ocean. They stand on a submarine ridge with a basal width at the south of forty to sixty miles but with a northern range of over two hundred miles. The islands are bordered on either side by deep trenches on the ocean floor. To the north and east is the Brownson Trough and its extension, the Tobago Trough, and to the south and west is the shallower, less well defined Grenada Trough. Barbados and Tobago islands, lying to the south and east, are geologically a part of South America rather than a part of the Caribbees.

All of the Volcanic Caribbees have well-preserved and still more or less active volcanic cones. Only two, however, Mount Pelée on Martinique and La Soufrière on St. Vincent, have had violent eruptions in historic time. The eruptions of these two in 1902, only eighteen hours apart, with the loss of thousands of lives are described in the following pages. Nearly all the islands have "soufrière," or gas-and-steam, vents and boiling or hot springs attesting recent volcanic activity. Hill (1902, p. 221), after describing the islands as "pearls on a necklace," says: "Across the throat of the Caribbean extends a chain of islands, which are really smouldering furnaces, with fires banked up, ever ready to break forth at some unexpected and inopportune moment." The northern islands of the chain, like Saba (2,820 ft.) and St. Eustatius (1,950 ft.) are simple piles of volcanic material with dominating crater cones. Likewise, St. Kitts is dominated by Mount Misery (4,314 ft.) with a summit crater 1,000 feet deep in which there is a crater lake. Montserrat consists of six adjacent mountain masses, each of which represents an old volcano modified by long-continued erosion (MacGregor, 1939). The youngest and the highest volcano is Soufrière Hills (3,002 ft.), which contains a number of active fumaroles. No eruptions have occurred in historic time and the rather considerable erosion since the last

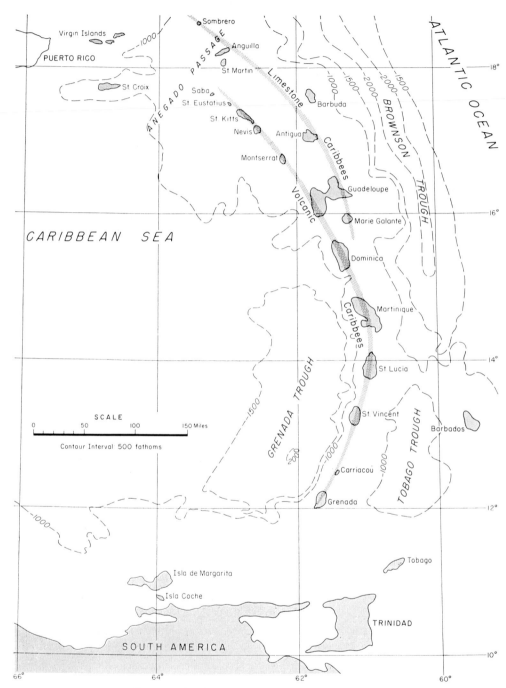

FIGURE 10. The Lesser Antilles, West Indies.

eruption indicates that possibly thousands of years have elapsed since the volcano was active. Near the center of the chain the five larger islands, Guadeloupe (4,869 ft.), Dominica (4,747 ft.), Martinique (4,800 ft.), St. Lucia (3,145 ft.), and St. Vincent (4,048 ft.) are each a complicated mass of old constructional and destructional volcanic forms. They indicate a series of eruptions in which, as the vent shifted, the cone was progressively destroyed and rebuilt.

Perret (1935, p. 114) believes that the volcanoes of the group, beginning with St. Kitts, illustrate an evolutionary sequence. Southward from St. Kitts are four great vents about equally spaced and progressively younger in the volcanic cycle. Mount Misery on St. Kitts is plugged by a massive lava dome and is probably extinct. The Soufrière on Guadeloupe is capped by a lava dome and its only activity is the emission of steam. Mount Pelée on Martinique is still active, but it is in the process of dome formation, while La Soufrière on St. Vincent thus far shows no signs of dome development.

In the earliest period of volcanic activity in this area extensive lava flows alternated with ash and fragmental debris. However, in recent eruptions the volcanoes erupted only fragmental material which formed the conspicuous cones and volcanic masses now present. The geologic history of the Lesser Antilles is not fully known but it is apparent that the older Limestone Caribbees began on a submarine ridge and by volcanic up-piling built a string of islands. These were then submerged and covered by limestone deposits. Schuchert (1935, p. 728) believes that they may have started as early as late Cretaceous and were submerged by early Tertiary time. This view is based on the fact that the oldest limestone known in the islands is of upper Eocene Age. The younger chain, the Volcanic Caribbees, may have existed as a submarine ridge as early as Oligocene time, but most of the islands do not contain coral reefs older than Pleistocene. Further, the chain probably developed progressively so that it is not of the same age throughout.

Studies at Bermuda, an isolated island 580 miles east of the coast of South Carolina and about 1,000 miles north of the Lesser Antilles, have been helpful in deciphering the geologic history of this region. Bermuda is a volcanic cone capped by limestone. A broad plain rising about six thousand feet above the ocean floor is surmounted by a typical volcanic cone six thousand feet in height. The cone was submerged (and doubt-less eroded) and a thick layer of coral limestone was deposited on the submerged crest, which now forms the surface rocks at Bermuda. The history could only be surmised until a well drilled in search of water revealed the complete story. The well penetrated 380 feet of limestone before passing into weathered basaltic material, showing that it had been washed to and fro by the sea. Below this material the top of the cone was encountered. The limestone was determined, on the basis of its fossil content, to be of Oligocene Age.

Mount Pelée, Martinique Island
Early history

Mount Pelée, or more properly Montagne Pelée, which prior to its catastrophic eruption of May 8, 1902, was scarcely known beyond its own little territory, makes up the northern end of the Island of Mar-tinique in the Lesser Antilles of the West Indies. When it was first de-scribed, about 1640, it was called "Bald Mountain," from a bare spot near its summit. The name Pelée was applied much later and presum-ably is from the French, (*pelé*, "peeled")for bald. However, the Hawaiian goddess of volcanoes is Pele, and one begins to wonder if there may not be some connection between the two. Definite knowledge concerning the history of Mount Pelée extends back only to the time of the first French settlement on Martinique in 1635. Prior to 1902 only two minor eruptions of Mount Pelée are recorded, neither of which was very serious or resulted in loss of life. The first was in 1792 and the other in 1851. The 1851 eruption, after some deep rumblings, threw out a column of ash, which settled over the southwest side of the moun-tain, extending as far as St. Pierre. The eruption was over in a few hours and did not cause alarm among the inhabitants.

The cone

Mount Pelée is a roughly circular cone culminating in a single peak from which the broken surface slopes in all directions to the sea, except on the southeast, where its slope meets the ruins of the older twin cone of Carbet (3,917 ft.). The slopes of Mount Pelée are deeply cut by ravines which radiate from the summit. Nearly all of them, not more

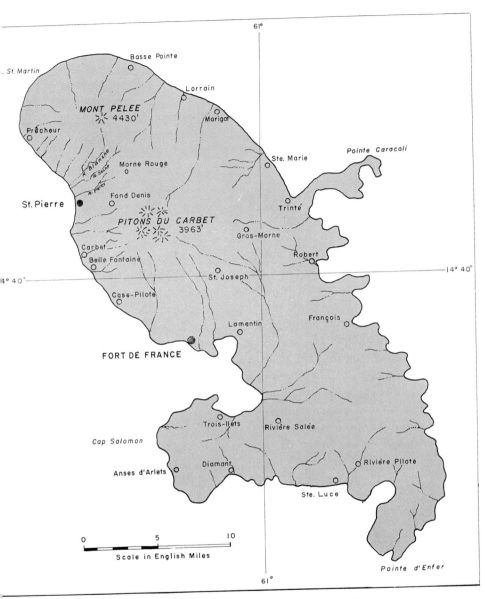

FIGURE 11. Island of Martinique, Lesser Antilles.

than four or five miles in length, discharge flood waters into the sea. They are the site of destructive floods during periods of heavy rain, carrying huge boulders and debris and spreading destruction in their path. The best known is that named Rivière Blanche, because of its connection with the 1902 eruption. It was the flow of boiling mud down its channel on May 5 which buried the sugar mill and caused the first loss of life in the eruption. Mount Pelèe appears to be a part of a complex volcanic mass which has been destroyed and rebuilt as the eruptive center shifts its location. Morne Siberie and Piton Pierreux, the latter nearly two thousand feet in elevation, are prominent relics of the older mass. The volcano itself covers an area of about fifty square miles.

A description of the condition of the summit and crater of the volcano at that time will be helpful in following the events of the 1902 eruption. Of course, the crater of a volcano is usually altered rather extensively by an eruption. The summit of Mount Pelée, before the eruption, was occupied by a bowl-shaped basin, the floor of an old caldera which had existed since prehistoric time. Around the rim of the basin was a series of peaks, of which Morne La Croix, the highest, stood about two thousand feet above the floor. On the floor of the caldera was a lake, L'Etang de Palmistes, a popular picnic spot. The crater which gave rise to the 1902 eruption, known as L'Etang Sec, was somewhat below the summit on the south side, overlooking the city of St. Pierre. It was an oval-shaped depression about one-half mile in diameter at the top and surrounded on all sides, except the southwest, by precipitous cliffs. On the southwest, through a great gash cutting fully a thousand feet below the rim, the crater drained into the canyon of the Rivière Blanche. This great cleft is an important element in the 1902 eruption because it was responsible for directing the explosions toward St. Pierre. In the 1851 eruption the lake in L'Etang Sec dried up, but there was no other evidence of any activity in the crater. For years prior to 1902 there was a small fumarole on the floor of L'Etang Sec.

The eruption of 1902

The first signs of activity were observed on April 2 by Professor Landes, of the natural science faculty of the St. Pierre Lycée, who noticed steaming fumaroles in the upper valley of Rivière Blanche. On April 23 a slight fall of ash and a strong odor of sulphur were noticeable in the streets of St. Pierre, and a few minor earthquake shocks caused dishes to fall from shelves. On April 25 explosions occurred in the basin of L'Etang Sec, sending ash clouds and rocks into the air. Visitors who climbed to the rim of the crater on April 27 reported that the normally dry bed of L'Etang Sec was occupied by a lake at least two hundred yards in diameter, and that a small cinder cone, hardly more than thirty feet high, had formed at one side. From its summit rose a column of steam, issuing with a vigorous "boiling" noise. Light falls of ash covered the streets of St. Pierre, giving a wintry look to the city. During the days that followed, the ash falls became heavier, blocking roads and forcing business houses to close. The roar of the explosions from the volcano and the continued fall of ash caused consternation among the inhabitants. Many birds and some larger animals were smothered by the ash or asphyxiated by poisonous gases from the ash. The local newspaper, *Les Colonies*, reported in its May 3 issue:

The rain of ashes never ceases. At about half-past nine the sun shone forth timidly. The passing of carriages in the streets is no longer heard. The wheels are muffled [in the layer of ash]. Puffs of wind sweep the ashes from the roofs and awnings, and blow them into rooms of which the windows have imprudently been left open.

This was followed by a list of closed business houses and an announcement that the excursion planned for L'Etang de Palmistes on the day following had been cancelled. Many of the inhabitants of St. Pierre were in fear and panic and they left the city in large numbers, but they were replaced by refugees from the outlying areas who crowded into the city to swell by several thousand its normal population of 26,000. The panic reached such proportions that some action seemed necessary.

A commission appointed by the French governor at Fort de France to investigate the danger from the volcano reported the existence of no immediate danger and no reason for abandoning the city. There is some suspicion that the governor and the newspaper were anxious to keep the people in St. Pierre until after an important election scheduled for

Sunday, May 10. The governor, in order to reassure the population, made a visit to St. Pierre with his wife for a personal inspection, and both were victims of the tragedy which overwhelmed St. Pierre.

Heavy rains sent floods of chocolate-colored water down all the valleys on the southwest side of Mount Pelée. Shortly after noon on May 5 the sugar mill at the mouth of the Rivière Blanche, two miles north of St. Pierre, was destroyed by a torrent of boiling mud which swept down the stream valley with express-train speed. Thirty or more workmen (the estimates run as high as 150) were entombed in the boiling mud, which left only the chimney visible to mark the location of the mill. The mud swept into the sea, extending the coast line and creating a huge wave which overturned two boats tied at anchor and washed the adjacent coast, flooding the lower portion of St. Pierre. The tragedy at the sugar mill was the first loss of life due directly to the volcano.

A later reconstruction of events explained how this catastrophe was caused. The accumulation of ash in the basin of L'Etang Sec formed a dam, which blocked the gorge and permitted a large quantity of water to collect in the old lake basin. The water, heated by volcanic action, broke the dam shortly after noon on May 5, because of an explosion or increased pressure, and rushed from its height of nearly three thousand feet as a deluge of mud and boulders down the Rivière Blanche. By the time it reached the lower slopes it had become an avalanche of mud, carrying huge boulders, rocks, and immense trees, and moving with precipitate speed. It swept over the sugar mill and on into the sea.

Jaggar (1949) takes exception to the view that the water causing the disastrous mudflow was from L'Etang Sec. He maintains that a fracture (rift zone) follows the gorge of Rivière Blanche from the crater to the sea and that eruptions of hot gases along this fracture converted the ground water into a flood of boiling mud. He argues that ground water must be involved since some of the hot mudflows occurred without corresponding rainfall on the upper slope of the mountain and further that the tremendous speed of the flows can be explained only by the migration of the eruptions along the fracture. Extension of crater blasts to lateral rift zones is a common feature in many volcanic eruptions and it is possible that such was the case in the eruption of Mount Pelée.

On the date of the disaster at the sugar mill, *Les Colonies* reported:

"A flood of humanity poured up from the low point of the Mouilage. It was a flight for safety, not knowing where to turn. The entire city was afoot. The shops and private houses are closing. Everyone is preparing to seek refuge on the heights." Although the volcano was in constant eruption, the people were expecting an earthquake or a tidal wave, and the danger from the volcano was not anticipated.

On May 6 the eruption was particularly violent, explosions being heard in the neighboring islands, and the exodus from St. Pierre continued on foot and by steamer to Fort de France and the neighboring island of St. Lucia. The governor ordered soldiers to guard the roads to halt the flight. *Les Colonies* on this date declared that the alarm was not justified, and on the next day, the eve of the catastrophe, said: "Mount Pelée is no more to be feared by St. Pierre than Vesuvius is feared by Naples. We confess we cannot understand this panic. Where could one be better off than at St. Pierre?"

The eruptions continued on May 7, with lightning flashing through the dense cloud of ash which rose with each outburst. All of the streams on the slopes of Mount Pelée were carrying torrents of mud and water, spreading destruction in their paths. These floods were due to the heavy rains on the slope of the mountain, which converted the fine ash into a mud. Such streams of mud are able to transport huge boulders, even up to many tons in weight. On the afternoon of May 7 news of the eruption of La Soufrière on St. Vincent, ninety miles to the south, was received. This gave the eruption-weary inhabitants of Martinique some hope, for it was generally believed that the eruption on St. Vincent would relieve the pressure on Mount Pelée and thus prevent a serious outbreak. It was with some degree of reassurance that the people retired to their homes for the last fateful night in the history of St. Pierre.

The morning of May 8 dawned bright and sunny, with nothing in the appearance of Mount Pelée to excite suspicion except the immense column of vapor rising from the crater. The column was not particularly dark in color but it did seem to be rising to an unusual height. At about 6:30 A.M. the ship *Roraima,* her decks covered with grey ashes, came into the port at St. Pierre and tied up alongside the seventeen other vessels in the roadstead. At 7:50 A.M. the volcano exploded with four deafening, gunlike reports, discharging upward from the main crater a black cloud pierced with lightning flashes. Another shot out laterally and with hurricane speed rolled down the mountain slope, keeping contact with the ground like an avalanche. In a short two minutes it had overwhelmed St. Pierre and spread fanlike out to sea. The clock on the tower of the Hospital Militaire was stopped at 7:52 A.M.—and practically instantly the entire population of nearly 30,000 was obliterated. The lateral and vertical discharges appeared to be identical except for direction. Observers who witnessed it from the side as well as from boats in the roadstead described it as a black, rolling cloud, like a blast from a huge cannon. Although some reported seeing flames in the cloud, the evidence on this is confusing, since many people associate flame with heat and, being burned by the blast, described it as flaming.

The blast consisted of superheated steam filled with even hotter dust particles traveling with a velocity of around a hundred miles per hour. The dust particles gave the cloud a greater density than normal atmospheric gases have. This unusual density increased the destructiveness of the cloud by keeping it in contact with the ground and by increasing its capacity for devastation, which was greater than that of a West Indies hurricane of the same wind velocity. All the houses in St. Pierre were unroofed, and otherwise demolished either in part or totally. The trees were stripped of leaves and branches down to the bare trunk. The force of the blast is shown by the fact that walls of cement and stone, three feet in thickness, were torn to pieces as though made of cardboard, six-inch cannon on the Morne d'Orange Battery were sheared from their mountings, century-old trees were uprooted, and a statue of the Virgin Mary, weighing at least three tons, was carried fifty feet from its base. Since there were no windows in the houses in St. Pierre, it being a tropical city, the highly heated gas quickly penetrated every part of the buildings and almost instantly the city was in flames. Those that were not instantly killed by the initial blast were doubtless burned in the fires that followed. Even at 11:30 A.M., three and one-half hours after the initial blast, the heat from the burning city was so intense that a ship from Port de France could not approach the shore.

All of the ships in the roadstead, save two, were capsized. The British steamer *Roddam*, set free by the parting of her anchor chain, succeeded in escaping to St. Lucia, where twelve of her men arrived dead and ten so severely burned that they had to be hospitalized. The other ship to survive was the *Roraima,* which had just arrived an hour earlier. Its mast, bridge, funnel, and boats were swept away and she took fire fore and aft. Of her crew of forty-seven, twenty-eight died from shock and burns, and only two of the passengers, a little girl and her nurse, escaped alive. Dr. Jaggar (1945, p. 142) personally interviewed the colored Barbados nurse of the little girl on the *Roraima,* who gave the following account:

We had been watching the volcano sending up smoke. The Captain (who was killed) said to my mistress, "I am not going to stay any longer than I can help." I went to the cabin and was assisting with dressing the children for breakfast when the steward (who was later killed by the blast) rushed past and shouted, "Close the cabin door—the volcano is coming!" We closed the door and at the same moment came a terrible explosion which nearly burst the eardrums. The vessel was lifted high into the air, and then seemed to be sinking down, down. We were all thrown off our feet by the shock and huddled crouching in one corner of the cabin. My mistress had the girl baby in her arms, the older girl leaned on my left arm, while I held little Eric in my right.

The explosion seemed to have blown in the skylight over our heads, and before we could raise ourselves, hot moist ashes began to pour in on us; they came in boiling splattering splashes like moist mud without any pieces of rock. In vain we tried to shield ourselves. The cabin was pitch dark— we could see nothing—.

A sense of suffocation came next [but] when the door burst open, air rushed in and we revived somewhat. When we could see each others' faces, they were all covered with black lava, the baby was dying, Rita, the older girl was in great agony and every part of my body was paining me. A heap of hot mud had collected near us and as Rita put her hand down to raise herself up it was plunged up to the elbow in the scalding stuff—.

The first engineer came now, and hearing our moans carried us to the forward deck and there we remained on the burning ship from 8:30 A.M. until 3:00 P.M. The crew was crowded forward, many in a dying condition. The whole city was one mass of roaring flames and the saloon aft as well as the forward part of the ship were burning fiercely; but they afterwards put out the fire.

My mistress lay on the deck in a collapsed state; the little boy was already dead, and the baby dying. The lady was collected and resigned, handed me some money, told me to take Rita to her aunt, and sucked a piece of ice before she died.

Assistant Purser Thompson, one of the survivors on the *Roraima,* describes the eruption as follows (Quoted by Leet, 1948, p. 8):

I saw St. Pierre destroyed. It was blotted out by one great flash of fire. Nearly 40,000 people were killed at once. Of 18 vessels lying in the Roads, only one, the British steamship Roddam escaped and she, I hear, lost more than half on board. It was a dying crew that took her out. Our boat arrived at St. Pierre early Thursday morning. For hours before we entered the roadstead, we could see flames and smoke rising from Mt. Pelée. No one on board had any idea of danger. Capt. G. T. Muggah was on the bridge and all hands got on deck to see the show. The spectacle was magnificent. As we approached St. Pierre, we could distinguish the rolling and leaping red flames that belched from the mountain in huge volume and gushed high in the sky. Enormous clouds of black smoke hung over the volcano. The flames were then spurting straight up in the air, now and then waving to one side or the other a moment, and again leaping suddenly higher up. There was a constant muffled roar. It was like the biggest oil refinery in the world burning up on the mountain top. There was a tremendous explosion about 7:45 soon after we got in. The mountain was blown to pieces. There was no warning. The side of the volcano was ripped out, and there hurled straight towards us a solid wall of flame. It sounded like a thousand cannon. The wave of fire was on us and over us like a lightning flash. It was like a hurricane of fire, which rolled in mass straight down on St. Pierre and the shipping. The town vanished before our eyes, and then the air grew stifling hot and we were in the thick of it. Wherever the mass of fire struck the sea, the water boiled and sent up great clouds of steam. I saved my life by running to my stateroom and burying myself in the bedding. The blast of fire from the volcano lasted only for a few minutes. It shriveled and set fire to everything it touched. Burning rum ran in streams down every street and out into the sea. Before the volcano burst, the landings at St. Pierre were crowded with people. After the explosion, not one living being was seen on land. Only 25 of those on the Roraima, out of 68, were left after the first flash. The fire swept off the ship's masts and smoke stack as if they had been cut by a knife.

Of the entire population of St. Pierre, only two survived the catastrophe. Auguste Ciparis, a twenty-five–year–old Negro stevedore, was a prisoner in an underground dungeon at the time of the blast. It will be recalled that the destruction of the city occurred at 7:52 A.M. on Thursday, May 8. Because of the hot ashes, which prevented rescuers from entering the area, it was not until Sunday that the cries of the prisoner were heard and he was rescued. His cell was windowless and the only opening was a small grated space in the upper part of the door. Auguste Ciparis was badly burned on his back and legs, but he survived and was able to give a coherent account of his experience.[1]

He related that he was waiting for the usual breakfast on the eighth, when it suddenly grew dark, and simultaneously hot air and ashes entered his cell through the door grating. His flesh was immediately burned and though he called for help, none came. The intense heat lasted only for an instant, and during that time he almost ceased to breathe. He did not recall any noise or odor, other than his "own flesh burning." He was wearing at the time, a hat, shirt, and trousers, but no shoes. Some of the most severe burns were on his back beneath his shirt. When seen by Kennan the burns were almost too horrible to describe and it seemed doubtful that he would survive. However, Auguste Ciparis recovered and later as "the prisoner of St. Pierre" became a side-show attraction in a circus.

Later it was discovered that Leon Compere-Leandre, a Negro about twenty-eight years old and strongly built, had also survived. He was a shoemaker by trade. He described his experience as follows:[2]

On May 8, about eight o'clock in the morning, I was seated on the doorstep of my house, which was in the southeast part of the city——. All of a sudden I felt a terrible wind blowing, the earth began to tremble, and the sky suddenly became dark. I turned to go into the house, made with great difficulty the 3 or 4 steps that separated me from my room, and felt my arms and legs burning, also my body. I dropped upon a table. At this moment four others sought refuge in my room, crying and writhing with pain, although their garments showed no sign of having been touched by flame. At the end of ten minutes one of these, the young Delavaud girl,

[1] Reported by George Kennan, who interviewed him a few days after he was rescued and before his burns had been treated, in Outlook, Vol. 71, July 26, 1902.

[2] Quoted by A. Heilprin in Mount Pelée and the Tragedy of Martinique, p. 119, 1903.

aged 10, fell dead; the others left. I then got up and went into another room, where I found the father Delavaud, still clothed and lying on the bed, dead. He was purple and inflated, but the clothing was intact. I went out and found in the court two corpses interlocked; they were the bodies of the two young men who had been with me in the room. Re-entering the house, I came upon the bodies of two men who had been in the garden when I returned to my house at the beginning of the catas-trophe. Crazed and almost overcome, I threw myself upon a bed, inert and awaiting death. My senses returned to me in perhaps an hour, when I beheld the roof burning. With sufficient strength left, my legs bleeding and covered with burns, I ran to Fonds-Saint-Denis, 6 kilometers from St. Pierre. With the exception of the persons of whom I have spoken, I heard no human cries; I experienced no degree of suffocation, and it was only the air that was lacking to me. But it was burning. There were neither ashes nor mud. The entire city was aflame.

At the time of the catastrophe St. Pierre was the most important commercial city on Martinique and one of the best-known in the entire region. It was located in a crescent-shaped strip about a mile long and one-fourth mile wide, lying between the curving beach and a corre-sponding curving ridge or steep hill on the landward side. The main street, Rue Victor Hugo, ran from one end of the crescent to the other and was crossed at intervals by shorter streets leading from the water-front and ending against the high, partly terraced ridge on the landward side. Although there were a number of large buildings such as the cathe-dral, the town hall, and the military hospital, in the main the city con-sisted of two- and three-story stone buildings with red tile roofs, located on narrow, crooked streets, such as is typical of the tropics. It was a gay, water-front city sometimes called the "Paris of the West Indies."

After the catastrophe the destruction of the city was almost beyond imagination. The wrecked walls, the cover of grey ash, and the absence of signs of life made the ruins appear ancient. It was impossible to realize that only a few minutes before the blast it had been the site of a flourishing city. No building remained standing and the destruction was so complete that the greater number of building sites were un-recognizable even to those familiar with the city. Only bare walls were left standing, most frequently those which were parallel to the direction

PLATE 5. Ruins of St. Pierre after its destruction by a *nuée ardente* on May 8, 1902. Photograph by Lacroix (1904). Courtesy Académie des Sciences (France).

of the blast. In most instances all that remained of the houses was their foundations, covered with a heap of rubble mixed with bedsteads, twisted iron braces, and mangled sheets of metal roofing—some of which were wrapped around posts as though they were made of cloth. Iron girders and steel bars were twisted into a mangled mass as if they were made of rope. There is no way of describing a city so completely wrecked other than to say that it was a chaotic mass of rubble, plaster, roofing tile, and shattered walls, with here and there a fire-scorched branchless trunk of a big tree.

The greater part of the destruction was the result of the highly heated hurricanelike blast together with the hot dust, which set fire to inflammable objects. The highly heated ash fell only in moderate amounts in comparison to the ash falls in many volcanic eruptions. Heilprin reported

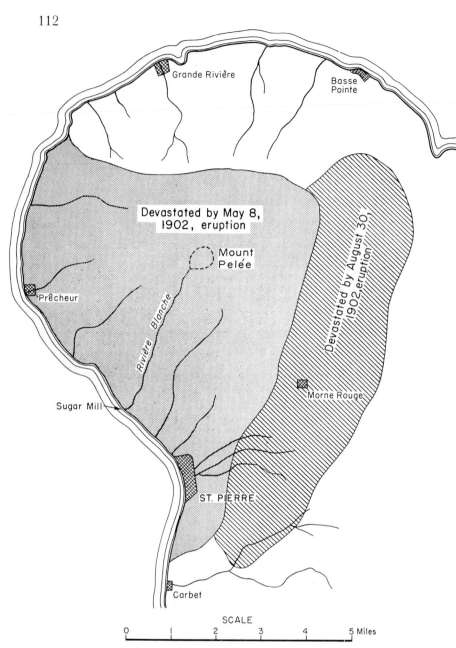

FIGURE 12. Devastated areas in the May 8 and the August 30, 1902, eruptions of Mount Pelée.

May 8th area after Hovey (1902) and August 30th area after Heilprin (1903).

that in drifts it rarely exceeded three to four feet in depth and that over the greater part of the city it was hardly more than a foot. Compared to the twenty-five or more feet which buried Pompeii this is insignificant. The death and destruction were not due to ash alone. Water, perhaps from the steam in the eruption cloud, mixed with the ash in the air to form a mud which plastered everything.

The temperature of the blast can be only estimated from its effect on objects where no conflagration took place. Glass objects were softened (650°–700° C.), green juicy fruits were carbonized, wooden decks of ships in the roadstead well offshore were set afire, but the melting point of copper, (1,058° C.) was not reached. Perret (1935) concluded from his study of similar eruptions of Mount Pelée in 1929–1932 that the temperature at the point of emission at the crater was around 1,200° C. The powerful expansion incident to escape of the gas would cause much cooling, but it is apparent that it still retained a heat of several hundred degrees centigrade when it reached St. Pierre, eight kilometers from its source.

In many cases the victims at St. Pierre were stripped of their clothing by the force of the blast. Some showed signs of momentary struggle but the great majority gave no evidence that they had stirred after the fiery blast struck them. Death was the result of inhaling the highly heated gases or from burns, and in many cases it appeared to have been almost instantaneous. It is unfortunate that no autopsies were performed on any of the victims to determine the true cause of their deaths.

The zone of destruction covered an area of about eight square miles. In the middle (Fig. 12) was a belt in which complete annihilation occurred, gradually decreasing in intensity toward either margin, where at the extreme edge objects were only scorched. Heilprin concludes, quite correctly, that the blast consisted of superheated steam, charged with incandescent particles of matter. Magma rising in the chimney of the volcano is highly charged with steam and under enormous pressure. As the magma rises it reaches a point where the weight of the overlying rocks in the throat or a weak spot in the walls of the chimney is unable to contain the pressure, and it is suddenly released with a tremendous explosion. The magma is shattered into fine dust which, mixed with superheated steam, is shot out like the discharge from a colossal gun.

Such blasts, unknown or unrecognized prior to the eruption of Mount Pelée, are now known to be characteristic of the gas-rich acid magmas which give rise to the most explosive types of eruptions. From his study of the 1902 eruption of Mount Pelée, Lacroix (1908) described such blasts as *nuées ardentes* or "glowing clouds." He believed from his study at Mount Pelée that the force of the blast was due to the direction of expulsion from the vent, more like a directed blast. Anderson and Flett (1902), representatives of the Royal Society of London and experienced observers of volcanoes, on the evening of July 9, 1902, were studying the effects of the great May 8, 1902 disaster. From a vessel a short distance offshore near Carbet they observed the eruption of a *nuée ardente* from Mount Pelée. Their description, one of the first of a *nuée ardente* by a trained observer, is as follows:

As darkness deepened a dull red reflection was seen in the trade wind cloud which covered the mountain summit. This became brighter and brighter and soon we saw red stones projecting from the crater, bowling down the mountain slopes and giving off glowing sparks. Suddenly the cloud was illuminated and the sailor cried, "The mountain bursts!" In an incredibly short span of time a red-hot avalanche swept down to sea. We could not see the summit owing to the intervening veil of clouds; but the fissure and the lower part of the mountain were clear, and the glowing cataract poured over them right down to the shore of the bay. It was dull red, with a billowy surface, reminding one of a snow avalanche. In it there were large stones, which stood out as streaks of bright red, tumbling down and emitting showers of sparks. In a few minutes it was over. A low angry growl had burst from the mountain when this avalanche was launched from the crater. The time occupied by the avalanche to reach the sea was "possibly a couple of minutes." There is no doubt that the eruption we witnessed was a counterpart of that which destroyed St. Pierre. . . . a mass of incandescent lava rises and rolls over the lip of the crater in the form of an avalanche of red hot dust. It is lava blown to pieces by the expansion of the gases it contains. It rushes down the slope of the hill, carrying with it a terrific blast which mows down everything in its path. The mixture of dust and gases behaves in many ways like a fluid. . . . They [the gases] consist apparently of steam and sulphurous acid.

This accurate and vivid description reveals many of the character-

PLATE 6. *Nuée ardente* eruption at Mount Pelée, December 16, 1902. Height of the eruption cloud is 13,000 feet.

Photograph by Lacroix (1904). Courtesy Académie des Sciences (France).

istics of a *nuée ardente,* which have been verified by subsequent investigators. It has been clearly shown by Perret (1935) in his studies of the 1929–1932 eruption of Mount Pelée, in which many *nuées ardentes* were emitted, that it is the expansion and compression of the gases being constantly emitted by the magma fragments in their downward rush that give the *nuées ardentes* their great speed and power. In effect, the explosions (rapid expansion) of the gases in the glowing cloud continue as the mass moves forward at a tremendous velocity. Such a mass, in which the solid particles are suspended in a gas, is an example of fluidization as described by Reynolds (1954). MacGregor (1951), in a critical review of published observations on the 1902 eruption of Mount Pelée, confirms Perret's conclusion that the mobility of the *nuées ardentes* was created by the "self-explosive (gas-generating) properties of fragments of new lava."

The Peléan type of eruption is characterized by the expulsion of *nuées ardentes.* All of the magma is expelled in this type of activity as pumice and ash and no liquid lava flows develop. In the final stage of the eruption, as is described later, a mass of viscous lava may accumulate in a domelike formation in the crater. This happens when the gas content of the magma is reduced to the point that it no longer shatters the magma on reaching the surface. Instead, it is pushed up into a dome or, as in the case of Mount Pelée, into a huge spine projecting from the crater like a giant stopper.

Following the destruction of St. Pierre on May 8, 1902, Mount Pelée continued intermittent eruptions of the same type (*nuées ardentes*) for several months. One of these, following almost the identical path traversed by that of May 8, and equal to it in violence, on May 20 completed the destruction of St. Pierre. Any walls which had survived the first blast were leveled. Other violent eruptions occurred on May 26, June 6, July 9, and August 30. The path of the last extended somewhat to the east of the previous ones (Fig. 12) and annihilated or partially destroyed five villages, adding two thousand victims to the death toll of Mount Pelée. Among the villages was Morne Rouge, a spot from which many observed the initial blast of May 8.

The Tower of Pelée

About the middle of October a domelike mass of lava, too stiff to flow, formed in the L'Etang Sec crater, and from its surface a spine or obelisk was protruded. This remarkable "Tower of Pelée," with a diameter of 350 to 500 feet, in a few months reached a maximum height of 1,020 feet above the crater floor (5,200 feet above sea level). There is some uncertainty as to the exact date at which the lava dome began to form in the crater. Some reports indicate that it began to appear as early as July or August, but it did not attract attention until the spine began to rise from it. The French Scientific Commission reported the spine on October 15, 1902, and by the end of November it had reached a height of 800 feet, rising like a giant stopper from the crater. Its rise was irregular but it averaged about 30 feet per day. Huge blocks were continually breaking from the top and its height was lowered only to be replaced by upheaval. The maximum height was reached on May 30, 1903, when it was 1,020 feet above the crater floor. At that time an eruption caused 180 feet of the top to crumble, and thereafter the upheaval did not keep pace with the crumbling. By the middle of August it had been reduced to a height of about 500 feet, and the eruptions, which became more frequent during August, September, and into November, aided in the disintegration. Even after the spine ceased to rise it continued to grow by swelling near the base as a result of the addition of stiff lava rising from below.

The phenomena attending the growth of the lava dome were the same as those accompanying an eruption. Great steam clouds carrying some ash rose 10,000 to 12,000 feet above the summit and loud detonations accompanied frequent discharges of "black clouds" of ash. Many of the "black clouds" were in fact, *nuées ardentes*. Heilprin reported that the dome appeared brilliantly incandescent and at night a red glow was reflected on the clouds overhead. During this period of renewed activity the spine was again pushed upward through its own rubble until it reached a height of 500 feet. The most rapid development was on August 31, 1903, when it rose 78 feet in one day. Thereafter the dome continued to disintegrate until it consisted only of a stump in the middle of a heap of rubble. There was some activity until the early part of 1904.

Significance of the spine

As was true of *nuées ardentes*, the nature of such lava domes was not appreciated prior to the eruption of Mount Pelée in 1902. Since then, such features have been recognized in many volcanoes and their significance is better understood. In volcanoes of the more acid type, such as Mount Pelée, since the lava is very stiff and viscous the chimney is commonly sealed after an eruption. The situation is quite different in the more basic types of volcanoes, such as Stromboli, in which the lava in contact with the air may remain liquid and the gases may continue to escape. In the Peléan type, with the chimney sealed, the gases accumulate until the upper part of the magma column becomes thoroughly gas-saturated. The initial stage of a new eruption consists of the explosive expulsion of the highly gas-charged magma, which is shattered into dust particles by the rapidly expanding gas, forming *nuées ardentes*. It must be remembered that this material is as truly primary magma as the more conventional liquid lava which flows from the more basic volcanoes. Following the expulsion of the highly gas-charged material, which in the 1902 eruption of Mount Pelée required about four months (May through August), there is a decrease in the explosive activity. The lava, now relatively gas-free, and therefore highly viscous, begins to rise in the conduit and slowly accumulates in the crater as a lava dome (known as a "tholoid"). It is accompanied by *nuées ardentes* of decreasing intensity. Occasionally spines, or, as in the case of Mount Pelée, giant monoliths, are forced up from cracks in the surface of the lava dome. One surface of the great spine of 1903 on Mount Pelée was molded by the curving wall of the crevice through which it emerged, showing grooved and striated surfaces indicating its semirigid nature. The core of the spine is more fluid and lava often exudes from the base.

Dome formation is an indication that a volcano is in the final stage of its history. In the early stages of the history of a volcano of this type the eruptions keep the crater clear, and, in fact, they frequently decapitate the cone, leaving a huge caldera. New eruptions begin on the floor of the caldera, build up cones, only to be destroyed again. Mount Pelée shows remnants of several ancient calderas of which L'Etang Sec, the site of the 1902 eruption, was one. The formation of a lava dome in the

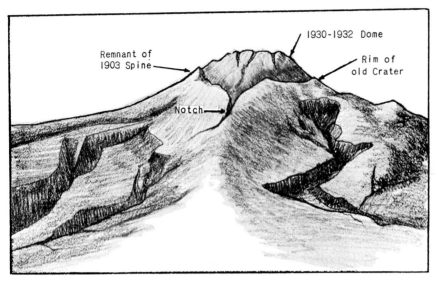

FIGURE 13. Lava dome in the crater of Mount Pelée, April 30, 1934.
Sketched from a photograph by Perret (1935).

crater is an indication that the eruptive force is decreasing. The dome may be disrupted or even partially destroyed and rebuilt by succeeding eruptions but its presence is an indication that the eruptive history of the volcano is nearing its end.

Eruption of 1929

The next major eruption of Mount Pelée, following the 1902 outbreak, began on September 16, 1929, and lasted until near the close of 1932, or a little more than three years. The eruption was similar to that of 1902, although of somewhat less intensity. St. Pierre, which by this time had grown to be a town with a population of about 1,000, and other villages on the western side of the volcano, were evacuated; so there was no loss of life. Many *nuées ardentes* were emitted, and this phase of activity reached a maximum about the middle of December. Although of considerable violence, they did not compare in intensity with those of May 8, May 20, or August 30, 1902. Following the culmination of the *nuées ardentes* phase, the explosive activity gradually declined and a lava dome began to pile up in the crater immediately to the east of the stump of the 1903 spine. The new dome eventually covered the older one on the south and east but it did not reach the western rim, which remained as an excellent reference point (Fig. 13). Numerous spines, some reaching heights of 150 feet, rose from the dome but they soon crumbled. When the new lava dome began to form in the crater, Perret, who was observing the eruption, was able to assure the inhabitants that the eruption was declining and that the "worst was over."

Whether the lava dome now occupying the crater of Mount Pelée has effectively sealed the vent and the eruptive activity is ended, only time will tell. There was an interval of twenty-seven years between the last eruptions (1902 to 1929), and if this pattern is maintained the next few years may hold the answer.

La Soufrière, St. Vincent Island

The volcano La Soufrière occupies the northern end of the island of St. Vincent, ninety miles to the south of Martinique. The island itself is a complex mass of volcanic material, similar to Martinique. The summit of La Soufrière, which rises 4,048 feet above sea level, consists of two craters, the 1812 crater and the so-called "old" crater, immediately to the southwest, which was the site of the 1902 eruption. The old crater has a diameter of about one mile and a depth of 1,600 to 2,400 feet below the rim. Up to the time of the 1902 eruption it was occupied by a beautiful crater lake which stood at 1,930 feet above sea level. The 1812 crater, about one-half mile in diameter and 500 feet deep, is separated from the old crater by a saddle, which, at its lowest point, is 3,550 feet above sea level or about 500 feet below the highest point on the rim of the old crater. As on Mount Pelée, numerous valleys radiate from near the summit of La Soufrière and follow individual courses to the sea. The sides of the mountain are covered with a dense growth of tropical vegetation.

Two eruptions at La Soufrière prior to the 1902 outbreak are known. In fact, these are the only two historic eruptions of any significance known in the entire Lesser Antilles prior to 1902. The first occurred in 1718, and, according to reports, the whole island and the ocean far out

FIGURE 14. Spine of Mount Pelée with ruins of St. Pierre in foreground. Photograph by Lacroix (1904) March, 1903. Courtesy Académie des Sciences (France).

FIGURE 15. Spine of Mount Pelée on March 15, 1903.
Photograph by Lacroix (1904). Courtesy Académie des Sciences (France).

to sea were buried by ash. It is quite probable that in this eruption the top of a more lofty cone was blown away, leaving the caldera which is now known as "the old crater." The next reported eruption occurred in 1812. In this eruption "vast clouds [of ash] darkened the sun for an entire day" and in the eruption a new crater, immediately adjacent to the old crater, was formed.

The first symptoms of unrest in the volcano were evident in April, 1901, slightly more than a year before the great eruption of May 7, 1902. Earthquakes were severe enough that people living on the western slope of La Soufrière became alarmed and some considered leaving the area, but the shocks ceased and the people resumed their normal activities until in April, 1902, when the shocks were again felt. By the first of May the inhabitants on the leeward side of the volcano north of Chateaubelair had sought refuge elsewhere. If this had not happened, the death toll of the eruption would have been much higher. Those living on the windward side were not particularly disturbed and continued their activities as usual. It was felt that in the event of an eruption the ash and gases would be carried towards the west by the prevailing winds. When the great eruption occurred on May 7, few people were killed on the leeward side (one report says only one) while 1,350 were killed on the windward side (other estimates place the loss of life as high as 1,600).

On May 5 fishermen crossing the mountain near the summit noticed that the water in the crater lake was discolored and agitated. The first visible outburst of steam was reported at 2:40 P.M. on May 6, and similar outbursts continued at intervals of one to two hours through the afternoon and night. By 10:30 A.M. on May 7 the eruptions had become an almost continuous roar and the steam cloud was estimated to have reached a height of 30,000 feet. At 1:00 P.M. large stones could be distinguished in the ascending cloud. At about the same time people who attempted to cross the Rabaka Dry River found a raging torrent of boiling mud and water more than fifty feet deep, which was rushing down the valley and out into the sea. This doubtless represented a discharge of at least a portion of the water from the crater lake into the headwaters of the stream. About 2:00 P.M. the already great activity increased markedly. A dense cloud of hot dust and steam spread down

124

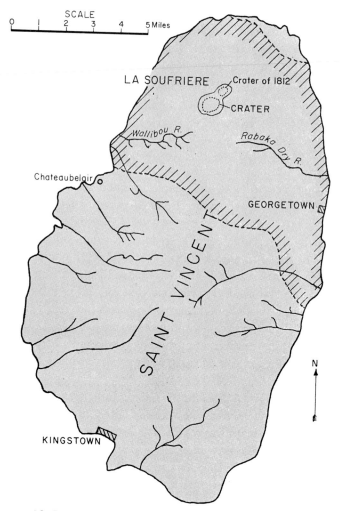

SCALE
0   1   2   3   4   5 Miles

LA SOUFRIERE   Crater of 1812

CRATER

Wallibou R.   Rabaka Dry R.

Chateaubelair

GEORGETOWN

SAINT VINCENT

N

KINGSTOWN

FIGURE 16. Island of St. Vincent. Area devastated (shaded) by
eruption of May 7, 1902.   After Hovey (1902).

the mountain sides as a hurricanelike blast, and from it red-hot rocks fell in torrents. One observer who described the cloud as "a terrific, huge, reddish-and-purplish cloud" advancing toward him escaped by taking to a boat which he had in readiness. The dust-laden steam expanded with explosive violence, both horizontally and downward, following the configuration of the mountain. It was a true *nuée ardente* but of somewhat less intensity than the blasts at Mount Pelée. Observers reported that a portion of the cloud traveling eastward seemed suddenly to split and send a part back toward the volcano. Thus windows on the side away from the volcano were broken. This unexplained feature was also reported at Mount Pelée. Perhaps an inrush of air toward the crater was due to a vacuum created by the explosion.

The hot blast overturned trees, scorching them on the side facing the volcano, destroyed houses, and set fire to inflammable objects. The hot ash, which fell in great quantities, killed all vegetation and devastated an area comprising about one-third of the island (Fig. 16). Hills and ridges provided some protection for vegetation on their immediate lee side, indicating that the blast swept past without touching the ground at these spots. A partially encircling ridge on the northeast side of the volcano accounts for the escape from destruction of a narrow fringe on the northeast edge of the island. Red-hot stones up to six inches in diameter fell in Georgetown, five and one-half miles from the crater. From the orientation of trees blown down, it was apparent that the blast swept outward in all directions from the crater. At Mount Pelée the blast was concentrated in a relatively narrow sector, which fact may account for its greater intensity. A feature of the La Soufrière eruption not marked at Mount Pelée was the enormous amount of ash which was distributed over a wide area, even far out to sea. Ash began to fall on the *Jupiter*, a ship enroute from Africa, at 2:30 A.M. on May 8, when it was 830 miles east-southeast of Barbados. This indicated that the ash cloud traveled at a speed of sixty miles per hour to have reached the vessel at that time. The ash was spread like a gray mantle over the island, generally decreasing in thickness from the crater outward, but collecting in vast deposits in favorable valleys. In the valley of the Wallibou deposits of more than sixty feet were formed, while in the Rabaka Dry River thicknesses up to two hundred feet were reported. These huge accumulations remained hot for weeks, and violent explosions were common when surface water seeped into the heated interior. Hovey (1902) describes one such eruption in the Wallibou Valley in which the steam column reached a height of more than a mile. Such eruptions, which were frequently believed to be new craters opening on the volcano, continued for weeks.

On the outer margin of the area the hot steam seems to have condensed to scalding water, which, mixed with the ash, formed a hot mud that adhered to everything it touched. The once dense tropical vegetation which covered the region was replaced by dull gray ash. The greatest loss of life was on the Georgetown side near the Rabaka Dry River. The deaths were due to inhalation of the hot dust, burns from steam and dust, and contacts with falling stones. Those who escaped injury were saved by seeking refuge in cellars in which the opening was on the side away from the volcano. The most striking example of such protection was at Orange Hill, two and one-half miles north of Georgetown, where 132 persons escaped injury by seeking shelter in an empty rum cellar. The cellar, only partly underground, had one window and a door on the side away from the volcano, these openings being equipped with heavy shutters which were kept closed during the eruption. Those killed in the eruption suffered burns in exactly the same manner as did the victims at St. Pierre. The tornadic force of the blast appears to have been considerably less than the more violent of the eruptions from Mount Pelée and the destruction was not so appalling because no large city was in its path.

Following the major outburst at 2:00 P.M. on May 7, tremendous detonations continued at such short intervals as to merge into an almost continuous roar, lasting all through May 8 and until early on the morning of May 9. Other eruptions, similar to the May 7 outburst, occurred on May 18 and September 1 and 3, but no additional loss of life was reported. The eruptions in September were equal to or even more violent than the May 7 blast and the devastated area was extended to the southwest beyond the limits of the earlier area affected.

When the crater of La Soufrière was first visited after the May 7 and May 18 eruptions, on May 31, all that could be seen was a small lake of boiling water from which a strong column of steam rose. The level of the lake was estimated to be 1,200 feet above sea level, whereas before the eruption it had stood 730 feet higher. The 1812 crater was not disturbed in the eruption. La Soufrière has shown no signs of "dome" development, such as that at Mount Pelée, and it must therefore be considered capable of further destructive eruptions.

In addition to the two examples of Peléan-type eruptions described in this chapter, the caldera-making eruptions of Coseguina in 1835 and Krakatoa in 1883, described in Chapter 6, are good examples of this type. The Peléan-type eruption, the most violent of all volcanic eruptions, is, rather strangely, associated with the final phase of activity of a volcano. A volcano appears to react with almost human traits, and, as a "last fling" before becoming extinct, stages a stupendous (Peléan-type) eruption.

Above the smoke and stir of this dim spot which men call Earth.

MILTON

8. THE VULCANIAN TYPE OF VOLCANIC ERUPTION

THE VULCANIAN TYPE of eruption, occupying an intermediate position in the classification scheme, includes many of the active volcanoes of the world. In a typical Vulcanian eruption the crater crusts over solidly between infrequent eruptions. Gases accumulate beneath the congealed crust and in time the upper part of the magma column becomes thoroughly gas-saturated. Finally, with strong explosions, sometimes sufficient to partially disrupt the cone, and accompanied by a great "cauliflower-shaped" eruption cloud, dark in color because of the high ash content, the obstruction is blown out. As the pressure is suddenly reduced the gas-charged magma is disrupted by the explosively expanding gases into pumice and ash. Following the clearing of the vent, lava flows may issue from the crater or from fissures on the sides of the cone. The initial phase of a Vulcanian eruption and that of the Peléan type are markedly similar. However, the characteristic *nuée ardente* of the Peléan type is not present in a Vulcanian eruption. Vulcano, in the Lipari Islands off the coast of Sicily, was the example used by Mercalli (1891) and later adopted by Lacroix (1908) and others for the Vulcanian type of eruption, but many consider Vesuvius to be an even better example. These volcanoes have had long interesting histories and the writer feels that it will be worth while to describe both of them as examples of the Vulcanian type.

Mount Vesuvius

Prestige of Vesuvius among volcanoes

Mount Vesuvius, on the shore of the Bay of Naples in central Italy, is probably the best-known volcano in the world. Located in the midst of one of the most densely populated areas of Europe, it is also in the area where the first Greek settlements were made more than eight hundred years before the beginning of the Christian era and from which civilization spread over Western Europe. The record of activity is, therefore, far more complete for Vesuvius than for any other volcano, and many of the ideas concerning volcanoes were developed from observations at Vesuvius. The Vesuvian Volcano Observatory, one of the few such institutions in the world, was dedicated in 1845. The city of Naples, which spreads out fanwise along one of the most beautiful bays in the world opposite Vesuvius, is built on a series of old craters. The steep slopes which distinguish the city, such as the Posilipo, are the inner walls of a group of intersecting crater rims.

Italy has long been a favorite recreation center, first for Western Europe and now for the entire world, and Vesuvius is one of its chief scenic attractions. Thousands of tourists have visited Vesuvius and to many the terms *volcano* and *Vesuvius* are synonymous. Many of the leading geologists of the world have at some time visited Vesuvius, and each, of course, has written an article or a book about it. A bibliography

(Johnston-Lavis, 1918) of the scientific articles and books on Vesuvius, published in 1918, contains over 2,000 entries, and a great many have been added since that time.

Detailed observations on the activity of Vesuvius extend back for several hundred years. From a close study of these records, Professor Palmieri, then director of the Vesuvian Volcano Observatory, announced in 1872 that the eruptions of Vesuvius follow a cyclic pattern which makes it possible to predict, at least to some extent, the pattern of activity of an eruption. The recognition of the cyclic behavior of Vesuvius stimulated other workers to try to establish patterns for other volcanoes, and the results of their efforts proved to be an important step in the advancement of volcanology.[1]

Vesuvius is but one of a series of volcanoes which are located along a line, or "trend," that parallels the west coast of Italy extending northward from Naples through Rome to the vicinity of Siena. This trend, located along a fracture which resulted from the sinking of the Tyrrhenian Sea and the uplift of the Apennine Mountains, is marked by a series of more or less evenly spaced volcanic vents. The Tyrrhenian Sea is the section of the Mediterranean lying between Italy and the islands of Sardinia, Corsica, and Sicily. The volcanic activity along this trend began at the north and shifted progressively southward until it reached the Naples area. Although the activity along this belt is of very recent age, from a geologic standpoint, the only eruptions which have occurred in historic time are in the Naples area.[2]

Vesuvius is but one of many volcanoes in the Naples area. Another is Ischia, an island in the Bay of Naples, which was in vigorous eruption in ancient times long before Vesuvius was even known to be a volcano. The last eruption of Ischia was in 1302, but a severe earthquake, at Casamicciola, in 1883 indicates that the volcanic energy is not entirely extinct. The Phlegraean Fields (Campi Flegrei), five miles west of Naples, is an area containing many craters, the last of which, Monte Nuovo, was formed in 1538. The volcano Solfatara is one of the craters of the Phlegraean Fields. It last erupted in 1198, sending out a stream of lava

---

[1] A discussion of volcanic cycles, with several examples in addition to Vesuvius, is given in Chapter 12.

[2] See Chapter 14 for further details.

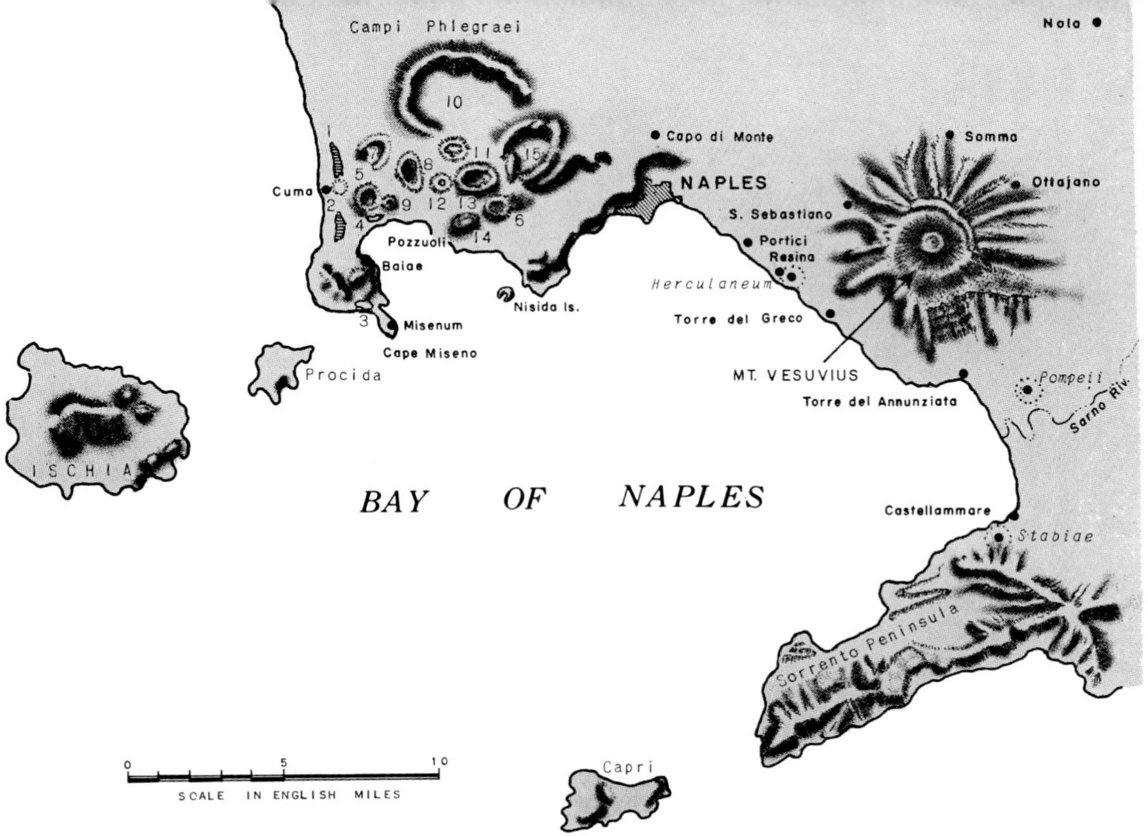

FIGURE 17. Bay of Naples and surrounding area. Herculaneum, Pompeii, and Stabiae, destroyed in the A.D. 79 eruption of Vesuvius, are located on the map. Index to areas in Campi Flegrei: 1. Lago di Licola. 2. Lago di Fusaro. 3. Mare Morto. 4. Lago Lucrino. 5. Lago Averno. 6. Lago di Agnano. 7. Monte Grillo. 8. Monte Barbaro. 9. Monte Nuovo. 10. Piano di Quarto. 11. Fossa Lupara. 12. Monte Cigliano. 13. Astroni. 14. Solfatara. 15. Pianura.   After Phillips (1869).

PLATE 7. Lake Avernus, Phlegraean Fields, Italy.

which reached the sea near the harbor of Pozzuoli. Since that time it has maintained a constant emission of gases, from which the name *Solfatara* (Italian for "sulphur mine") is derived. The term has been incorporated in the terminology of volcanology to indicate that any volcano which emits only gases is in the "solfataric stage."

The Phlegraean fields

Vesuvius, the location of the present volcanic activity in the Naples area, is interestingly related to the Phlegraean Fields. The Phlegraean Fields, with nineteen separate craters concentrated in an area of about twenty-five square miles, is indeed a unique feature. It is the scene of many classic fables, the theme of Roman poets, and a land that excited the imagination of the ancient world. Here the gaseous emanations, deep hollows, scorched rocks, and subterranean passages might well be taken for the ruins of an older world, or imagined to be the entrance to the realm of Pluto. Indeed it was the fumes from the Solfatara which inspired Dante's *Inferno*.

Several of the craters in the Phlegraean Fields contained beautiful lakes. Some, such as Agnano, which is now used as a race track, have been drained in recent years for various reasons. Lake Avernus, one of the best-known in ancient times, remains today. It is a circular lake about one-half mile in diameter, occupying the crater of a volcano. The name was derived from the belief that gaseous emanations from the lake killed any birds flying over it, hence the name which means "without birds." Certainly today the birds have no difficulty in flying over it at will.

Virgil (70 B.C.–A.D. 19), the great classic Roman poet, spent his last years in Naples and was, of course, familiar with the Phlegraean Fields. In his great classic poem, the *Aeneid*, he locates the entrance to the realms of Pluto (and the infernal region) on the underground road at Lake Avernus.

History of Vesuvius to A.D. 79

It is likely that Vesuvius first began as a submarine volcano in the Bay of Naples, then emerged as an island, and finally was joined to the land by the filling and upbuilding of its eruptive products. Its first eruptions are believed to have occurred after the retreat of the last Ice Sheet (Pleistocene), and if this is true its age is somewhere in the neighborhood of 10,000 years. Vesuvius is younger than the first eruptions of the volcanoes in the Phlegraean Fields, since these tuffs are found beneath Vesuvian material.

Because the ancients made no reference to Vesuvius as a volcano, it must be assumed that a long period of repose intervened between its early activity and the eruption of A.D. 79, which gave rise to the modern cone. The Greeks of the seventh century B.C. and, later, in the fourth century B.C., who were driven from their homes on Ischia by volcanic eruptions would hardly have settled on the slopes of Vesuvius had they recognized it as a volcano. Certainly some of the Greeks who had seen Mount Etna or Vulcano in eruption must have recognized the volcanic nature of Vesuvius, but there were no legends of any activity. Diodorus Siculus, a native of Sicily, and certainly familiar with Mount Etna, describes the area as it appeared to him about 45 B.C.: "The whole region was named Phlegraean, from the culminating point, which is now called Vesuvius, bearing many indications of having emitted fires in ancient time" (Lib. iv. c. 21). At about the same time (30 B.C.) the noted geographer Strabo observed the rich fields on the slopes of Vesuvius, except at the summit, which for the most part was flat and quite barren, and comments on the cindery aspect as if it had been "eaten by fire." He speculates that in ancient times the country was in a state of burning, being full of fiery cavities, though now extinct for want of fuel (Strabo, Geog. Bk. v.). We learn from a still earlier source, which tells the story of the revolt of the Roman gladiators under Spartacus[3] about 72 B.C., that the summit was covered with a mass of tangled vines. Plutarch's (Dryden, Vol. 2, p. 279) *Life of Crassus* relates the story as follows:

Clodius the Praetor, with 3,000 men, besieged them in a mountain having but one narrow and difficult passage, which Clodius kept guarded; all the rest was encompassed with broken and slippery precipices, but upon the top grew a great many wild vines: they cut down as many of their boughs as they had need of, and twisted them into ladders long enough to reach from thence to the bottom, by which, without any danger, all got down save one, who stayed behind to throw them their arms, after which he saved himself with the rest. The Romans were ignorant of all this; and, therefore, coming upon them from the rear, they assaulted them unawares and took their camp."

The barren top described by the usually accurate Strabo does not check with the description of the vine-covered summit which enabled Spartacus to escape. Nevertheless, we may conclude that Vesuvius at this time had a broadly truncated summit and that the deep crater was intact except for a narrow opening on one side. From a distance it appeared as a broad flat-topped mountain and the presence of the crater would not have been revealed except from the summit. It is not sur-

[3] Spartacus, a deserter from the Roman army and later a slave placed in a training camp for gladiators at Capua, escaped from Capua with seventy-eight fellow gladiators and sought refuge on the summit of Vesuvius. Plutarch's account of the Spartacus revolt gives us one of the few descriptions of the crater of Vesuvius during this general period.

prising then that it was not recognized as a volcano except by a few of the scholars of the time.

The first sign of renewal of activity at Vesuvius was a severe earthquake on February 5, A.D. 63. According to Seneca it destroyed a considerable portion of Pompeii and did much damage in Herculaneum and the surrounding area, including Naples. In Pompeii the temple of Isis was so badly damaged that it had to be rebuilt. When a private citizen bore the expense of the reconstruction the city in gratitude erected on the building a plaque, which was found when the area was unearthed from beneath the ejecta of the later eruption. Suetonius[4] has preserved a notice of this earthquake in connection with his account of the first appearance of Nero on the stage in Naples. Nero, believing that he was a gifted singer, was giving a trial concert in Naples before he appeared in Rome: "This singular 'master of the world' loitered and amused himself much in the city of Syren, and amid the waters of Baiae. To be singing while Vesuvius thundered, and fiddling while Rome burned, was not unfitting the imperial madcap" (Phillips, 1869, p. 12). The earthquakes continued intermittently for the next sixteen years, finally culminating on the night of August 24, A.D. 79, in extremely violent shocks which immediately preceded the historic eruption on that date.

In the great eruption of A.D. 79 about one-half of the cone was destroyed and a new cone, the present Vesuvius, was started. The remnant of the old cone, which now partly encircles Vesuvius, is known as Mount Somma (Fig. 18).

The term *somma* is now applied to the remnant of any cone which bears to its parent mountain the relationship of Mount Somma to Vesuvius. In this eruption the cities of Pompeii and Herculaneum were completely buried and several other cities were badly damaged, most notable perhaps being Stabiae, where Pliny the Elder lost his life. The only eye-witness account describing the great eruption of August 24, A.D. 79, which has survived today is given by Pliny the Younger in two letters written some years afterwards to his friend the historian Tacitus.

[4] Suetonius (A.D. 70–A.D. 160) was a friend and contemporary of the younger Pliny. For a time he was the imperial secretary to Trajan and as such had access to the imperial archives.

136

FIGURE 18A. Vesuvius prior to the eruption of A.D. 79.

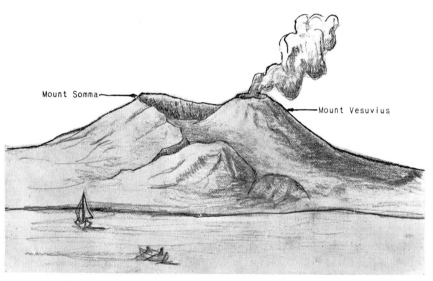

Mount Somma

Mount Vesuvius

FIGURE 18B. Vesuvius today.

The younger Pliny, apparently, was born at Como in northern Italy in A.D. 61, since he states that he was eighteen years old at the time of the eruption. His father died at an early age, and as was the custom at that time, he and his mother went to live with his uncle, Caius Plinius Secundus (generally known as Pliny the Elder), who was an ardent student of natural history, making written notes on every book he read as well as on his own observations. He was an important person, friend of the Emperor, and held various offices. At the time of the eruption he was in command of the Roman fleet at Misenum. Of his numerous writings only his *Natural History* survives. He died in the eruption of Vesuvius in A.D. 79 at the age of fifty-six.

The younger Pliny, brought up in his uncle's household, studied under the best scholars of the time. He was much devoted to literature and less inclined to scientific matters than was his uncle. Ten books of Pliny's letters have survived. The majority of the letters were written for publication rather than as actual correspondence.

Pliny the Elder was at Misenum (near Baiae) at the time of the eruption. Misenum, or rather Capo Miseno, marks the northern boundary of the Bay of Naples at its westernmost point. The Bay, then, as now, one of the most beautiful spots in the world, was crowded with villas of Roman nobility. Baiae, immediately adjacent to the Roman fleet base at Misenum, was the site of many large and elaborate baths. Puteoli (now Pozzuoli) was a busy harbor, and Neapolis (Naples) was one of the most important cities of the Empire. Herculaneum, Pompeii, and Stabiae were coastal towns on the Bay, behind which the flat-topped summit of Vesuvius rose to a height of four thousand feet. It was covered with dense vegetation and neither history nor tradition preserved any records which might serve to warn the cities at its base of its volcanic nature.

Pliny's account of the A.D. 79 eruption

Caius Cornelius Tacitus was the leading historian of his time. Although he was a little older than Pliny the Younger they were intimate friends. Apparently, several years after the great eruption of A.D. 79, in which Pliny the Elder lost his life, Tacitus was compiling a history, and since Pliny the Elder was one of the prominent men of the day, the details of his death were of importance. Accordingly, he wrote to Pliny the Younger and asked him to set down the events leading up to his uncle's death. It should be understood that Tacitus was interested in Pliny the Elder and not in an account of the eruption of Vesuvius. Pliny's letter to Tacitus is in reply to this request. Since this letter, like all of Pliny's letters, was undated, the time interval between the letter and the event he described is not known. It seems likely that the letter was written when Pliny was twenty-four years of age, or about six years after his uncle's death.

The best-known translation of Pliny's letters is the one by William Melmoth, published in 1746. This translation, a rather free version, has been used by numerous authors, who usually have made further modifications in style. The letters reproduced here are from the Melmoth translation as revised and corrected by Bosanquet (1907). His alterations in the Melmoth version were made "in the direction of greater literalness in the text," and it seems to the writer that he has been quite successful in preserving the style and spirit of the original letters. The letter describing his uncle's death follows: [5]

Your request that I would send you an account of my uncle's death, in order to transmit a more exact relation of it to posterity, deserves my acknowledgement; for, if this accident shall be celebrated by your pen, the glory of it, I am well assured, will be rendered forever illustrious. And notwithstanding he perished by a misfortune, which, as it involved at the same time a most beautiful country in ruins, and destroyed so many populous cities, seems to promise him an everlasting remembrance; notwithstanding he has himself composed many and lasting works; yet I am persuaded, the mentioning of him in your immortal writings will greatly contribute to render his name immortal. . . . It is with extreme willingness, therefore, that I execute your commands; and should indeed have claimed the task if you had not enjoined it.

He was at that time with the fleet under his command at Misenum. On the 24th of August, about one in the afternoon, my mother desired him to observe a cloud which had appeared of a very unusual size and shape. He had just taken a turn in the sun, and after bathing himself in cold water, and making a light luncheon, gone back to his books; he immediately arose and went out upon a rising ground from whence he might get a better sight of this very uncommon appearance. A cloud, from which mountain was uncertain at this distance, was ascending, the form of which I cannot give you a more exact description of than by likening it to that of a pine tree, for it shot up to a great height in the form of a very tall trunk, which spread itself out at the top into a sort of branches; occasioned, I imagine, either by a sudden gust of air that impelled it, the

[5] Pliny's Letters, Book 6. Letter 16. to Tacitus.

force of which decreased as it advanced upwards, or the cloud itself being pressed back again by its own weight, expanded in the manner I have mentioned; it appeared sometimes bright and sometimes dark and spotted, according as it was either more or less impregnated with earth and cinders. This phenomenon seemed to a man of such learning and research as my uncle extraordinary, and worth further looking into.

He ordered a light vessel to be got ready, and gave me leave, if I liked, to accompany him. I said I would rather go on with my work; and it so happened he had himself given me something to write out. As he was coming out of the house, he received a note from Rectina, the wife of Bassus, who was in the utmost alarm at the imminent danger which threatened her; for [from] her villa lying at the foot of Mount Vesuvius, there was no way of escape except by sea; she earnestly entreated him therefore to come to her assistance. He accordingly changed his first intention, and what he had begun from a philosophical, he now carried out in a noble and generous spirit. He ordered the galleys to put to sea, and went himself on board with an intention of assisting not only Rectina, but the several other towns which lay thickly strewn along the beautiful coast. Hastening then to the place from whence others fled with the utmost terror, he steered his course direct to the point of danger, and with so much calmness and presence of mind as to be able to make and dictate his observations upon the motion and all the phenomena of that dreadful scene.

He was now so close to the mountain that the cinders, which grew thicker and hotter the nearer he approached, fell into the ships, together with pumice stones, and black pieces of burning rock; they were in danger too not only of being a-ground by the sudden retreat of the sea, but also from the vast fragments which rolled down from the mountain, and obstructed all the shore. Here he stopped to consider whether he should turn back again; to which the pilot advising him, "Fortune" he said, "favors the brave; steer to where Pomponianus is."

Pomponianus was then at Stabiae (now Castellammare), separated by a bay, which the sea, after several insensible windings, forms with the shore. He had already sent his baggage on board; for though at that time he was not in actual danger, yet being within sight of it, and indeed extremely near, if it should in the least increase, he was determined to put to sea as soon as the wind, which was blowing dead in-shore, should go down. It was favorable, however, for carrying my uncle to Pomponianus, whom he found in the greatest consternation; he embraced him tenderly, encouraging and urging him to keep up his spirits, and, the more effectually to soothe his fears by seeming unconcerned himself, ordered a bath to be got ready, and then, after having bathed, sat down to supper with great cheerfulness, or at least (which is just as heroic) with every appearance of it.

Meanwhile broad flames shone out in several places from Mount Vesuvius, which the darkness of the night contributed to render still brighter and clearer. But my uncle, in order to soothe the apprehensions of his friend, assured him it was only the burning of the villages, which the country people had abandoned to the flames: after this he retired to rest, and it is most certain he was so little disquieted as to fall into a sound sleep: for his breathing which, on account of his corpulence, was rather heavy and sonorous, was heard by the attendants outside. The court which led to his apartment being now almost filled with ashes and stones, if he had continued there any time longer, it would have been impossible for him to have made his way out. So he was awoke and got up, and went to Pomponianus and the rest of his company, who were feeling too anxious to think of going to bed. They consulted together whether it would be most prudent to trust to the houses, which now rocked from side to side with frequent and violent concussions as though shaken from their very foundations; or fly to the open fields, where the calcined stones and cinders, though light indeed, yet fell in large showers and threatened destruction. In this choice of dangers they resolved for the fields: a resolution which, while the rest of the company were hurried into by their fears, my uncle embraced upon cool and deliberate consideration. They went out then, having pillows tied upon their heads with napkins; and this was their whole defense against the storm of stones that fell round them.

It was now day everywhere else, but there a deeper darkness prevailed than in the thickest night; which however was in some degree alleviated by torches and other lights of various kinds. They thought proper to go farther down upon the shore to see if they might safely put out to sea, but found the waves still running extremely high, and boisterous. There my uncle, laying himself down upon a sail cloth, which was spread for him, called twice for some cold water, which he drank, when immediately the flames, preceded by a strong whiff of sulphur, dispersed the rest of the party, and obliged him to rise. He raised himself up with the assistance of two of his servants, and instantly fell down dead; suffocated, as I conjecture, by some gross and noxious vapor, having always had a weak throat, which was often inflamed. As soon as it was light again, which was not till the third day after this melancholy accident, his body was found entire, and without any marks of violence upon it, in the dress in which he fell, and looking more like a man asleep than dead. During all this time my mother and I, who were at Misenum—but this has no connection with your history, and you do not desire any particulars besides those of my uncle's death; so I will end here, only adding that I have faithfully related to you what I saw as an eye-witness myself or received immediately after the accident happened, and before there was time to vary the truth. You will pick out of this narrative, whatever is most important; for a letter is one thing, a history another; it is one thing writing to a friend, another thing writing to the public. Farewell.

This account, written from the recollections of an eighteen-year-old student some years afterwards, contains some significant facts as well as some inconsistencies. It seems likely that the author's memory, or the information given to him in regard to the final scene of his uncle's death, was in part at least, in error. We can hardly assume that "flames" could have reached as far as Stabiae, ten miles from the crater. Perhaps there were "noxious gases" in the eruption cloud which enveloped them and in the falling ash, which did irritate the throat, but others in the party were not stricken. It seems more probable that Pliny's death was due to a heart attack rather than to the cause ascribed by his nephew in the letter to Tacitus. If this were not the case it is difficult to explain why he did not escape with the others. Pliny's description of the eruption cloud as resembling a pine tree has become a classic, and today the scientific name for such an eruption cloud is "pino," the Italian word for pine tree. Eruptions displaying "pinos" and of the violence of the eruption of Vesuvius are described as "Plinian eruptions." Pliny's letter to Tacitus, Book 6, Letter 16, may quite properly be considered as the beginning of modern descriptive volcanology.

Tacitus was so interested in Pliny's account that he wrote to him and asked what happened to him and to his mother at Misenum after his uncle left. This Pliny describes in a second letter to Tacitus:[6]

The letter which, in compliance with your request, I wrote to you concerning the death of my uncle has raised, it seems, your curiosity to know

[6] Pliny's Letters, Book 6, Letter 20, to Tacitus.

what terrors and dangers attended me while I continued at Misenum; for there, I think, my account broke off:

"Though my shock'd soul recoils, my tongue shall tell."[7]

My uncle having left us, I spent such time as was left on my studies: (it was on their account indeed that I had stopped behind), till it was time for my bath. After which I went to supper, and then fell into a short and uneasy sleep. There had been noticed for many days before, a trembling of the earth, which did not alarm us much, as this is quite an ordinary occurence in Campania; but was so particularly violent that night that it not only shook but actually overturned, as it would seem, everything about us. My mother rushed into my chamber, where she found me rising in order to awaken her. We sat down in the open court of the house, which occupied a small space between the buildings and the sea. As I was at that time but eighteen years of age, I know not whether I should call my behavior in this dangerous juncture courage or folly; but I took up Livy, and amused myself with turning over that author and even making extracts from him as if I had been perfectly at my leisure.

Just then a friend of my uncle's, who had lately come to him from Spain,[8] joined us, and observing me sitting by my mother with a book in my hand, reproved her for her calmness, and me at the same time for my careless security; nevertheless I went on with my author. Though it was now morning, the light was exceedingly faint and doubtful; the buildings all around us tottered, and though we stood upon open ground, yet as the place was narrow and confined, there was no remaining without imminent danger; we therefore resolved to quit the town.

A panic-stricken crowd followed us, and (as to a mind distracted with terror every suggestion seems more prudent than its own) pressed on us in dense array to drive us forward as we came out. Being at a convenient distance from the house, we stood still, in the midst of a most dangerous and dreadful scene. The chariots, which we had ordered to be drawn out, were so agitated backwards and forwards, though upon the most level ground, that we could not keep them steady, even by supporting them with large stones. The sea seemed to roll back upon itself and to be driven from its banks by the convulsive motion of the earth; it is certain at least the shore was considerably enlarged, and several sea animals were left upon it.

[7] From Virgil.

[8] Pliny the Elder had served as governor of Spain and had many friends there.

On the other side, a black and dreadful cloud, broken with rapid, zigzag flashes, revealed behind it variously shaped masses of flame: these last were like sheet lightning but much larger. Upon this our Spanish friend, whom I mentioned above, addressing himself to my mother and me with great energy and urgency: "If your brother," he said, "if your uncle be safe, he certainly wishes you to be so too; but if he perished, it was his desire no doubt, that you might both survive him; why therefore do you delay your escape a moment?" We could never think of our own safety, we said, while we were uncertain of his. Upon this our friend left us, and withdrew from the danger with the utmost precipitation.

Soon afterwards the cloud began to descend and cover the sea. It had already surrounded and concealed the island of Capreae (Capri) and the promontory of Misenum. My mother now besought, urged, even commanded me to make _my_ escape at any rate, which, as I was young, I might easily do; as for herself, she said, her age and corpulency rendered all attempts of that sort impossible; however she would willingly meet death if she could have the satisfaction of seeing that she was not the occasion of mine. But I absolutely refused to leave her, and, taking her by the hand, compelled her to go with me. She complied with great reluctance, and not without many reproaches to herself for retarding my flight.

The ashes now began to fall upon us, though in no great quantity. I looked back; a dense dark mist seemed to be following us, spreading itself over the country like a cloud.

"Let us turn out of the high-road," I said, "while we can still see, for fear that, should we fall in the road, we should be pressed to death in the dark by the crowds that are following us."

We had scarcely sat down when night came upon us, not such as we have when the sky is cloudy, or when there is no moon, but that of a room which is shut up, and all the lights put out. You might hear the shrieks of women, the screams of children, and the shouts of men; some calling for their children, others for their parents, others for their husbands, and seeking to recognize each other by the voices that replied; one lamenting his own fate, another that of his family; some wishing to die from the very fear of dying; some lifting their hands to the gods; but the greater part convinced that there were now no gods at all, and that the final endless night of which we have heard had come upon the world. Among these there were some who augmented the real terrors by others imaginary or willfully invented. I remember some who declared that one part of

Misenum had fallen, that another was on fire; it was false, but they found people to believe them.

It now grew rather lighter, which we imagined to be rather the forerunner of an approaching burst of flames (as in truth it was) than the return of day; however, the fire fell at a distance from us; then again we were immersed in thick darkness, and a heavy shower of ashes rained upon us, which we were obliged every now and then to stand up to shake off, otherwise we should have been crushed and buried in the heap. I might boast that, during all this scene of horror, not a sigh, or expression of fear, escaped me, had not my support been grounded in that miserable, though mighty consolation, that all mankind were involved in the same calamity, and that I was perishing with the world itself. At last this dreadful darkness was dissipated by degrees, like a cloud or smoke; the real day returned, and even the sun shone out, though with a lurid light, like when an eclipse is coming on. Every object that presented itself to our eyes (which were extremely weakened) seemed changed, being covered with deep ashes as if with snow.

We returned to Misenum, where we refreshed ourselves as well as we could, and passed an anxious night between hope and fear; though, indeed, with a much larger share of the latter; for the earthquake still continued, while many frenzied persons ran up and down heightening their own and their friends' calamities by terrible predictions. However, my mother and I, notwithstanding the danger we had passed, and that which still threatened us, had no thoughts of leaving the place, till we could receive some news of my uncle.

And now, you will read this narrative without any view of inserting it in your history, of which it is not in the least worthy; and indeed you must put it down to your own request if it should appear not worth even the trouble of a letter. Farewell.

Although this account by Pliny is vivid in its description and conveys the feelings of the writer, along with a certain amount of youthful boasting, it is scarcely satisfactory as a narrative of facts. Pliny does not tell us the direction they took in their flight, although we may infer from what he says about the invisibility of the Island of Capri that they were along the shore of the Bay. From other positions Capri would have been hidden from view by the high land of the promontory of Misenum. Again

Pumice

PLATE 8. Excavations in progress at Pompeii, Italy, in 1952.

he says nothing about the time covered by his narrative. Since no mention is made of spending a night in the open, we may assume that they returned to the villa at Misenum on the afternoon of the same day, August 25.

The destruction of Pompeii and Herculaneum

Pliny[9] makes no mention of the destruction of Pompeii and Herculaneum. He may have felt that Tacitus was already familiar with this aspect of the eruption or that it was not connected with his narrative. Strangely, there is an almost total lack of reference to the fate of these two cities in the literature which has come down to us from that time. Tacitus, in the preface to his *History,* states that he will record, along with descriptions of other events, how "cities in the richest plains of Campania were swallowed up and overwhelmed." Unfortunately this portion of his works has been lost, and no contemporary account of the calamity exists. Indeed, other than the mention of the unfortunate cities in an epigram by V. Martial, written twelve years after the catastrophe, the first reference to them is found in the writings of Dion Cassius[10] about A.D. 230, one hundred and fifty years later. Based on legends of the great eruption which he heard while living in Campania, Cassius reconstructs a fantastic tale in which he describes huge giants leaping through the smoke and tearing the mountain asunder, day turning into night, and the general belief among the people that the earth was returning to Chaos. He further states (Phillips, 1868, p. 27) that "an inexpressible quantity of dust was blown out, which filled land, sea and air; which did much other mischief to men, fields and cattle, . . . and besides buried two entire cities, Herculaneum and Pompeii, while the population was sitting in the theatre." The people were not in the theatres, but the wild rumor recorded by Cassius has nevertheless per-

[9] A view of the Roman Empire, based on Pliny's Letters, is presented by Alfred Church and W. J. Brodribb (1872) in Pliny's Letters, published by William Blackwood and Sons, London. This volume, which is not a free translation of Pliny's letters but a history of the time, based on the letters, is a part of the Ancient Classics for English Readers series. It contains a chapter on the eruption of Vesuvius.

[10] Dion Cassius (A.D. 150–235) is the author of a history of Rome from the founding to A.D. 229. It was written in Greek, and twenty-six of the eighty volumes are extant.

sisted. It is not surprising, therefore, that in time all knowledge of these cities vanished and a thousand years later a town (Resina) had grown up on the site of Herculaneum without the inhabitants knowing that the buried city was beneath them.

The Last Days of Pompeii, a romantic novel written by Edward Bulwer-Lytton (Lord Lytton) in 1834, reanimated the scene in a most realistic manner. The final events, including a description of the eruption of Vesuvius, are based on the letters of Pliny.

The destruction of Pompeii and Herculaneum by the great eruption of Vesuvius in A.D. 79 has been described by many writers and is a subject with which everyone is somewhat familiar. Most of the works on this subject have dealt primarily with the art, customs, or life of the people of the time rather than with the physical destruction of the cities. The only surviving account of the eruption is the letters of Pliny the Younger, which have already been discussed, but unfortunately since they do not mention the destruction of Pompeii or Herculaneum, we are forced to reconstruct the tragedy from the nature of the debris which buried the cities and from evidence uncovered in the excavations.

Pompeii was a well-established Roman city which had existed as a center of commerce for centuries. At the time of its destruction it had a population of about twenty thousand. The fifteen to twenty-five feet of pumice and ash which buried the city not only killed many of the inhabitants, but also preserved, in a unique fashion, a record of the life and customs of the times. In all parts of the city the basal eight to ten feet of the material which buried the city consists of uniformly stratified, light-colored, pumiceous lapilli, varying from the size of a pea up to fragments two to three inches in diameter. Overlying this bed is a somewhat hardened layer of ash with a thickness of six to seven feet, showing evidence of compaction by heavy rains either during or soon after its fall. Doubtless some material has been added by later eruptions but this is not an important factor at Pompeii. For the most part the pumice is loose and unconsolidated, a factor which makes excavation much easier than at Herculaneum. A good topsoil has developed on the surface, and today trees and cultivated fields of corn and other grains are growing on the unexcavated part of Pompeii.

There has been much speculation as to how the people were killed at

Pompeii. From experience in later eruptions it is known that the ash is hot when it falls, although not in an incandescent state. Pliny mentions the hot ashes and Perret (1924, p. 91) in connection with his study of the 1906 eruption states that a "bucket of fine, hot ash was too hot to touch at the end of 24 hours." Such material, since it is primary magma converted into pumice and ash by the sudden release of pressure, would contain a considerable amount of residual gases and these would continue to escape for some time after it had fallen.

The debris which buried Pompeii was primary pumice with insignificant quantities of material from the old cone of Mount Somma. This lends support to the conclusion that the disappearance of a portion of Mount Somma during the eruption was largely a result of collapse rather than distribution through explosion. Williams (1941, p. 311) uses the term *sector graben* for this type in which a segment of the cone collapses into the magma chamber as a result of the rapid expulsion of primary pumice, such as occurred in the A.D. 79 eruption of Vesuvius. The problems concerning the origin of a sector graben, which is a type of caldera, are discussed in Chapter 6. Many have speculated that the deaths in Pompeii were due to *nuées ardentes,* such as destroyed St. Pierre in the eruption of Mount Pelée in 1902. Although there are many similarities in the two tragedies, the evidence does not support the conclusion that a *nuée ardente* overwhelmed Pompeii.

About one-half the area of the city of Pompeii has been excavated, and some two thousand skeletons have been found. Many were discovered with their hands or cloths to their mouths, apparently trying to keep out the lethal gases. We may conclude that these persons died of asphyxiation. Others were killed by falling roofs, or were trapped in buildings in which they sought refuge. In one wine cellar alone eighteen bodies were found. Many of the skeletons are found about two feet above the base of the pumic layer, indicating that they endured the eruption for a time before succumbing. During an excavation in the presence of Queen Carolina Murat, in 1812, several bodies were uncovered ten feet above the base of the pumice layer and separated from the upper surface by only a thin bed of ash and lapilli. One of the dead was holding a bag which had decomposed, spilling its contents of 360 silver coins, 42 bronze pieces, and 8 bright imperial gold medallions. The presence of these bodies near the top of the pumice layer indicates that they survived most of the eruption before perishing. The discovery of a great many bodies near the sea indicates that the victims were fleeing, often with some of their most precious belongings. It is possible that suffocation from the great quantity of fine dust in the air was a cause of the death of many of the inhabitants, or it may have been a contributing factor along with asphyxiation by the gases in the ash.

The great loss of life at Pompeii must have occurred in the initial hours of the eruption when the ash fall was at its maximum. Pliny tells us that it was the morning of the third day before the wind began to remove the black cloud which had cast darkness over the entire area. Since the darkness was due to the dense ash cloud we can infer that the heavy ash falls continued during this period.

The situation at Herculaneum was entirely different. Although Herculaneum is nearer to the cone of Vesuvius than Pompeii, it apparently was not in the direct path of the heavy and destructive ash falls. Instead, the city was covered by a mudflow which in places exceeded sixty-five feet in thickness. The material shows no stratification but consists of a confused mass of fine ash, lava fragments, and pumice, which penetrated every nook and crevice. Breaking through openings, it filled the buildings, but in some instances the roofs, because of the support from the inside, did not collapse. The mudflow which destroyed Herculaneum is similar in all respects to those which have devastated numerous towns on the slopes of Vesuvius in almost all of the violent eruptions. A mudflow, on drying, becomes hardened and is frequently called a "volcanic tuff," a term applied to any consolidated ash which breaks into lumps. Such is the material which entombed Herculaneum. The consolidated nature of the material, as well as the depth to which Herculaneum is buried, makes the excavations difficult, thus only a small section of the city has been uncovered. Only a few skeletons, probably not more than thirty, have been found. This fact indicates that most of the inhabitants were able to escape.

Although many accounts state that Pompeii and Herculaneum were destroyed on the same day, this seems unlikely. The mudflow would have been more likely to occur after the eruption had progressed long enough to cover the upper slopes of Vesuvius with a thick layer of ash.

Then heavy rains, which almost invariably accompany an eruption, would convert the ash into an avalanching mass of mud. The mudflow which destroyed Herculaneum may have occurred a day or two after Pompeii was buried. At least sufficient time elapsed after the eruption began for those who wished to seek refuge elsewhere to do so. After the avalanche of mud passed over Herculaneum it was so completely sealed that its site was forgotten and it became a "lost" city. At Pompeii it was quite different. After the eruption, the tops of many of the buildings projected above the debris and doubtless many of the former inhabitants returned to see if they could recover any of their belongings. Without much effort they were able to dig away some of the ashes and enter a room. When one room had been cleared, the next room was reached by breaking a hole in the wall. However, when the most accessible places had been emptied, the search became so difficult that it was abandoned. Relatively few houses in Pompeii, however, were untouched either by former inhabitants or plunderers. Some of the stone in the walls was quarried for use elsewhere. However, weeds soon began to grow over the buried city and later ash falls helped to conceal it. In time, the last vestiges of the buried city were gone and all memory of its exact location was lost.

The discovery of Pompeii and Herculaneum

The discovery of the buried cities is a fascinating bit of history which is worth recounting. For nearly fifteen hundred years following the catastrophe the buried cities were seldom mentioned, and they seem to have been completely forgotten. In the fifteenth and sixteenth centuries speculation as to the location of Pompeii occurred, a vine-clad hill known as Civita being frequently mentioned as the probable site. However, no investigations were made and little notice was taken of such suggestions. About 1592 a canal was constructed to carry water from the River Sarno to Torre Annunziata, which lacked a suitable water supply. The canal crossed the site of Pompeii, and during excavation for it marble fragments and even some coins of the time of Emperor Nero were discovered, but these latter quickly disappeared into the pockets of workmen and no immediate conclusions were drawn from the other discoveries. By 1607, however, from excavations made during the

PLATE 9. Excavations at Herculaneum. Note mudflow on right, on top of which the present city of Resina is located.

construction of the water-supply system, it was established that the site of some ancient place lay beneath the Civita. But even this seems to have been forgotten, especially after the violent eruption of Vesuvius in 1631, which again spread ash over the entire countryside.

In 1689 excavations were undertaken at some distance from Naples in search for water. The workers noticed several distinct layers of different kinds of ash and found in the deepest layers some stones which contained inscriptions, including one on which was the name *Pompeii*. Although some felt that it was the site of the ancient city of Pompeii, others maintained that it was simply a Pompeian country house which they had encountered. Apparently, stimulated by these reports as well as by the earlier bits of information, Guiseppe Macrini, an explorer of Vesuvius, examined the hill called Civita and in his book, *De Vesuvio*, published in 1699, announced that Pompeii was in fact in the Civita area. His claims were not taken seriously and no excavations were undertaken.

The chronologic sequence of the story now shifts to Herculaneum. The actual discovery of the ruins at Herculaneum is generally credited to Prince d'Elboeuf, an Austrian army officer who in 1710 was in command of the guard at the court of Naples, which at that time was under Austrian rule. D'Elboeuf had spent a summer in the villa of a friend near Resina (actually at Portici), which, it will be remembered, was built over the site of Herculaneum, though its inhabitants did not know of the existence of a city beneath them. Becoming engaged to a Neapolitan princess, D'Elboeuf bought a tract of land on the sea near Resina, intending to build a house on it. He was interested in decorative stone for his proposed house and upon inquiry learned that a peasant, while digging a well at Resina, had found some unusual stones. The peasant, in order to increase the supply of water in his well, had deepened it. In so doing he found some white and yellow marble and other "costly" stones, which appeared to be parts of ancient pillars. The peasant was not particularly impressed and sold the best pieces to a marble dealer. Prince d'Elboeuf was much interested and he subsequently purchased the land from the peasant and began to carry on excavations of his own. Numerous statues were discovered, and three of the best were smuggled out of the country as a present to Prince Eugene at

Vienna. After the initial success, few statues were found, and, since the digging was difficult because of the hard nature of the material, interest in the project lagged. There was no indication that anyone realized that the ancient city of Herculaneum was the source of the material. When Prince d'Elboeuf was transferred to France he sold his villa, which subsequently was again resold.

The political fortunes of Italy now changed, and in 1735 Naples and Sicily came under Spanish rule. The eldest son of the King of Spain, nineteen-year-old Charles of Bourbon, became the absolute monarch of the Two Sicilies. The royal youth, much interested in fishing and hunting, acquired for his pastime the house formerly belonging to Prince d'Elboeuf. Still in the house were many of the statues which Prince d'Elboeuf had recovered from his diggings. In 1738 young King Charles married Maria Amalia Christini, whose father, Augustus III of Saxony, was a great patron of the arts. It should be recalled here that Augustus had purchased the three statues, smuggled out to Prince Eugene at Vienna, and hence these were known by his daughter. When the King brought his young Queen to Naples she was fascinated by the ancient statuary, especially that found by Prince d'Elboeuf, and she begged her husband for more pieces. He organized a digging force and work was started at the original well which D'Elboeuf had taken over from the peasant. The first discovery consisted of three pieces of a statue of a huge bronze horse. Next they found the torso of three marble figures in Roman togas and another bronze horse. As work progressed a flight of stairs was discovered, and on December 11, 1738, a plaque bearing the inscription "Theatrum Herculanensem" was unearthed. Thus by sheer luck, it appears that D'Elboeuf had unwittingly hit upon the front of the stage of a theatre, on which had collapsed, under the impact of the mudflow, the wall which served as wings and background with its marble facing and numerous statues. This was one of the few spots, perhaps the only one, where sculpture was literally piled one piece upon the other. Thus Herculaneum was discovered.

King Charles and his Queen, keenly interested in the excavations, over a period of years made a splendid collection of statues and other articles, and assembled them in a museum which they established at Portici. The king, at first, tried to keep his discovery a secret but in time the news leaked out. In March, 1748, when they were having little success at Herculaneum, it was suggested to the king that the work be suspended and a serious attempt be made to explore the Civita area.

Some held this to be the ancient city of Pompeii while others maintained that it was Stabiae.[11] The king agreed, and on April 1, 1748, twelve workers began digging at Civita, at what turned out to be a lucky spot. However, in spite of the uncovered remains of numerous houses, no one seemed to realize that they were in the middle of a town; it was still thought that this was a part of an isolated villa. On April 6 the first painted frescos were uncovered. On April 19 the first dead was found, a skeleton lying on the ground, that of a man from whose hands had fallen a number of gold and silver coins of the time of Nero and Vespasian. The excavations went on with redoubled vigor, but since they were motivated by curiosity and greed rather than historical or archaeological interest, the search was not systematically conducted. In November work was shifted to an oval-shaped depressed area, which turned out to be the amphitheatre. It was called the "Stabian Theatre," under the delusion that the town was Stabiae. The death of King Ferdinand VI of Spain, on August 10, 1759, was a serious blow to the excavations. King Charles of the Two Sicilies, being his step-brother and heir to the Spanish throne, was obliged to give the kingdom of the Two Sicilies to his son and to ascend the Spanish throne. Unfortunately, his son, then only eighteen years of age, was a very backward boy and the affairs of the country were run largely by his ministers. King Charles and his Queen had for more than twenty years enthusiastically carried on the excavations, and, while the ministers continued the work, many complications which it is not possible to detail here, hampered progress. That the diggings at Civita were actually Pompeii was definitely established for the first time on August 16, 1763, when the workers unearthed a statue of white marble and a nearby pedestal bearing the following inscription: "In the name of the Emperor and Caesar Vespasian Augustus, the tribune T. Svedius Clemens has restored . . . to the public

[11] Stabiae had been buried by ash in the A.D. 79 eruption of Vesuvius and its location was by this time long forgotten. Castellammare now stands, at least in part, upon the ruins of Stabiae.

possession of the Pompeians those places which belong to them and has been taken into private possession."

The progress of the excavations at Pompeii and Herculaneum were largely dependent on the interest of the royal family. By good fortune it so happened that usually some member of the ruling family, most often the queen, was interested in the excavations, and the work was continued. One of the most enthusiastic supporters was Queen Carolina, daughter of the Empress of Austria (House of Hapsburg), who married King Ferdinand of Bourbon in 1768. She became intensely interested in the excavations and was largely responsible for having the work continued during the long reign of her husband. The Bourbon rule of Naples was interrupted during the period of the French Revolution and the Napoleonic Wars by a brief period of French occupation. During this time King Ferdinand and Queen Carolina sought refuge in Sicily. Even the French rulers, however, were patrons of the excavations, and so the work was not interrupted.

In 1808 the French Marshal Joachin Murat and his wife, another Carolina, the twenty-six–year–old sister of Napoleon, were placed on the Naples throne. Queen Carolina Murat was even more enthusiastic about the excavations than was her Bourbon predecessor. She was a frequent visitor at the excavations and took an active part in organizing the work. It was a common practice for the workmen to place skeletons and statues back in their original position and cover them lightly, and "find" them when the Queen was present. The Queen's consistent rewarding of the workers for unusual discoveries greatly stimulated the work. Many royal visitors were entertained at the excavations and prepared "finds" were staged for them.

With the defeat of Napoleon in 1815 the French rule in Naples ended and the Bourbons returned from their exile in Sicily to the Naples throne. King Ferdinand, who died in 1825, after sixty-six years on the throne, was succeeded by his son, who died in 1859 as a result of wounds inflicted in a plot on his life about two years earlier. After a short interval, through the leadership of Giuseppe Garibaldi, the Bourbons were displaced and Italy was united under King Victor Emmanuel II of the House of Savoy. The new king regarded it as his patriotic duty to resume the excavations at Pompeii and Herculaneum, which in recent years had been neglected by the Bourbons.

An archeologist, G. Fiorelli, who was placed in charge, carried on the work vigorously. Following a systematic plan, he had the results published in a *Journal of the Excavations at Pompeii*. Thus for the first time the work was placed on a scientific rather than a treasure-seeking basis.

During Italy's participation in World War I the excavations were halted, but after Mussolini's ascent to power, a renewal of national pride gave fresh impetus to the work. It was at about this time that Professor A. Maiuri, at present and for many years in charge of the excavations, became connected with the work. During World War II work was again suspended, but following the war, with Marshall Plan funds, the work has been continued under Professor Maiuri's direction on an even larger scale.[12]

The great care with which the work is now done, with reconstruction being carried out as the excavations are made, insures accurate restorations. But the progress is slow. About two-fifths of the area within the walls of Pompeii remains to be excavated, and the area outside the walls is limitless. At Herculaneum the work is even slower, although electric boring machines and mechanical shovels are used. The town of Resina, a thickly populated community, is a serious obstacle to expansion of the project, since it sits above Herculaneum. Fortunately, the lava flow of 1631, which is prominent along the streets in Resina, flowed on either side of the site but did not actually overflow Herculaneum. Apparently the mudflow which buried Herculaneum raised the level of the surface sufficiently to divert the lava flow to the sides of the mudflow.

Vesuvius since A.D. 79

For many hundreds of years following A.D. 79 only passing references to the eruptions of Vesuvius were made. It is probable that only the eruptions which resulted in loss of life or widespread damage were described in the literature and many of the writings have not survived.

[12] There are numerous and extensive works dealing with the excavations at Pompeii and Herculaneum. One which the writer found interesting and which was used freely in the preparation of this section is The Destruction and Resurrection of Pompeii and Herculaneum by E. C. C. Corti, first published in 1940, in German, and in 1951 in English by Routledge and Kegan Paul, London.

Dion Cassius, to whom reference has been made in connection with the legends of the destruction of Pompeii, describes an eruption which occurred in A.D. 203, from which the following is a brief excerpt (from Phillips, 1868, p. 41):

> . . . and the summits are clothed with trees and vines, but the interior circle is abandoned to fire, and throws up smoke by day and flame by night as if many and various kinds of incense were rising. And it is always so with more or less intensity, and often ashes are projected and fall in great quantity, and stones thrown up and under the influence of the wind. And the mountain echoes and bellows, because it has not wide but narrow secret air passages.

Cassius is here expressing Aristotle's view that volcanoes were caused by "pent-up" winds.

An eruption occurring in A.D. 472 is reported to have spread ashes over all Europe and caused alarm as far away as Constantinople. During the next six hundred years only four eruptions are recorded, in 512, 685, 993, and 1036. The eruption of 1036 is of particular significance because it was during this eruption that the first lava flows of the historic period occurred. The accounts relate that the eruption occurred not only at the top but also on the sides, and that "its burning products ran into the sea."

Vesuvius, in its early history as a submarine volcano and later as an island in the Bay of Naples, had given rise to lava flows, as is typical of the early history of all volcanoes. Then for a thousand years or more before the beginning of the Christian era and until 1036, it produced only fragmental materials, building the cones now known as Mounts Somma and Vesuvius. These cones were superimposed on the older lava and ash beds formed by its early activity. There is evidence that Mount Somma had been disrupted and rebuilt at least once before the eruption of A.D. 79, in which it was again destroyed, in part, and the present cone of Vesuvius was formed. Thus Vesuvius was following a pattern repeated in many volcanoes, in which the final stage is marked by cone-disrupting explosions and the ejection of only fragmental material. As the magma becomes more acid, and as a result more viscous, the explosive release of the gases shatters it into pumice and ash and no lava is emitted. Such eruptions, at Mount Pelée and elsewhere, have already been described as characteristic of the Peléan type of volcanic activity. Normally, they indicate that the volcano is in its final phase of activity, and that from the geologic viewpoint, the end is in sight. We may well inquire, then, why Vesuvius seems to have had a "rejuvenation" and started an entirely new cycle. The first indications of the "new life" were the lava flows in 1036. Other flows followed, but the great eruption of 1631, with its flood of lava, left no doubt that Vesuvius had embarked upon a new type of activity.This new activity resulted from a change in the composition of the Vesuvian magma, which will be described in a later section.

There are records of eruptions in 1049, 1138 and 1139, the latter two, according to Alfano and Friedlander (1928), being the most important eruptions prior to that of 1631. Sir William Hamilton,[13] who compiled a list of the eruptions of Vesuvius and Etna, states that no eruptions occurred at Vesuvius from the year 1139 to the great eruption of 1631. He comments that the list of eruptions which he gives could not have been compiled but for the curious fact that sacred images and vestments of the church were used by the priests to stop the fury of the volcanoes, the veil of St. Agatha in Sicily and the relics of St. Januarius in Naples, and that the record of the triumphant interference of the saints was carefully recorded by the priests.

The eruption of 1631, occurring after about five hundred years of repose, is one of the great historic eruptions of Vesuvius. It also marks a turning point in the pattern of activity of Vesuvius, for prior to this eruption it had been relatively inactive with long periods of repose, but since 1621 it has been in a more or less constant state of activity. The eruption began on December 16, 1631, with strong explosions and a great ash-filled pino cloud rising from the crater. It soon spread nightlike darkness over the area, and cinders and ash began to fall. As the eruption continued thousands of the inhabitants from villages on the

---

[13] Sir William Hamilton (1730–1803) was the British envoy to the Court of Naples from 1764 to 1800. Holding this post for thirty-six years is in itself something of a record. He was a keen student of volcanoes and made many significant observations which provide one of the best records of the activity of the period. His letters to the Royal Society of London were published under the title Campi Phlegrei, 1776.

slopes of Vesuvius fled to Naples. On the morning of the seventeenth, at an elevation of about three thousand feet, two fissures opened on the southwest side of the cone. From them floods of lava issued, and, breaking into numerous streams, rushed down the slope with great speed, invading S. Giorgio a Cremano, Portici, Pugliano, La Scala, and the western part of Torre del Greco. The flows reached the sea in numerous tongues, covering the six kilometers from the source to the sea in about two hours.

On the evening of the seventeenth it began raining mud in Naples while great mudflows invaded villages on the slopes of Vesuvius, as well as on the north slope of Mount Somma. Mudflows invaded S. Giorgio a Cremano, Portici, and Resina (site of ancient Herculaneum) and formed a long peninsula of land extending into the sea. Another lava flow developed, issuing from a fissure on the south side. Dividing into three streams it passed between Camaldoli del Torre and Torre Annunziata. Strong explosions accompanied by pino clouds continued through the eighteenth, but thereafter the violence decreased, although the eruption continued with some periods of calm into January, 1632.

The destruction by mud, lava, and ash in the densely populated and intensely cultivated area was of tremendous proportions. Six towns were destroyed by lava, nine were wrecked by mudflows, and the entire region suffered from ash falls. About one foot of ash and cinders fell in Naples. To add to the damage, tremendous deluges of rain fell during the last week in December, particularly on the north slope of Vesuvius, where the ash fall was the heaviest. The death toll was placed at four thousand people and six thousand domestic animals. In the eruption the cone lost 168 meters in height and the crater was enlarged to more than twice its diameter before the eruption.

Since the grand eruption of 1631 Vesuvius has followed a pattern in which a cyclic repetition of the eruptive activity can be recognized. This pattern, or the Vesuvian cycle, is described in some detail in Chapter 12 on "Volcanic Cycles." However, a brief résumé of the cycle at this point will enable the reader to follow more intelligently the eruptions of Vesuvius which are described in the following paragraphs. The eruptive cycles vary in length but the two latest cycles ran thirty-four and thirty-eight years respectively. The cycle begins with a repose period, averaging about seven years, in which only gases issue from the crater. The renewal of explosive activity begins with the building of small cinder and scoria cones on the crater floor. Outpourings of lava may also occur in the crater until the crater is gradually filled. Sometimes the lava flows spill over the top or issue from fissures in the crater rim, but such flows are of small volume and cause little damage. This type of moderate activity may continue for years (perhaps twenty to thirty years). When the cinder cones and the lava flows have filled the crater, the stage is set for the culminating eruption of the cycle. The column of lava now stands high in the throat of the volcano and it is under tremendous pressure and saturated with gases. Finally, when the pressure becomes too great to be contained by the surrounding material the eruption begins. Accompanied by sharp earthquakes and strong explosions, which give rise to great ash clouds (pinos), the cone splits. From the fractures, which frequently extend from the crater rim to the base, floods of lava pour out and flow rapidly down the side of the cone. These actions constitute the paroxysmal eruption which marks the end of a cycle. Such eruptions usually last for two or three weeks and are followed by a repose period which is the beginning of a new cycle.

Sir William Hamilton, whose work on Vesuvius has already been mentioned, gives a detailed account of an eruption which began on October 17, 1767. This paroxysmal eruption is typical of those which mark the end of a cycle. After strong explosions which lasted for two days and were felt in Naples, fissures opened on the northwest and south sides of the cone on October 19, and streams of lava poured out. One was directed toward the town of Salvatore while the other flowed in the direction of Torre Annunziata. Padre Torre, an ardent observer of Vesuvius, was on the mountain near the point where one of the fissures opened and his vivid account of his experience, as well as the events which followed, is worth repeating here:

I was making observations upon the lava, which had already, from the spot where it first broke out, reached the valley, when, on a sudden, about noon, I heard a violent noise within the mountain, and about a quarter of a mile from the place where I stood, the mountain split; and with much noise from this new mouth a fountain of liquid fire shot up many feet high and then like a torrent rolled on directly towards us; in an instant clouds

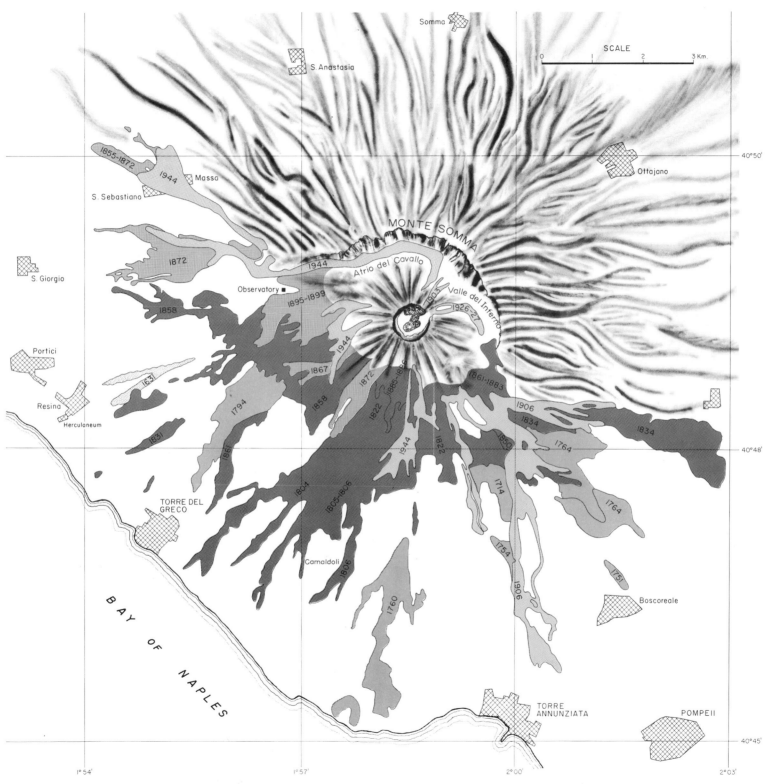

PLATE 10. Lava flows of Mount Vesuvius.
Compiled from Alfano and Friedlander (1928) and others.

of black smoke and ashes caused total darkness; the explosions were much louder than any thunder I ever heard, and the smell of sulphur was offensive. My guide, alarmed, took to his heels . . . [and] I followed close and we ran nearly three miles without stopping as the earth continued to shake beneath our feet. I was apprehensive of the opening of a fresh mouth which might cut off our retreat. . . . besides the pumice stones, falling upon us like hail, were of such a size as to cause a disagreeable sensation upon the part where they fell.

I observed on my way to Naples, which was in less than two hours after I left the mountain, that the lava had actually covered 3 miles of the very road through which we retreated. . . . Portici and Naples were in the extremity of alarm; the churches were filled; the streets were thronged with processions of saints, and various ceremonies were performed to quell the fury of the mountain. In the night of the 20th [October] the situation became critical, the prisoners in the public jails attempted to escape and the mob set fire to the gates [of the house] of Cardinal Archbishop because he refused to bring out the relics of St. Januarius. The 21st was quieter but on the 22nd, at 10:00 A.M. [there was] the same thundering noise but more violent and alarming. Ashes fell in abundance in Naples, covering houses and balconies to an inch in depth. In the midst of these horrors, the mob growing tumultous and impatient, obliged the Cardinal to bring out the head of St. Januarius and go with it in the procession . . . and it is well attested here that the eruption ceased the moment the Saint came in sight of the mountain; it is true the noise ceased about that time after having lasted five hours, as it had done the preceding day. . . . on the 27th the eruption came to an end.

In the latter part of the eighteenth century Vesuvius appears to have been particularly active, with much shorter cycles than during the nineteenth and twentieth centuries. After a repose of only three years, following the 1767 eruption, Vesuvius renewed its activity, and after nine years of moderate activity, the paroxysmal eruption which ended the brief cycle began in May, 1779. A fissure opened on the north-northeast side and lava flowed from this opening throughout the month of June. On August 8, according to Hamilton, terrific explosions, accompanied by a liquid fountain of fire, began to rise from the crater to a height of about two miles. This blazing column was directed toward Ottaiano, and as it fell it covered the side of the cone with a band of red-hot scoria more than a mile in width. The inhabitants of Ottaiano, unable to see the crater because of the rim of Somma and unaware that they were in the path of the fiery blast, were suddenly enveloped by a deluge of red-hot scoria and cinders. Hamilton writes:

The sight of the place [Ottaiano] was dismal, half buried under black scoria and dust, all windows towards the mountain broken, some of the houses burnt, the street choked with ashes—in some narrow streets to a depth of four feet, so that roads had to be cut by people to reach their own doors. During the tempestuous fall of ashes, scoria, and stones, so large as to weigh a hundred pounds, the inhabitants dared not stir out—even with vain protection of pillows, tables, wine casks, etc. on their heads. Driven back wounded or terrified, they retreated to cellars and arches, half stifled with heat and dust and sulphur, and blinded by volcanic lightning— through 25 minutes this horror lasted; then suddenly ceased, and the people took the opportunity of quitting the country, after leaving the sick and bedridden in the churches. One more hour of this frightful visitation and Ottaiano would have been a buried city like Pompeii.

After the 1779 eruption Vesuvius was in repose for five years, followed by moderate activity until the great paroxysmal eruption of 1793, which ended the cycle. This eruption began on June 15, 1793, after strong explosions and earthquakes opened a fissure between Resina and Torre del Greco low on the southwest side of the old Somma cone. Along this fracture, said to have been one-half mile in length, lava poured from six *bocas*. The flows soon united in a single stream and in a matter of six hours (from 10:00 P.M. to 4:00 A.M.) invaded Torre del Greco, flowing down the main street with a front 1,200 to 1,500 feet wide, and extended 362 feet into the sea on a front 1,127 feet wide and 15 feet in height. It was the third time, but unfortunately not the last, that Torre del Greco had been invaded by lava. At the same time a lava flow of about half the volume of the Torre del Greco flow poured from a fissure almost directly opposite on the northeast side of the cone.

From the 1793 eruption to the middle of the nineteenth century paroxysmal eruptions, each ending a cycle, occurred in 1822, 1838, and 1850. There is some difference of opinion regarding the assignment of cycles from 1850 to 1872, but all agree that the eruption of 1872 was one of the all-time great eruptions of Vesuvius and without doubt marks the end of a cycle.

In the eruption of 1872 the cone split from top to bottom on the north flank and the lava from this fissure poured into the Atrio del Cavallo and through the Observatory gap, inundating the villages of Massa and San Sebastiano. From the main crater strong explosions with large pinos spread both fine and coarse ash over a wide area. The explosions, heard in Naples, were particularly strong on April 28, 29, and 30, the last three days of the eruption.

One of the best-known eruptive cycles of Vesuvius extended from 1872 to 1906. The repose period was interrupted briefly in 1874 when a small cone formed on the crater floor but the main renewal of activity began in 1877. Cone building and lava flows inside the crater followed the usual pattern of crater filling until the outbreak of the external flow of 1881. This flow issued from a fracture on the southeast side of the cone, above Torre Annunziata, but the lava was so sluggish that it accumulated around the opening, forming a cupola or dome-shaped mass of lava. Colle Margherita, a lava dome of the same type located in the Atrio de Cavallo, was formed in 1891–1894, and Colle Umberto, near the Vesuvian Volcano Observatory, was formed in 1895–1899. Colle Umberto rises 480 feet above the Atrio floor, and, while it obscures the view from the Observatory into the Atrio, it does serve as a barrier to protect the Observatory from future flows.

By April, 1906, the intercrater cone completely filled the crater and was, in fact, a continuation of the main cone. At this time Vesuvius reached its greatest height, having an elevation of 4,338 feet above sea level. The great eruption of 1906 began early on the morning of April 4 when a fissure opened on the south-southwestern side of the cone and a small lava flow issued from the upper end of the break at an elevation of 3,630 feet. Toward midnight another flow started from the same break but at a point 1,200 feet lower. During this time the activity in the crater increased in violence and enormous blocks of old lava, incandescent scoria, and cinders were constantly being ejected, rising hundreds of feet above the crater rim and falling on the sides of the cone or back into the crater. Dense pinos, in which lightning flashes were seen for the first time in this eruption, rose from the crater and spread ash over the countryside. On the morning of April 6 the third *boca* opened still lower, at an elevation of about 1,800 feet, and on the same zone of fractures but somewhat to the east of the previous vents. From it came the most imposing lava flow of the entire eruption, which covered a portion of Torre Annunziata. On April 7 still another flow issued from a point slightly east of the Torre Annunziata vent and a tongue of lava flowed toward Terzigno. In the early hours of April 8, enormous quantities of fresh scoria and rocks were thrown from the crater, a portion of which described a great arch over Mount Somma in the direction of Ottaiano and San Giuseppe.

This phenomenon was a repetition of what occurred in the eruption of 1779, previously described. About three feet of scoria and debris fell in Ottaiano and the roofs in many houses collapsed under the weight of the debris. In San Giuseppe 105 persons were killed when the roof of a church in which they had sought refuge collapsed. The culmination of the eruption was reached with a great "gas blow-off," which began at 3:30 A.M. on April 8 and continued for twelve to fifteen hours. This tremendous outrush of gas, which by its force enlarged the crater and carried away the upper part of the cone, was an awesome spectacle. Perret (1924, p. 45) who was an eye-witness of the eruption, gives a scale drawing of the "blow-off," which is reproduced as Figure 42, Phase 5. The gas eruption, with abundant ash, continued, but with decreasing intensity, for two days, and intermittently until the end of the eruption on April 22. The accumulation of hot ash on the upper slopes of Vesuvius gave rise to many "hot avalanches," which were a serious hazard to trips on the volcano during the closing days of the eruption. These masses of ash were very unstable and an earthquake or even a huge boulder falling on an accumulation might be sufficient to send it cascading down the slope like an avalanche of snow. Heavy rains toward the end of April, especially in the Ottaiano area, caused mudflows which did extensive damage. The cone lost 325 feet of height in the eruption, largely because of the gas "blow-off."

The next and latest full cycle at Vesuvius extended from 1906 to 1944. After April 22, 1906, Vesuvius was in a state of repose until May, 1913, although minor eruptions of cinders occurred in the bottom of the crater in May, 1910, and again in June, 1911. The typical pattern of cone

PLATE 11. Mount Vesuvius and the Bay of Naples.
Photo with infra-red film.

building and lava flows in the crater continued with varying intensity until the paroxysmal eruption of March, 1944, brought the cycle to a close. During this interval of about thirty years the crater was filled and the cinder cone, built up from the crater floor, could be seen from Naples projecting above the rim of the crater. The initial phase of the 1944 eruption began on March 12, when a section of the summit cone collapsed, obstructing the conduit. Another collapse on March 14 further blocked the conduit. By March 18 the conduit had been reopened by explosive activity and lava began to overflow the crater rim at a break on the east side. Moving rapidly it reached the walls of Somma in one-half hour and then moved westward in the Atrio de Cavallo and through the Observatory gap toward the towns of Massa and San Sebastiano. The lava reached these towns on March 21, and moving at the rate of fifty to one hundred meters per hour it passed through the towns leaving only a smoking lava field with the ruins of some of the houses to mark the site. Other lava streams poured from the west side of the cone, cutting and blocking the railway and the Funicolare Vesuviana. Accompanying the outpouring of lava, explosive activity in the crater increased in violence, throwing out great quantities of ash and scoria.

On March 21, when the outflow of lava from the fissures on the side had ceased, a new phase began. It was marked by the violent overflowing of the lava column and the ejection of fountains of lava to a height of not less than one-half mile. A large amount of the ejected lava fell on the east side of the cone forming a "pseudo-lava flow." These violent lava fountains, lasting about an hour, occurred at intervals throughout the day and into the night. A similar type of activity, which devastated Ottaiano, occurred in the 1779 and in the 1906 eruptions. The gas "blow-off" similar to that described in the 1906 eruption, began on March 22 and in its most violent phase lasted about ten hours. The eruption continued with the ejection of quantities of ash and cinders until March 29.

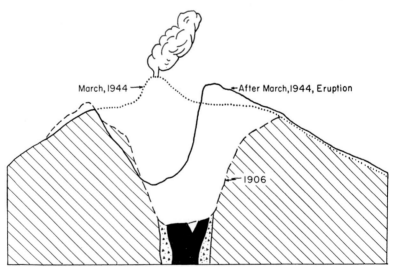

FIGURE 19. Profiles of the crater of Vesuvius since the 1906 eruption. After Imbo (1951).

Mount Somma

1944 lava flow

Volcano Observatory

PLATE 12. Mount Vesuvius and the harbor of Naples.

As in the 1906 eruption, marked changes occurred in the crater as a result of the 1944 eruption. These changes are believed to be due in a large measure to the "gas blow-off," which literally blows away the upper portion of the cone. At the close of the eruption the crater was an irregular, elliptical basin with a depth of about 900 feet and a long axis of about 1,800 feet in an east-west direction. Since the 1944 eruption the crater has been gradually filling by avalanching from the sides. When observed by the writer in 1952 the crater was about 700 feet deep and the huge dust clouds which rose when an avalanche from the sides crashed into the crater were frequently reported as new eruptions. Profiles of the crater at several periods since the 1906 eruption are shown in Figure 19. Following the 1944 eruption, Vesuvius lapsed into a repose period in which it remains today. For the past three hundred years the repose periods have averaged about seven years. Vesuvius is now in its sixteenth year of repose; so it is apparent that a renewal of activity is long overdue.

Depth of the magma reservoir at Vesuvius

The depth of the magma reservoir in a volcano can be determined only by indirect evidence. In most cases the depth of earthquakes which are associated with a volcanic eruption give a clue to the probable depth of the magma chamber. This is, of course, based on the assumption that the earthquakes originate in the magma reservoir. The depth of many such earthquakes has been recorded, and, surprisingly, a depth of around twenty miles is indicated in many cases.

Vesuvius is unique in that the geologic structure surrounding the volcano provides a means of establishing the depth of certain formations beneath Vesuvius and from this infomation the depth of the magma can be determined. Since this, in the case of Vesuvius at least, answers the oft-asked question, "How deep is a volcano?" it will be worth while to explain how the information is obtained.

The Bay of Naples is a faulted synclinal basin, with the Sorrento Peninsula (Amalfi) and the Island of Capri forming one of the uptilted edges, while a similar projection on the north, known as Mount Massico, forms the northern limb of the syncline (Fig. 20). Vesuvius as well as the other volcanic centers in this area, such as the Phlegraean Fields and

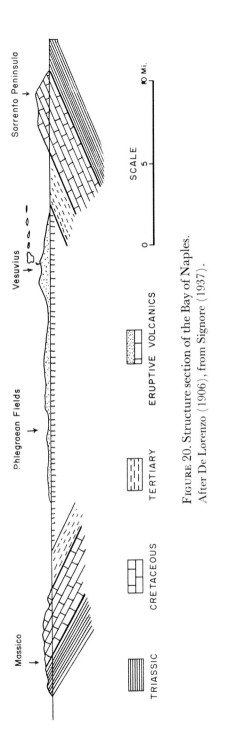

FIGURE 20. Structure section of the Bay of Naples. After De Lorenzo (1906), from Signore (1937).

Ischia, are located near the center of this synclinal basin. The rocks of the Sorrento Peninsula consist of Triassic and Cretaceous limestones and dolomites which dip to the northwest, that is toward Vesuvius. From the dip, the depth of these layers below Mount Vesuvius can be estimated. The conduit which connects the magma reservoir with the crater must, of course, pass through these layers of limestone. During an eruption blocks of these limestones are broken from the walls of the conduit, or from the roof of the magma chamber and ejected along with ash and pumice. Great numbers of such blocks are found among the tuffs of Mount Somma, and they can be identified on the basis of the contained fossils and lithologic characteristics.

Fragments of Tertiary rocks show little or no magmatic influence. Blocks of Cretaceous limestone are usually unaltered, or at most only recrystallized, indicating only a brief contact with the magma during their ascent in the conduit. In strong contrast, blocks of Triassic limestone are thoroughly altered, and frequently the entire rock has been metamorphosed to a silicate rock in which new minerals, largely lime silicates such as vesuvianite, have been developed. These rocks must have had a long enduring contact with the magma such as could take place only if they formed the roof of the magma chamber. Thus we can assume that the magma reservoir has reached the level of the Triassic rocks but has not reached the level of the overlying Cretaceous rocks (Fig. 21). Since the Triassic rocks crop out on the Sorrento Peninsula and their thickness and angle of dip are known, it is possible to estimate accurately their depth beneath Vesuvius. Rittmann, who was among the first to work out this relationship, estimated that the top of the magma reservoir of Vesuvius is approximately five kilometers below sea level.

It was mentioned earlier that Vesuvius, after reaching a stage in which its eruptive history should have been approaching an end, was rejuvenated and began a new cycle. The reason for this change can now be made clear from the preceding discussion. It will be recalled that in the initial stage of volcanic activity basic lavas are usually erupted and that these form plateaulike basements which underlie most volcanic areas, including Vesuvius. In time, due to magmatic differentiation (p. 57), the magma progressively becomes more acidic and in the final stage the eruptions consist mainly of ash and pumice. It is in this final

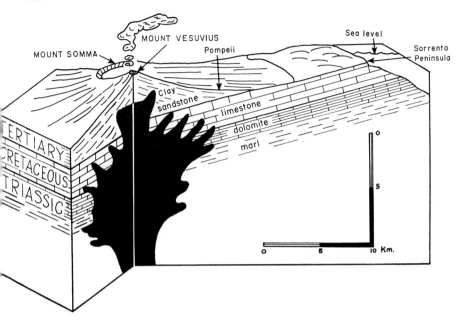

FIGURE 21. Depth of magma chamber at Vesuvius.
Based on Rittmann (1933) as interpreted by Umbgrove (1950).

stage that the cinder cone, surmounting the lava plateau, is built. Such was the condition of Vesuvius prior to A.D. 1036, when it began to pour out new flows of lava. Although for the next five hundred years the status of Vesuvius may have been open to question, the great floods of lava in the eruption of 1631 left no doubt that Vesuvius had embarked on a new type of activity.

The absorption of large quantities of limestone by the magma as it rose into the zone of the Triassic limestone would certainly have an effect on its composition. The added calcium would make the magma more basic and this is doubtless the explanation for its "rejuvenation." This change in composition of a magma by the absorption of limestone has been described by Rittmann (1933) as "magmatic-sclerosis." Many of the volcanoes in the Mediterranean area, in addition to Vesuvius, have erupted lavas (and other products) which indicate that the magmas have absorbed large quantities of limestone. These lavas, with a compo-

FIGURE 22. Map showing location of Larderello steam area, Italian volcanoes, and major structural trends.

sition distinct from the usual Pacific or Atlantic types, are placed in a special category known as the "Mediterranean" type. The classic limestone-assimilation hypothesis, described above, to account for alkalic lavas has been a point of controversy for a number of years. It is particularly unsatisfactory in areas in which no significant amount of limestone exists in the bedrock to be assimilated. Holmes (1950), with good evidence, proposed that rocks of this type were formed by reaction between carbonatite magma (one rich in carbonates) and granitic rocks of the sial. Thus Holmes has turned the limestone-assimilation hypothesis upside down. Instead of a silicate magma assimilating limestone to produce alkalic magma, he suggests that a carbonatite magma assimilates granite.

The well-documented record of the activity of Vesuvius through the ages has provided much information on which some of the basic concepts of volcanism are founded. Its future activity will be watched closely by scientists in order to verify some of the current theories concerning volcanic activity and to obtain possible clues to the problems of volcanology.

Vulcano

The Vulcanian type of eruption was named for the volcano Vulcano, which from ancient times until late in the nineteenth century was one of the most active volcanoes in the Mediterranean region. Its last eruption was in 1888–1890. However, under existing conditions Mount Vesuvius is perhaps a better example of the Vulcanian type of eruption. But even though other volcanoes may now be better examples of this kind of eruption, the type is still called after Vulcano. Vulcano is one of two volcanoes in the Aeolian Islands which have given their names to types of volcanic eruption, the second one being Stromboli. A description of these Islands, noted for their volcanic activity, will assist in the understanding of Vulcano as an example of the Vulcanian type of eruption, as well as of other volcanoes.

The Aeolian Islands

The Aeolian Islands lie in the Tyrrhenian sea between the toe of Italy and Sicily. About twenty-five miles off the northern coast of Sicily,

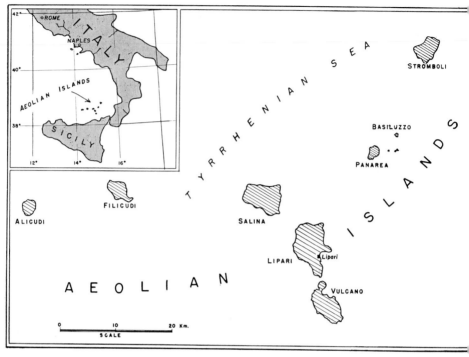

FIGURE 23. Aeolian Islands.

for governmental purposes they fall within the province of Messina, Sicily. The islands are known also as the Lipari Islands, from the largest island in the group. However, the Italian name *Isole Eolie*, or the English equivalent, *Aeolian*, is a name which has been used since ancient times.

The Islands were frequently mentioned in classical mythology as the home of Eolus, God of Wind, and they were twice visited by Ulysses in his wanderings. According to one version, Eolus was a Greek prince ruling a colony on the Islands. Being a shrewd man, he acquired some fame by his success in predicting the weather from the nature of the vapor cloud over the active volcano believed to have been Stromboli. The people were fishermen and the weather was an important element in their daily lives. The power of forecasting events is often confused with that of bringing them to pass; and the prophets of one generation frequently become the gods of the next. Hence, it is not surprising to find Eolus in later mythologies referred to as the "God of Wind." Stromboli is still believed by the inhabitants, not without some justification, to respond like a barometer to changes in atmospheric pressure, and the density of the vapor column rising from the crater faithfully reflects the moisture content of the air. A native of Stromboli will look up at the vapor column rising from the crater and confidently predict the weather for the next day! However, to the writer, who experienced some of the sudden and fierce storms which sweep the surrounding sea and was stranded on Stromboli for two weeks by a storm, it does not seem necessary to look to Greek mythology for the name of the Island.

The Aeolian Islands consist of seven inhabited islands and a number of uninhabited rocks, all of volcanic origin. The largest and most populous island is Lipari, with an area of 14.5 square miles. The highest peak on Lipari is 1,975 feet above sea level. The other inhabited islands, with the area and the highest point of each are: Stromboli—area 5 square miles, elevation 3,040 feet; Panarea—area 1.24 square miles, elevation 1,381 feet; Salina—area 10.25 square miles, elevation 3,155 feet; Vulcano—area 8 square miles, elevation 1,637 feet; Filicudi—area 3.75 square miles, elevation 2,542 feet; and Alicudi—area 2 square miles, elevation 2,185 feet. The islands rise from a depth of around 7,000 feet below sea level to a maximum height on Salina of 3,155 feet above sea level. Thus, only the top one-third of Salina is exposed above the sea, and on some of the other islands the ratio of exposed height to submerged depth is even less.

The volcanoes of Italy, in general, are located along a trend which parallels the Apennine Mountains and the Tyrrhenian coast. The uplift of the Apennines in mid-Tertiary time, in common with that of the Alps, was accompanied by a subsidence of the Tyrrhenian basin, and the volcanoes of Italy, with the exception of Mount Vulture and Mount Etna, are at the juncture of the depressed area and the upstanding block. Beginning in the vicinity of Siena, in northern Italy, and extending southward through Rome and on to Naples, volcanic centers are more or less evenly spaced along this trend. The Apennine Mountains, which make up the backbone of Italy, extend the length of Italy, through Sicily and are continued in the Atlas Mountains of North Africa. This

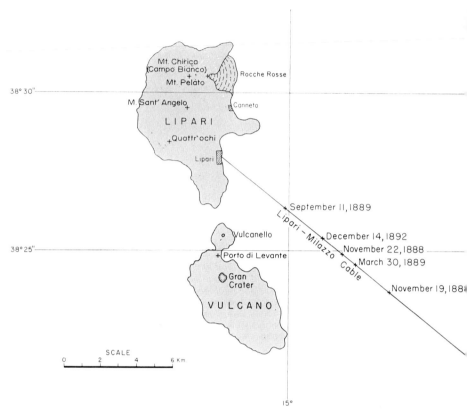

FIGURE 24. Lipari and Vulcano, Aeolian Islands.

trend of folding, the general position of the major fracture lines, and the volcanic centers are shown on Figure 22. It will be observed that the Aeolian Islands are located in the sharply curved portion of the belt. The arrangement of the Islands in a three-prong, starlike pattern has prompted several writers to propose radiating fractures, as indicated on Figure 23, with activity beginning at the center and progressing outward along radii. It is true that the only active vents, Stromboli and Vulcano, are at the opposite ends of two of the radii, but this relationship may be more apparent than real. Reference has already been made to the subsidence of the Tyrrhenian basin, which doubtless was broken into a series of blocks parallel to the edge of the basin, conforming with

PLATE 13. Vulcano from Quattr'ochi on Lipari Island. Refer to Plate 15 for location of Quattr'ochi.

the trend of the Apennines. In many volcanic regions the location of vents is determined by fractures which intersect subsiding blocks at almost right angles. This is probably the case in the Aeolians. If so, the various islands may not be on a continuous fracture but on separate fractures each of which intersects a subsiding block of the earth's crust.

With the exception of Panarea, which is probably only the remnant of a former cone, all the islands contain cones with well-marked craters. Filicudi, Alicudi, and Stromboli are each single cones, while Salina consists of twin cones. Lipari and Vulcano are more complex, each consisting of the ruins of several intersecting cones. Only Vulcano and Stromboli have erupted during recorded history, and these two are still active today.

Vulcano lies directly to the south of Lipari, a channel less than one kilometer in width separating the two islands (Fig. 24). However, the trip from the town of Lipari, where boats are obtained, to the landing point on Vulcano, Porto di Levante, is about six and a half kilometers. Good views of Vulcano can be obtained from almost any high point on Lipari. A favorite spot with the writer is that from Quattr'ochi, about three kilometers to the northwest of the town of Lipari, where the view of Vulcano is unobstructed and where on a clear day Mount Etna, a hundred miles distant on Sicily, can be seen in the background.

The central part of the Island of Lipari is occupied by Mont Sant'Angelo (1,952 feet) with a great axial crater and several small cones on its western flank. Judd (1875) considers Mont Sant'Angelo to be the product of what he terms the second period of volcanic activity in the history of the Islands. This period, during which most of the now exposed cones in the Aeolian Islands were formed, was characterized by lavas (trachytic type) and volcanic tuffs. The cones of Alicudi, Filicudi, and Salina and the central cone of Stromboli belong to this period. The first period of volcanic activity was, of course, largely submarine. Monte Pelato, better known as Campo Bianco (White Field), a volcanic cone composed entirely of pure white pumice, makes up the northeastern part of the Island of Lipari. It is in part surrounded by the relic of a large cone (a Somma ring) which culminates in Monte Chirica (1,975 feet), the highest point on the island. The steep walls of the crater of Campo Bianco are four hundred to six hundred feet high on all sides except

PLATE 14. Obsidian flow from crater of Campo Bianco, Lipari Island.

the northeast, where it was breached by a stream of volcanic glass (obsidian) emerging from the crater in the final phase of activity. This one-half-mile-wide stream of glassy lava, extending as a cascade down the side of the cone and into the sea, is a striking sight. The flow, now covered with a reddish brown coating of iron oxide as a result of weathering, is known as Rocche Rosse ("red rock"). The regular interisland steamers pass near the sea front of the obsidian flow, affording splendid views of this unique feature. (Plate 14).

The pumice and ash deposits at Campo Bianco have long been famous and, prior to World War II, were the world's chief source of high-grade pumice and ash. Pumice is used as an abrasive and ash is the chief constituent in many scouring powders. As a result of the interruption of shipping routes during the war, which made Lipari pumice unavailable, deposits in other parts of the world were developed and Lipari has not been able to regain its former position in world markets. The ash and pumice which form the cone of Campo Bianco belong to the third and last period of volcanic activity in the Lipari area. Thus Campo Bianco conforms to the usual pattern, previously described, with lavas of basaltic or intermediate composition in the early stages (first and second periods of activity) and with ash and pumice eruptions and a dome of acidic lava filling the crater in the final stage. In the case of Campo Bianco the obsidian flow represents the lava dome. The obsidian flow of Campo Bianco is well known to geologists because the material had been described as a separate rock type under the name of "liparite."

The contrast of the blue waters of the Mediterranean and the snow-white cones of pumice, such as Campo Bianco, presents a most impressive view. Judd (1875) in an outburst of almost poetic extravagance, describes the scene as follows:

Lofty cinder cones of snowy white pumice, their vast craters breached by lava streams of solid glass, their surface coated with a reddish brown crust, arise amidst the blue waters of the Mediterranean, and displaying in that clearness of outline and that vividness of coloring which only the brilliancy of an almost tropical sky can impart, they constitute scenery of startling novelty and wondrous beauty—the impression produced by it is as hopeless to convey as it is impossible to forget.

Vulcano in mythology

In ancient mythologies Vulcano is identified as the location of the forge of Vulcan, the Roman god of fire. It was Herodotus (475 B.C.) who first mentioned Vulcano under the name Hiera, as the vent of the forge of Hepaestus, the Greek god of fire. Vulcan, the Latin equivalent. was the blacksmith of the gods, maker of the finest armor, the breast-plate of Hercules, the shield of Achilles, as well as the arrows of Apollo and Diana. Vulcan's wife, according to the *Odyssey,* was Venus. The fire and smoke which came out of a volcano were believed to come from the forge. Later historians and geographers gave a more exact description of the phenomena displayed at Vulcano and in time the name came to be applied to all mountains where similar activity occurred—thus it is the prototype of all volcanoes. It should be recalled that prior to A.D. 79, Vesuvius was inactive, and in fact was not generally recognized as a volcano. However, Vulcano and Stromboli were frequently in eruption, and, since they were the only active volcanoes (other than Etna) with which the ancient Greeks and Romans were familiar, it is not surprising to find many myths and legends surrounding these islands.

Early history of Vulcano

Early accounts of the activity of Vulcano lead us to conclude that it was in a much more violent state of activity than has been the case in recent centuries. Its eruptions were also more explosive than those of either Stromboli or Etna. Thucydides, one of the most prominent of the early Greek historians writing in the fifth century B.C., speaks of Vulcano as throwing out considerable smoke by day and flame by night. Aristotle, who died in 322 B.C., states (Meteorologica 2. viii) that: ". . . in the Island of Vulcano part of the ground swelled up and rose with a noise in the form of a hillock, giving vent to a great quantity of air, carrying with it flame and ashes, the latter in sufficient quantity to cover all the town of Lipari."[14] In the third century B.C. Callias described Vulcano as having two craters, one of which was two hundred feet in circumference and threw out great stones with a noise which could be

[14] Aristotle advocated "pent-up" winds imprisoned in subterranean channels as a cause of earthquakes and volcanoes.

heard for a distance of fifty miles. Pliny records that an island emerged from the sea among the Lipari Islands early in the second century B.C., and later Grosius gives the date as 182 B.C. Apparently on the strength of these references and on the assumption that the island was Vulcanello, the British Admiralty Handbook gives the date for the birth of Vulcanello as about 183 B.C. Judd (1875), DiFiore (1922), and others have accepted this date for the birth of Vulcanello. It is the one commonly found in the literature.

Recent studies attempting to trace the wanderings of Odysseus as narrated by Homer throw some doubt as to the accuracy of 183 B.C. as the date of the birth of Vulcanello. The reader will recall that in the *Odyssey* Homer describes the adventures of Odysseus, King of Ithaca, in his journey home following the fall of Troy and the end of the Trojan War. Classical scholars have long been divided as to whether the places described are actual localities known to Homer, or whether they are entirely mythical. It is beyond the scope of this volume to review this interesting topic. However, we are dependent on the classics, especially the writings of Homer and Virgil, for much of our information on the activity of the Mediterranean volcanoes in ancient times and the source of such information cannot be entirely ignored. On the assumption that Homer was describing a region with which he was familiar, it should be possible by a careful analysis of his descriptions to detect clues which would identify the various areas visited by Odysseus. One of the best-known as well as most controversial works in this field is that by Samuel Butler (*Authoress of the Odyssey*), who concluded that the *Odyssey* had its origin at Trapani, Sicily, and was written by a woman. A study now under way by Professor L. G. Pocock of Canterbury University College, Christchurch, New Zealand, confirms in part and rejects in part the conclusions reached by Butler as to the route of Odysseus. A preliminary statement of Professor Pocock's conclusions has been released in a fifteen-page pamphlet entitled *Landfalls of Odysseus*. Professor Pocock makes a good case for the argument that the islands described as Charybdis, Scylla, and Planctae are Vulcanello (at that time still not joined to Vulcano), Vulcano, and Lipari respectively. Charybdis is described by Homer as not far from Planctae and within bow-shot of Scylla. The *Odyssey* was written about 650 B.C., and if Charybdis is Vulcanello, then the island described by Pliny as appearing in 183 B.C. must be some other island of the Aeolian group.

Regardless of the exact date at which Vulcanello appeared as an island, considerable volume was added by an eruption in 126 B.C., and by 91 B.C. sufficient debris had accumulated to form a platform surrounding it. Confusion as to the date of its birth may arise from the fact that new volcanic cones which appear in the sea are frequently destroyed by wave action in a short time, only to reappear when a new eruption occurs. This may have happened several times, before the cone attained enough volume to maintain itself against the attack of the waves, giving rise to conflicting dates as to its birth.

With the passing of the classical writers the history of Vulcano again becomes nebulous. The inhabitants of the Lipari Islands suffered from the invasions of pirates and slave hunters and acquired a reputation for ferocity which caused the islands to be bypassed by mariners. The long period of obscurity during the Dark Ages is marked by a brief reference to Vulcano in the fifth century, and another, perhaps legendary, account which appears in the biography of St. Willebald, who is believed to have lived from A.D. 701 to A.D. 786. In his biography the following passage (quoted by Judd, 1875, p. 101) refers to Vulcano:

The Saint, [wished] to obtain a view of the boiling crater, called the inferno of Theodoric, but they could not climb the mountain from the depth of ashes and scoria, so they contented themselves with a view of the flames, as they rose with a roaring like thunder, and the vast column of smoke ascended from the pit.

Modern history of Vulcano

The modern history of Vulcano begins with accounts by Frazello, a native of Sicily, who described the great eruption of February 4, 1444, which shook all of Sicily and was felt as far away as Naples. It is said that the sea "boiled" all around the island and that vast rocks were discharged into it. Submarine eruptions were indicated by reports that smoke was rising from the waves at a number of points. Following the eruption navigation around the island was totally changed because of the presence of many new rocks. Frazello later visited Vulcano and reported that Vulcanello was still a separate island, with a narrow channel between it and Vulcano. In 1727 M. d'Orville, after a visit to Vulcano, reported that it had two active vents and that the noise of the almost continuous explosions was so loud at Lipari, six miles away, that he could not sleep the whole night. At the time of Spallanzani's first visit to Vulcano, some sixty years later, only one crater existed. When and how the two craters were destroyed and a single cone formed is not recorded, although from the diary of Abbe Ignacio, published in 1761 by Signor Don Salvatore, we learn that between 1730 and 1740 Vulcano was in an almost constant state of eruption. In 1768 Sir William Hamilton, in passing near Vulcano by ship, observed the gas column rising from the crater and compared the activity to that of the Solfatara at Naples. Other travelers in the area in 1770 reported no "glow" over Vulcano at night; so it appears that this was a period of quiet. The repose was of short duration, for an eruption was reported in 1771 and another in 1775. The latter, according to Dolomieu, produced a large flow of obsidian on the north side of the cone. In 1786 a violent eruption, accompanied by subterranean roaring which could be heard over all the islands, threw out enormous quantities of cinders and incandescent rocks. The eruption lasted fifteen days. When Spallanzani visited Vulcano two years after this eruption the terror among the inhabitants was so great that he could not induce any of them to accompany him to the crater. From Spallanzani's description Judd concludes that no essential change in the crater took place until the eruption of 1873–1874.

The southern part of the island had been inhabited and under cultivation since ancient times, but the severe eruptions of the eighteenth century appear to have driven the inhabitants away and during these eruptions it was totally uninhabited. Following the great eruption of 1786, Vulcano was in a state of repose to such an extent that some writers, until activity was renewed in September, 1873, referred to it as extinct. During this eruption, which lasted intermittently for about eighteen months, rumblings were heard in Lipari, several fissures opened on the floor of the crater, and dense columns of vapor, accompanied by some stones, were discharged. Needless to say, the sulphur-mining operation which was under way in the crater was seriously hampered.

The next eruption of Vulcano, and the latest to date, began on August 3, 1888, and continued until May 17, 1890. An account of the eruption is given in English by Johnston-Lavis (1888), but the report by an Italian commission provides the most complete record. The commission, as originally established, consisted of Professor O. Silvestri (Catania) as president, Professor G. Mercalli (Milan), Professor Grablovitz (Seismological Observatory of Ischia), and V. Clerici (Messina) as engineer, with A. Cerati, Professor Ponte, and A. Silvestri as assistants. Professor Silvestri died before the publication of the report but not until some months after the eruptions ceased. After his death Professor Mercalli (1891), the largest contributor to the report, completed it.

During the eruption strong explosions were accompanied by a dense eruption cloud which spread ash and cinders over a wide area. Most observers commented on the whiteness of the ash, comparing it to snow. Masses of pumice, "bread crust" bombs, and incandescent rocks were scattered over the cone and the immediate surroundings. The explosions, which broke windows in the town of Lipari six miles away, occurred at intervals of a few minutes during the most violent periods. The strongest explosions usually followed a period of repose. Especially strong explosions were reported on August 4, 1888, December 26, 1889, and March 15, 1890. Some of the bombs were unusually large. One believed to have been ejected on March 15, 1890, in one of the last outbursts of the eruption, measured nine feet by six feet by six feet. It was a mass of older lava coated with a four-inch crust of new obsidian. Many of the bombs ejected in this eruption contained a core of older lava. No lava flows were produced, but bright "glows" over the crater following explosions indicated the presence of incandescent material. Analysis of the material ejected indicated a silica content of from 62 to 67 percent.

A submarine cable connects Lipari with Milazzo in Sicily. This cable runs about three miles to the east of Vulcano, where the water is from seven hundred to one thousand meters in depth. During the eruption the cable was broken five times. The first break occurred on November 22, 1888, and the last on December 14, 1892, nearly eighteen months after activity had ceased in the crater of Vulcano. At the point of the break, usually, a violent boiling of the sea occurred, and pumice or scoria appeared either on the bottom or floating near the location of the break. Without doubt the breaks marked points of eruption on the submerged flank of Vulcano. The positions of the breaks, which followed a definite

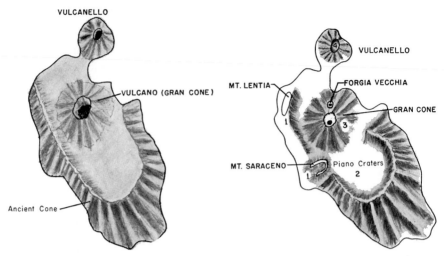

FIGURE 25A. Sequence of eruptions at Vulcano as interpreted by Scrope (1825) and Stoppanni (1900).

FIGURE 25B. Sequence of eruptions (No. 1 being the oldest) at Vulcano, according to DeFiore (1922).

alignment, are shown on Figure 24. After the eruption of 1888–1890, Vulcano lapsed into a state of mild solfataric activity which, with some fluctuations in volume, has continued to the present time.

The cones of Vulcano

During historic times, with the exception of the eruptions which formed Vulcanello, the activity has occurred in the crater of a broadly truncated, symmetrical cone which stands more or less isolated in the northern part of the island. The cone, frequently called the "Gran Cone," rises to a height of 1,266 feet. Gran Cone is encircled on the south and to some extent on the west by remnants (sommas) of earlier cones. All investigators, even from the earliest times, have recognized at least three stages in the history of Vulcano, marked by the progressive migration of the eruptive centers northward (Fig. 25A). Mercalli (1891) and DeFiore (1922) believed that four stages can be identified (Fig. 25B). The oldest part is a rocky mass directly to the west of Gran Cone known as Mount Lentia. The cone of which Mount Lentia is the western edge may have had its center near that of the present active

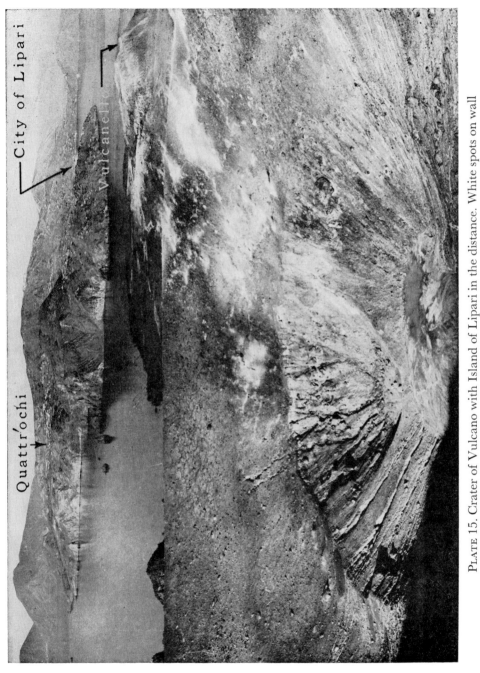

PLATE 15. Crater of Vulcano with Island of Lipari in the distance. White spots on wall of crater are sulphur deposits.

cone. The second center of activity was to the south of Gran Cone. Here were many eruptive centers, referred to collectively as the Piano Craters.[15] The area then collapsed, leaving a huge caldera, of which the south rim was formed by remnants of several of the Piano Craters and the west rim by Mount Lentia. Mount Saraceno, the most recent of the Piano Craters, remained active for a brief time after the subsidence. The sea doubtless flooded the collapsed area and washed against the steep sides of the surrounding rim, until the formation of Gran Cone, which has been in essentially its present condition throughout historic time.

The main crater (or fossa), which occupies an eccentric position, is roughly circular with a diameter of about one-fourth mile at the top and about one-half that at the bottom. The walls of the crater, which rise from four hundred to six hundred feet, are vertical in the lower part but open out into a funnel shape in the upper part. It appears that the bottom of the crater has subsided since the last eruption. When the writer visited Vulcano in December, 1952, many fumaroles were active on the north side of the crater walls, but none were present on the crater floor. Abundant deposits of sulphur were being formed around the more active vents. The composition of the gases from the main crater, as reported by Sicardi (1940), is as follows:

CO_2	55.0	to	69.0%
SO_2	6.0	to	21.0%
H_2S	11.0	to	20.0%
HCl	1.5	to	1.7%
N	1.9	to	2.7%

The reported range in temperature was from 99° C. to 480° C. Along the shore at Porto di Levante are several spots, both on the beach and a short distance offshore, where, because of vigorous agitation due to the escape of carbon dioxide, the water appears to be "boiling."

Sicardi showed that a marked increase in fumarolic activity, both in the temperature as well as in the number of fumaroles, developed around 1924. Maximum temperatures in excess of 600° C. were reported from vents in the main crater where previously the temperature

[15] *Piano* is an Italian word meaning a "level plain" or "floor." Here it means that the craters rise from a relatively flat surface.

had been only slightly in excess of 100° C. Although no eruptive activity occurred at this time, such a marked rise in temperature indicated the possibility of an outbreak. Sulphur had been obtained from the crater in small quantities since ancient times. Shortly after the middle of the nineteenth century a Scottish firm obtained a concession on the crater and installed a fairly extensive chemical works, which was, of course, destroyed in the eruption of 1873. Sulphur has also been obtained from the ruins of an old crater near the shore at Porto di Levante. But all sulphur operations at Vulcano were abandoned many years ago.

About halfway down the slope on the north side of the Gran Cone is the small, compound crater known as Forgia Vecchia, which DeFiore believes was formed early in the eighteenth century.

At the extreme north tip of the island is the cone of Vulcanello, the date of origin of which has already been discussed. It was a separate island for many centuries and was joined to Vulcano in 1550 by an accumulation of ash. Three small craters occupy the summit of Vulcanello. Waves have cut into the east side of Vulcanello, opening one of the craters into the sea and affording a striking cross section of the cone.

Vulcano's contributions to volcanology

Vulcano was the source of the name *volcano,* as has been already pointed out, and this in itself is sufficient to give it a leading place in volcanology. However, its chief contribution has been in serving as one of the types in the classification of volcanoes. It was in 1891, in the report of the commission appointed by the Italian government to study the 1888–1890 eruption of Vulcano, that Mercalli first used and defined the *Vulcanian type* of eruption. The terms *Plinian* and *Vesuvian,* as well as *Strombolian,* had previously been applied descriptively to types of eruptions, but since Vulcano did not fit the pattern of any of these, a new category was needed. As originally defined by Mercalli, the Vulcanian type was characterized by only the explosive removal of the crater plug and the discharge of bombs and scoria, accompanied by a dark, ash-filled eruption cloud. In this respect it resembled the initial outburst of the Vesuvian (Plinian) type. No lava streams were produced and only minor earthquakes accompanied the eruption. The characteristics of the Vulcanian type, as set forth by Mercalli were based, of course, on the 1888–1890 eruption of Vulcano. In this eruption the material discharged during the first three days consisted mainly of the old material blocking the crater. After an interval of thirteen days the second main period of eruption began and thereafter the products of the eruption consisted chiefly of new material in the form of ash, "bread crust" bombs, and scoria. The term *Vulcanian* was later used by other Italian writers and was incorporated into the classification of volcanoes as one of the major types. However, as the term is now used, Vesuvius is a better example of the Vulcanian type than Vulcano. As originally used by Mercalli, the term *Vulcanian* was restricted to those eruptions in which the crater obstruction was removed but no lava flows developed. A typical eruption at Vesuvius begins, like those at Vulcano, with the explosive removal of the crater plug, but then, unlike Vulcano, there are extensive outpourings of lava. In the explosive removal of the crater obstruction huge quantities of ash are produced, as the material is shattered by repeated explosions. This produces a dark eruption cloud heavily charged with ash, which is one of the characteristics of the Vulcanian-type eruption. If there is no outflow of lava the eruption would be of the Vulcanian type as originally defined by Mercalli. However, since lava flows commonly occur the Vulcanian type has been expanded to include such eruptions. It is perhaps unfortunate that Mercalli's original use of *Vulcanian* was not preserved and another type and term introduced to include the eruptions exhibited by Vesuvius. In its broader application, Vulcanian-type eruptions are perhaps the most common type among the volcanoes of the world. An example of a recent eruption is Parícutin Volcano, Mexico, which is described in detail in Chapter 13. Examples of eruptions which fall within Mercalli's original usage of the term are less common, but Lassen Peak, California, the only volcano in continental United States (excluding Alaska) to erupt in historic time, is an example.

*One might have thought that Nature
lived hard by and was brewing on a large.
scale.*   DICKENS

9. THE STROMBOLIAN TYPE OF VOLCANIC ERUPTION

THE STROMBOLIAN TYPE OF ERUPTION was introduced
into the literature by Mercalli and subsequently adopted
as one of the major types in the classification of volcanoes. The essential characteristics of a Strombolian
eruption are the throwing out of incandescent fragments of lava accompanied by a white eruption cloud.
The white color indicates that, in contrast to the Vulcanian eruption cloud, which is heavily charged with
ash and hence dark in color, it contains little ash. The
lava column crusts over lightly and at frequent intervals
mild explosions break the crust, hurling the pasty, incandescent fragments into the air.

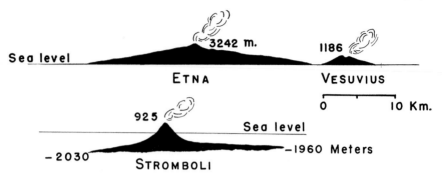

FIGURE 26. Relative sizes of Vesuvius, Stromboli, and Etna.

Significance of Stromboli

Stromboli occupies an important place in the study of volcanoes. It is one of the few volcanoes in the world which is in a state of permanent moderate activity. Records indicate that it has been essentially in its present condition since earliest times. Because of its convenient location and constant state of activity, Stromboli has been visited by many persons interested in volcanoes and there are many reports on its activity. Further, it was the "observations made by Spallanzani at Stromboli in 1788 which first exhibited the true nature of volcanic action," (Scrope, 1872, p. 31). In addition Stromboli was selected as the type example of one of the major divisions in the classification of volcanoes, to which it has given its name. It is apparent, therefore, that there are several reasons for including a description of Stromboli in this volume.

Appearance of Stromboli

Stromboli, the most northerly of the Aeolian Islands, is an almost perfect cone-shaped mass, with twin peaks, emerging directly out of the sea to a height of 3,040 feet. Rising from the floor of the Mediterranean in water 7,000 feet in depth, Stromboli stands above its submarine base at a total height of 10,400 feet, which exceeds the 9,425-foot elevation of Mount Etna above its sedimentary platform. Thus Stromboli may well be, as Professor Ponte has maintained, the "highest active volcano in Europe." Near sea level on the eastern and western sides of the island, on rocky benches formed by lava flows, are the villages of San Vincenzo

PLATE 16. Stromboli Volcano.

and Ginostra, where most of the eight hundred inhabitants of the island
live. The twin peaks forming the summit of Stromboli are remnants of
the rim of an ancient crater. On a terrace about six hundred feet below
the most northerly of the two peaks is the active crater or fossa of Stromboli. Thus, from the summit one has an unobstructed view into the active
crater below. Although it requires a strenuous climb of about three
hours to reach this favorable spot, the view into the crater is well worth
the effort. Scrope, who visited Stromboli in the early half of the nineteenth century, in commenting on the view from this position says:

We are there, indeed admitted almost into the recesses of Nature's laboratory, comparatively open to near inspection at all seasons, without risk,
since the explosions which characterize this phase rarely exceed an average
ratio, and the crater can consequently be approached and its interior
viewed at leisure with complete impunity (p. 31, 1872 ed.).

The crater, which is described more fully in a later paragraph, is an
oval-shaped basin, filled in part with lava and blocks which have ava-

lanched from the sides. On the mountain side the crater is bordered by vertical walls, but on the seaward side it merges into a long, smooth slope called the Sciara del Fuoco ("ski of fire"), which extends from the crater to the sea (Plate 17). Practically all the material ejected from the crater, other than that which falls back into it, rolls down the Sciara del Fuoco. Lava flows also emerge from the crater from time to time and cascade down the Sciara and into the sea.

The Sciara del Fuoco is a unique feature, and many observers have speculated upon its origin. One of the first as well as one of the simplest explanations was advanced by Scrope (1872), who held that an explosion blew away a large segment of the cone and the resulting depression was gradually filled with debris in the nature of a talus slope, forming the Sciara del Fuoco. The eccentric position of the present crater, at the head of the Sciara, would seem to support this explanation. However, this idea was discarded by later workers, notwithstanding its simplicity, largely because of the fact that on the sea floor along the northwest side of the Aeolian Islands is a sharp, almost clifflike slope which becomes steeper near the Sciara del Fuoco than elsewhere. It does not appear to the writer that this necessarily precludes the possibility that the cone of Stromboli was ruptured by an explosion, but it does offer the alternative of rupture by faulting or by avalanching from the precipitous slope. Williams (1941) accounts for the Sciara del Fuoco by collapse and uses it as an example of what he terms a "sector graben."

Eruptive Activity of Stromboli

Although Stromboli is mentioned less frequently by ancient writers than Vulcano, it is referred to in the writings of Aristotle, Diodorus Siculus, Strabo, and others. Most remarkable, perhaps, is the description in the first century of the Christian era by Pliny, who described it in terms still applicable today. The ancient name for the island was Strongyle, a name which is still used by some of the local inhabitants and which referred to the circular form. Stromboli has been known since ancient times as the "Lighthouse of the Mediterranean" because of the red glow which flashes from its summit after each explosion. The red glow, reflected on the clouds above the crater, quickly fades, only to reappear in

PLATE 17. Stromboli and Sciara del Fuoco.

fifteen to thirty minutes, when the next explosion occurs. The oft-described activity of Stromboli, while differing from day to day, follows the same general pattern. Spallanzani, one of the early Italian scientists interested in volcanoes, visited Stromboli in 1788 and described the eruption as follows (quoted by Judd, 1875, p. 148):

On the western side a large number of fumaroles were discharging steam, while deposits of yellow salts were forming around the openings; on the eastern side one large orifice poured out a continuous column of vapor about 12 feet in diameter. In the center there was a funnel-shaped tube which contained liquid lava. This incandescent mass was agitated, rising and falling in the tube—the vertical motion a maximum of 20 feet, sometimes slow, other times fast. On reaching a certain height, large bubbles were seen to collect and these bursting with a sharp report carried innumerable fragments in a fiery shower into the air. The lava would then sink in the tube and begin to rise again.

Spallanzani mentions that the explosions were at intervals of two to three minutes, but with varying degrees of intensity.

In 1831 and early 1832, Friedrich Hoffman spent several weeks at Stromboli. He described the eruptions as follows (quoted by Judd, 1875, p. 151):

The largest opening occupied the center of the crater floor and gave forth vapors only, which produced yellow crusts on its sides. To the southwest, nearly under the crater wall, another mouth about 20 feet in diameter was seen. In the glowing red throat of this chimney, a fluid column of lava could be seen rising and falling, perhaps 20 to 30 feet. Through this column of lava bubbles of steam burst, the puffs taking place regularly at intervals of about a second giving rise to globes of vapor, which carried up bladders of lava. This action continued for more than 15 minutes, then suddenly a louder explosion followed by the violent escape of steam from the opening carrying thousands of fragments of glowing lava to great height. Where the crater joins the steep slope of the Sciara, a third and much smaller opening was seen, from which a small stream of lava, like a perennial fountain, flowed down the Sciara towards the sea, which, however, it did not reach, becoming solid before it arrived at the bottom; some portions of the congealed mass were becoming detached and rolling down into the water.

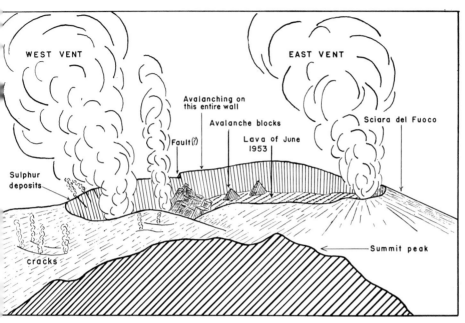

FIGURE 27. Crater of Stromboli on June 21, 1952.
Sketched from a photograph (Bullard, 1954b).

The aspect of the crater, as observed by the writer on three separate visits in 1952, is shown in the accompanying sketch (Fig. 27). The left end, in the sketch, was so deep and the walls so steep that it was not possible to see the bottom of the crater from the observation point on the summit. The floor of the crater, which had a diameter of about four hundred feet, was covered with recent lava, doubtless partly the product of the June, 1952, lava flow. The two most active vents were at the east and west ends of the crater terrace with a smaller vent nearer the center. The east vent, near the edge of the Sciara del Fuoco, was an oval-shaped opening about thirty or forty feet in diameter from which a grayish gas issued. At intervals, a dense white, cauliflower-shaped cloud of steam poured from this vent. There was no noise accompanying the emissions. The west vent was the most active of the three, sending out a vapor cloud, with a distinct chlorine odor, which frequently filled the entire crater. It was accompanied by a continuous roar, which may be compared to the sound of the steam exhaust from a locomotive, but with an irregular rhythm. Then at intervals of from fifteen to twenty minutes a tremendous outrush of gas (not an explosion but a "rushing" sound like many rockets being discharged simultaneously) carried incandescent fragments of lava to a height of from five hundred to a thousand feet above the crater floor. Following a discharge, the crater would clear momentarily of steam, permitting a view which otherwise was obscured by the steam column. The central vent could not be seen from the observation point but a gas column rising at irregular intervals from this point was proof of its existence. With the exception that the lava column was not visible, the eruption was essentially the same as that described by Hoffman 125 years earlier. A stream of lava had issued from the crater and poured down the Sciara del Fuoco and into the sea shortly before my first visit to Stromboli. It is probable that this outpouring of lava reduced the lava level in the crater to the extent that it was no longer visible from the observation point. The fact that lava was present is indicated by the incandescent slag which was thrown up with each explosion.

The persistence of the three vents within the crater of Stromboli is one of the puzzling features of this volcano. The normal pattern is for vents to shift from time to time rather than to maintain their positions. Sir William Hamilton, in 1768, reviewed all earlier reports and concluded that the three vents, then present, had persisted for at least 150 years. In relation to this repeatedly discussed problem it is of interest to note that the observations of the writer show that three vents are still active today, in much the same position as described by previous investigators. Perret thought that they represented diverging outlets from a single conduit but the lack of synchronous activity in the vents invalidates this explanation. Since the vents have persisted for a considerable period of time, it must be concluded that they are deep-seated channelways along which the gases from the underlying magma are reaching the surface. Washington (1917) reviewed the problem and concluded that the persistence of the vents is to be explained by Daly's "gas-fluxing" hypothesis. It is not possible to go into this controversial topic further than to say that it is based on the idea that gases rising from the magma would collect in pockets (cupolas) at the top of the chamber. The highly heated gas would react with the wall rock and, in a process described as "gas-fluxing," would melt ("blowpipe") its way to the surface, forming the vents now present in the crater. It is of interest to note that the persistence of the vents at Stromboli has been used as a proof of the "gas-fluxing" concept.

In recent years more detailed studies of Stromboli have shown that the so-called "normal" Strombolian activity is interrupted at intervals by more vigorous eruptions, which are comparable to those of the Vulcanian type. It is also becoming more apparent that lava flows are far more common at Stromboli than was formerly believed to be the case. These eruptions are accompanied by violent explosions which shake the entire island and during which a dark eruption cloud, a "pino," rises over the crater and spreads red-hot scoria, lapilli, and cinders over the island, forcing the inhabitants to seek shelter indoors to escape the falling debris. Fortunately, the rim of the old crater, which now forms the observation point on the summit, serves as a shield to protect the two villages on the island from the full fury of the eruptions. Nevertheless, the eruptions cause considerable damage and occasionally lives are lost. Lava flows usually develop on the Sciara del Fuoco and frequently one or more streams will reach the sea. Infrequent observations of Stromboli, particularly prior to the present century, make it impossible even to catalog the violent eruptions. During the past two decades strong eruptions have occurred at intervals of two to three years. A particularly violent eruption, in which several lives were lost and in which the property damage was high, occurred in 1930.

The lava from Stromboli is basic in character (50 to 51 percent silica) and is classified as a basalt. As long as the lava column is kept open by frequent explosions, normal activity prevails. If the vent becomes clogged, then more vigorous explosions are required to remove the obstruction. Such explosions pulverize the material and therefore result in a dark, ash-filled cloud. Eruptions of this kind, even though they occur at Stromboli, are properly classified as Vulcanian in type.

Small but well-formed augite crystals are exceedingly abundant in the ash and cinders making up the cone of Stromboli. Augite is one of the early minerals to crystallize from a basaltic magma and apparently the augite stage has been reached at Stromboli. As the lava is shattered by the explosions the augite crystals are deposited along with the resulting ash and cinders.

Varying theories as to Stromboli's continuing state of activity have been advanced. Some geologists believe that this peculiarity is related to the Sciara del Fuoco, the position of which causes most of the ejected material to roll into the sea, rather than falling back into the crater and clogging the conduit. Without this accumulation of debris, which would stop activity until enough pressure develops to remove the obstruction, Stromboli continues its more or less regular eruptions. It may be argued that volcanic orifices become clogged *because* the eruptive force is exhausted or "peters out" and that it is the result rather than the cause of the end of an eruption. Whatever the explanation, Stromboli is almost unique among the volcanoes of the world in that it has been in an almost constant state of activity for more than 2,500 years.

In most volcanoes, eruptions, particularly lava flows, frequently develop on the flanks of the main cone. This is strikingly shown on Mount Etna, where more than two hundred eruptive centers occur on the flanks of the mountain. At Stromboli two-thirds of the cone is submerged and it is not known how many eruptions or lava flows have occurred on the submerged flanks, or even when one is in progress.

One of the problems posed by the classification of volcanoes is well illustrated by Stromboli. It is apparent from the foregoing description that the eruptions of Stromboli show considerable variation and that they do not always conform to the so-called Strombolian type. Rather, Stromboli has a Strombolian phase, a Vulcanian phase, and sometimes, when no activity is in progress, a Solfataric phase. Similarly, many volcanoes may exhibit characteristics of more than one type, even in a single eruption. For many years, because of the selection of Stromboli as a type in the classification of volcanoes, it was believed that it had a constant, uninterrupted activity consisting of a series of rhythmic explosions in which pasty material was ejected and that it did not have outpourings of lava. This, of course, is far from true, but the idea is still widely held because of the terminology of the classification.

A Visit to Stromboli

Soon after the writer's return from Stromboli an article describing the visit was prepared for a local magazine. Entitled "Stromboli, Lighthouse of the Mediterranean,"[1] it presents some of the details of the trip as well as conditions on the island. It is reproduced below with a few excisions:

"On my first of three trips to Stromboli, my wife and I boarded the steamer *Eolo* at Naples at 6:30 P.M. on Friday, June 20, 1952. . . .

"About daybreak of the next morning, the perfect cone-shaped outline of Stromboli appeared on the horizon. No 'red' glare could be seen, but a prominent column of white vapor was rising from the crater, and at infrequent intervals a denser cloud of yellowish brown gas was emitted. As the boat steamed around the edge of Stromboli, the big 'scar' on the slope, known as Sciara del Fuoco, stood out prominently. This remarkable feature with a slope of 35° and a width of about three-quarters of a mile is like a tremendous talus slope and extends from the crater to the sea, a distance of about four thousand feet. Much of the material, including lava flows ejected from the crater, lands on the Sciara del Fuoco and rolls directly into the sea. The origin of the Sciara del Fuoco is uncertain, but it appears to represent a great depression formed by an eruption which destroyed one side of the cone. The accumulation of debris in the depression has built up the present talus-like slope. The crater of Stromboli is on a terrace at the top of the Sciara del Fuoco, about six hundred feet below the summit peak.

"As Stromboli has no harbor facilities, the steamer anchored some distance from shore, and small boats came out to pick up the passengers and freight. The landing was made at the little village of San Vincenzo on the east side of Stromboli. Its whitewashed houses stand out in sharp contrast against the black sand beach and the deep blue water of the Mediterranean. As our rowboat landed on the beach, a group of small boys scrambled for the baggage and endeavored to take us to the hotel of their choice.

"On Stromboli are no automobiles, no electricity, no radios, no

---

[1] The Alcalde, Vol. 42 (June, 1954), pp. 284–289. Small editorial changes have been made in the text.

donkeys, in fact, not even a dog. With several small boys carrying our baggage, we picked our way across a beach strewn with boulders of lava, and followed a narrow winding street to the hotel, Locando Miramare. The Locando is built of thick blocks of lava, and even the roof is of stone. The thick stone walls keep out the sun, making the inside pleasantly cool. The hotel room was primitive, with pitcher and bowl and an oil lamp, but the sheets were clean and the air pleasant. There is no water on Stromboli, except rain water which is caught from the roofs of the buildings and stored in cisterns. Thus, during the dry summer months, water is at a premium. . . .

"After we were settled in our quarters, I arranged with a local guide, Signor Salvatore Di Lose, to climb with me to the summit the next morning. In the summer the midday sun is quite hot; so we decided to leave at 4:00 A.M. in order to reach the summit while it was still cool. When Salvatore knocked on my door the next morning the sky was already showing some color in the east, and it was light enough to walk without difficulty. The barefooted guide carried my pack, which contained three cameras (movie, color, and black-and-white), notebook, water, and some lunch. As we walked through the town over the narrow cobblestone streets and the ancient lava flows, we passed many two-storied houses built of lava rock, plastered white and adorned with the vines of grape and bougainvillea. Many of these homes had a well or cistern at the front, with an oven of rock and a garden enclosed by a rock wall.

"In about forty-five minutes we arrived at the ruins of the abandoned Observatory pavilion, Semafor di Labronzo, which had been destroyed by the earthquake and eruption of 1930. The real climb begins at this point. The first thousand feet is over a well-established trail which winds with numerous switchbacks through a zone with some vegetation. Leaving this zone behind, the trail then enters barren slopes covered with ash, cinders, and lava flows. The trail is often indistinct, and the loose cinders make upward progress tedious and tiring. Numerous vantage points permit a view of the Sciara del Fuoco, where the recent lava flow stands out prominently. After three hours of wearisome climbing, . we reached the summit of the north peak, where we were able to look down into the crater.

"From an oval-shaped depression about a thousand feet in its longest diameter, and so deep that the bottom is not visible from our position on the summit peak, two prominent columns of vapor boil out like smoke from a ship's funnel. The one on the right, adjacent to Sciara del Fuoco, has a well-defined cone, and the large steam column is noiseless as it pours out. The one on the left, the larger of the two, is accompanied by peculiar sounds. The noise is more of a 'sloshing,' or like the sound of quickly escaping steam as a locomotive slides its wheels to start. This exhaustlike noise was interrupted at intervals of fifteen to twenty minutes by a more violent outburst—not like an explosion but with a tremendous outrush of gas which hurled rocks and debris to the level of our position six hundred feet above the crater floor. The crater floor and the sides of the cone are covered with yellow sulphur and greenish-yellow ferrous chloride; the presence of these gases was readily detected when the wind shifted slightly toward us.

"We remained on the summit peak overlooking the crater until midday, checking the intervals between explosions and studying the nature of the outbursts. I was disappointed that no liquid lava was visible in the crater, and none of the fragments ejected appeared to be red-hot. The guide had seemed disturbed for some time and had tried to tell me, in Italian, that the cinders were hot. This, I thought, was reference to the fact that the cinders were hot when they were blown out of the craters. However, on the way down, I realized that he was referring to the cinders getting hot from the noonday sun, and, since he was barefooted, they were hot enough to burn his feet. We took a short cut on the return trip down, taking giant strides as we almost cascaded down the slope of loose cinders. Salvatore stopped frequently on a rock to let his feet 'cool.' In an hour and a half, we were back at the Locando, the return trip having taken only half the time required for the ascent.

"My second trip to Stromboli was made in early December, on my return from a study of Vulcano. I was unable, however, to make the climb to the summit this time because of the density of the fog and the onset of a heavy rain. Weather conditions being what they were, I decided to leave Stromboli and sail to Naples on the *Eolo*. It was already dark as the *Eolo* left Stromboli, and a light mist was falling. I remained on deck to watch Stromboli disappear in the distance, thinking perhaps it was my last sight of the volcano. As I watched Stromboli grow smaller, I detected a red glow at its summit showing even through the fog which still covered the summit. Watching with renewed interest, I saw the red glow fade and reappear. Suddenly, I saw a brilliant flare, and then heard the sound of a tremendous explosion. Even at several miles' distance I could distinguish red-hot fragments hurled into the air. Two such explosions occurred during the hour I stood on the deck and watched this 'Lighthouse of the Mediterranean.' This was certainly the time to observe activity in the crater, and I regretted that I had not stayed at Stromboli. However, I resolved to return on the very next boat.

"One week later, at 6:00 P.M. on December 12, I boarded the *Eolo* in Naples for my third trip to Stromboli. Going on deck just before daylight the next morning, I was fortunate in seeing two bursts which gave a red glow to the steam column over the crater. I was, therefore, very hopeful that my trip would be rewarded, and I resolved to climb Stromboli that very day, if at all possible.

"A stiff breeze was blowing from the northwest, and the steam-and-gas column was drifting across the summit peak, which is the only point from which one can see into the crater. My guide, Salvatore, and I agreed that if the wind did not change, the trip would be useless. The wind held during the day; so we postponed the climb until the following morning. When Salvatore knocked on my door at 7 A.M. the next day the weather was not much better; low clouds were drifting over the peak, and Salvatore did not think it advisable to make the climb, but I was afraid the weather might get worse. So we decided to go. At the summit overlooking the crater terrace the wind was blowing a gale so strong that it was difficult to stand against it. The wind brought the steam and crater gases directly into our faces so that we could see little of the crater floor.

"We sought shelter from the cold by crouching below the rim and digging 'foxholes' in the soft ash. To my great surprise, the ash was very hot a few inches below the surface, too hot to hold our hands against, and any small hole soon became an active steam fumarole! Digging a large foxhole, I tried to warm myself, but soon the steam condensed on my clothes, and I began to get damp, which made me still colder. Then I was alarmed to discover that the whole top of the cone was hot! Activity in the crater was much the same as on my previous visit in June except that the steam column was denser, because of increased condensation due to the colder air temperature. There were frequent strong explosions, and while I could hear rocks falling on the crater walls and rolling back into the crater after each explosion, the dense steam column obscured the view. Occasionally, after an explosion, the crater would be free of steam for a few seconds, permitting a glimpse of the crater floor. I realized that it would be useless to try to observe activity in the crater, even if the day was clear, unless the wind was from the south and the steam column was drifting away from the observation point on the summit peak. We descended on the south talus slope, and I arranged with Salvatore that if the wind changed directions we would make that climb again.

"For the next two days, the weather developed into storm proportions and life on Stromboli came to a complete standstill—as did our plans to climb the volcano. After the storms abated, Salvatore came to my room at seven one morning, reminded me that I had asked him to come if the wind direction shifted. He asked me to take a look at the summit peak. Certainly the wind had changed, and the gas 'flume' was now drifting to the north, away from the observation point. The sky was overcast, but there was no rain; so in less than an hour we were on the trail.

"The wind was cold, but even so, the exertion of climbing caused one to perspire. We maintained a steady pace, and in two hours we reached the summit. A gale was blowing at the top, even stronger than on the previous trip, but this time the steam column was blowing away from our position, and we could see the crater floor clearly. I got out the movie camera, but the wind was so strong I was afraid it would blow over. Digging a small bench on which to stand below the edge of the crater rim, I set up my cameras and crouched below the rim to escape the fury of the wind. While I was getting ready, an explosion sent up a shower of red-hot scoria from the west vent. I was so startled that I forgot to turn on the movie camera, but having learned where to expect the outbursts, I trained my camera on this spot and waited for the next explosion. In approximately twenty minutes it occurred, and I was successful in recording it with the movie camera.

"During the three hours we were on the summit, there were seven explosions at intervals of twenty to thirty minutes. Each explosion threw quantities of red-hot scoria to a height of six hundred to a thousand feet above the crater floor—our position being six hundred feet above. All the red-hot fragments came from the west vent and all fell back into the crater. The east vent continued to emit large quantities of steam accompanied at irregular intervals by a shrill whistling-like noise, like the violent exhaust of a locomotive.

"About 1:00 P.M. the wind began to shift, and the last two explosions, which I was waiting to photograph, occurred while the crater was obscured by steam. However, the thud of the falling fragments made it evident that the outbursts were the same as the earlier ones. Soon the wind definitely shifted to the north, and we were enveloped in a cloud of steam and volcanic gases. Hastily gathering up our equipment, we started down the talus slope on the south side. Our descent was made in a drizzling rain, and when I returned to my hotel, I had to dry my clothes over Signor Costa's charcoal burner."

*And the mountain burned with fire unto
the midst of heaven, with darkness, clouds,
and thick darkness.*

DEUTERONOMY 4:11

10. THE HAWAIIAN TYPE OF VOLCANIC ERUPTION

History of the Hawaiian Islands

FIFTEEN HUNDRED MILES across the central Pacific
stretches the line of islands, reefs, and shoals which
make up the Hawaiian Archipelago (Fig. 28). Beginning with Ocean (Kure) Island at the northwest, they
include Midway and Gardner islands, French Frigate
Shoals, Necker, Nihoa, and Kaula islands, all of which
are small, low islands, then the eight major islands of
the Hawaiian group proper, which in order southeastward are Niihau, Kauai, Oahu, Molokai, Lanai, Ka-
hoolawe, Maui, and Hawaii.

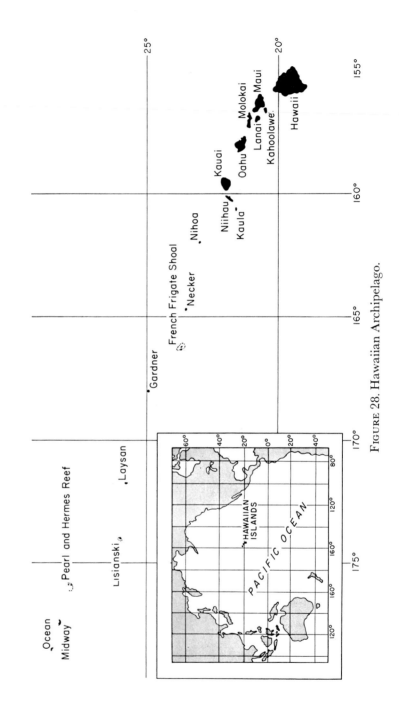

FIGURE 28. Hawaiian Archipelago.

The Hawaiian Islands, the most important Polynesian group in the North Pacific, were discovered by Captain Cook in 1778 and named the "Sandwich Islands" in honor of the Earl of Sandwich, first lord of the British Admiralty at the time of the discovery. Captain Cook was welcomed by the inhabitants and treated as a god, although in the following year he was killed by a native when he landed in Kealakekua Bay on Hawaii. The natives, who numbered about 200,000 in the Islands when Cook arrived, are closely allied, ethnologically, to the Maoris of New Zealand. At the time of Cook's visit each island had its chief, but later the chief of the Island of Hawaii, Kamehameha, conquered the other islands and united them under his rule. The death of Kamehameha V in 1872 ended the long line of Kamehamehas. Following a short reign by two chiefs who followed Kamehameha, Princess Liliuokalani succeeded to the throne in 1891. At constant variance with her legislature and advisors, the Queen was deposed in 1894, and the new government promptly sent a commission to Washington to invite annexation to the United States. The annexation question was a lively political issue for several years, but finally after vigorous opposition the annexation resolution was passed by Congress and signed by President McKinley on July 7, 1898.

Geology of the Hawaiian Islands

Only tiny dots on the map of the Pacific, the Hawaiian Islands are in reality the tops of a range of volcanic mountains, one of the greatest mountain ranges on earth, built up from the sea floor by thousands upon thousands of lava flows. The Hawaiian Islands rise in water which averages about fifteen thousand feet in depth, thus even the lowest of the islands are mountains over fifteen thousand feet in height (above their base), while the highest rise nearly thirty thousand feet above the ocean floor base. The volcanic peaks rise along two main trends, N 70° W and N 55° W. Shorter trends crossing the main axis at approximately right angles have probably determined the location of the vents, which are spaced at about twenty-five–mile intervals. Outpourings of lava formed great domelike piles of basaltic lava, which in time accumulated to a sufficient thickness to reach the surface of the sea. When the volcanoes

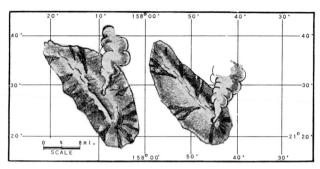

Stage 1. Waianae Volcano (left) is in the old-age phase with the caldera practically filled. Koolau Volcano (right) is actively building, chiefly along the northwest rift zone.

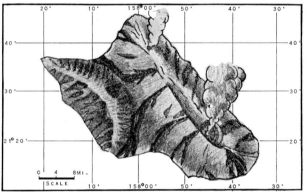

Stage 2. Koolau Volcano (right) is in the collapse phase with a large caldera at its summit. Koolau and Waianae Volcanoes are joined to form a single island (Oahu).

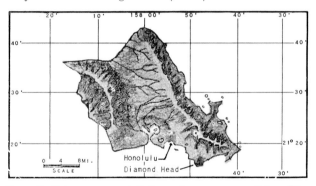

Stage 3. Submergence of Oahu to its present condition. Diamond Head, a secondary cone, is related to the last phase of volcanic activity.

FIGURE 29. Stages in the development of Oahu Island, Hawaii. After Stearns (1946).

began to rise above the sea, they were then subjected to the destructive attack of the waves and other erosive agents which sought to destroy them. So long as the volcanoes were active the islands continued to grow, but when volcanic activity died out the power of erosion was unchallenged. In time great canyons were carved into the slopes by streams, and waves continually battered away at the shores, cutting them back into high cliffs with a broad bench of shallow water (wave-cut terrace) on the seaward side. Finally, in some instances, the whole mass was worn away, leaving a shoal a few fathoms below sea level cutting across the volcanic cone.

Before the final stage of erosion is reached, coral reefs begin to form in the shallow water offshore. In an early stage the reefs surrounding a volcanic island are attached to the shore and are known as "fringing reefs," such as are now found on the island of Oahu, especially off Waikiki beach at Honolulu. In later stages, perhaps because of submergence, the fringing reef becomes separated from the shore by a lagoon and is known as a "barrier reef." If the island disappears entirely, either by wave erosion or submergence, the barrier reef forms an "atoll," a ring-shaped coral island enclosing a lagoon.

Volcanic activity appears to have started at the northwest end of the great fissure on which the Hawaiian Islands are located and to have shifted progressively to the southeast. The accumulation of great piles of volcanic debris over the fissure eventually sealed the opening at that point, and the activity shifted to the southeast. This pattern was repeated for each of the islands until today the only active volcanoes in the entire Hawaiian Archipelago are on the Island of Hawaii, the southeasternmost island. The relative age of the islands in the archipelago is indicated by the extent to which they have been destroyed by erosion. Thus, the exposed parts of Ocean and Midway islands, at the northwest end of the archipelago, are composed entirely of coral limestone, but it seems quite certain that at a comparatively shallow depth the limestone rests on the truncated summits of great volcanic mountains. At French Frigate Shoal a tiny pinnacle of volcanic rocks projects through the limy reefs. Necker and Nihoa islands are remains of once much larger volcanic islands, and Niihau has lost a great slice of its eastern slope by wave erosion.

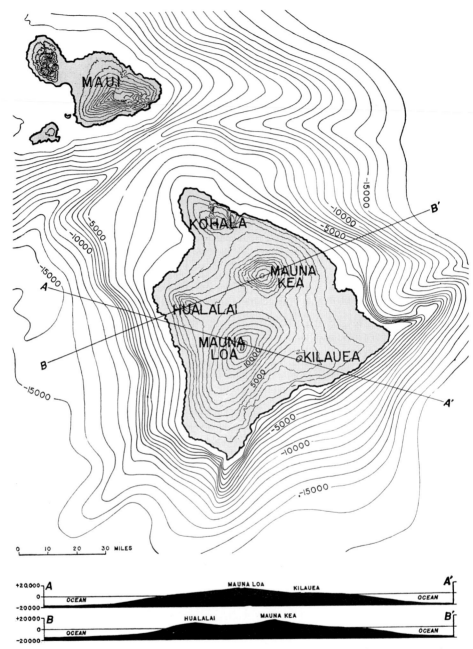

FIGURE 30. Map of Hawaii including the submerged area. Contours are in feet.   After Stearns and Macdonald (1946).

On Kauai sufficient time has elapsed since volcanic activity became extinct for weathering to decompose the rocks, and a mature topography with wide, soil-covered valleys has developed. Kauai is often called the "garden island" because of its beautiful green valleys and excellent soil. This is in contrast to the other islands to the southeast, which because of their younger age are more rocky and have developed less soil.

Oahu, on which the city of Honolulu is located, is the most populous and the best known of the islands. As described by Stearns (1946), Oahu consists of two major lava domes, Waianae and Koolau volcanoes, which formed along parallel fissures. Eventually the two masses joined to form a single island. Erosion and fluctuations of sea level, the last being a submergence, have determined its present outline (Fig. 29).

The Island of Hawaii, known as the "Big Island," has an area of 4,030 square miles, which is slightly less than the area of Connecticut, but it is more than twice the combined area of all the other islands of the archipelago. Hawaii consists of five volcanoes (lava domes) which have combined to form the island (Fig. 30). Of the five, Mauna Loa and Kilauea[1] are still active, while Hualalai, the only other to erupt in historic time, poured out a large lava flow in 1800–1801, but it has shown no signs of activity since that time.

When the fissure on which the Hawaiian Islands are located first began to emit lava is not known. The oldest rocks of the major islands now visible above sea level date from late Tertiary time, or about ten million years ago. Obviously the rocks at the base of the pile on the ocean floor must be much older.

Characteristics of the Hawaiian Type of Eruption

In the Hawaiian type of eruption, of which Mauna Loa and Kilauea volcanoes are examples, basaltic lava issues more or less quietly from a fissure which may extend for a number of miles. A series of earthquakes usually precedes the eruption as the fissure opens to allow the magma to reach the surface. The lava is quite fluid, and the gases escape readily without the disruption of the lava into ash or cinders which occurs in the Peléan type of eruption. Less than .5 percent of the portion of the

[1] Mauna Loa and Kilauea will be described in some detail in a later section.

Hawaiian Islands exposed above sea level consists of fragmental material, thus attesting to the great predominance of the outpourings of lava at these vents.

In the initial stage of an eruption spectacular lava fountains play at many points along the fissure, hurling streams of lava hundreds of feet into the air. The lava fountains, known as "curtains of fire," are caused by the frothing of the top of the lava column when the pressure is suddenly reduced by the opening of the fissure, and the contained gases explosively expand. Great floods of lava issue from the fissure and flow in rivers down the mountainside. Sometimes the lava flows reach the sea, and as the red-hot material strikes the water it disrupts violently, forming cones of fragmental material or providing the black sand which forms beaches along the coast, as at Kalapana. Historic eruptions have lasted from a few days to ten months. The vents from which the lava is issued open from time to time at different points along the fissure, so that eventually an elongate dome-shaped mass of lava is built over the fissure by the accumulation of successive lava flows. These large, flat lava domes, known as "shield" volcanoes, are characteristic of the Hawaiian type of eruption. The absence of soil layers between successive flows, or at best very thin soil beds, indicates rapid accumulation of the flows.

All of the Hawaiian volcanoes have passed through, or probably will pass through, more or less similar stages in the course of their development. Some of the latter stages have already been mentioned in discussing the development of coral reefs on the eroded stumps of the volcanic masses, and the earlier stages, now exhibited by the still active volcanoes of Mauna Loa and Kilauea, will be described presently. The stages as outlined by Stearns (1946) are as follows:

Stage I

Building of the volcano from the ocean floor to sea level. Large quantities of ash are produced as the lava comes in contact with sea water in the eruption. When the cone first rises above sea level it is composed of weakly consolidated ash, and it is rapidly eroded by the waves. Soon, however, new lava flows veneer the cone, and the erosive effect of wave action is greatly reduced.

Stage 2

The dome-shaped mass is formed by thin sheets of highly fluid primitive-type olivine basalt, which flows from major rift zones.

Stage 3

The volcano collapses over the vent area to form a caldera on the summit and shallow grabens along the rift zone. This is the stage now represented by Kilauea and Mauna Loa.

Stage 4

When the amount of lava poured out exceeds the amount of the collapse, the caldera and grabens are partly or entirely obliterated. High lava fountains now characterize most eruptions, and large cinder cones and some bulbous lava domes are formed. Ash beds increase in number and thickness, and the profile of the dome steepens. Hualalai, Mauna Kea, and Kohala on Hawaii are in this stage.

Stage 5

Erosion partly destroys the volcanic dome.

Stage 6

Extensive submergence partly drowns the island and extensive fringing reefs develop.

Stage 7

Volcanic activity is renewed, with the new vents showing little or no relationship to the ancient rift system of the volcano on which they form. Eruptions of this stage commonly began in middle and late Pleistocene and Recent times on such volcanoes as Haleakala, West Maui, Koolau, Waianae, and others. Following submergence the fringing reef becomes a barrier reef.

Stage 8

If submergence continues or if the island is planed off by wave erosion during the fluctuations of sea level of the Pleistocene, an atoll may develop on the eroded and submerged volcanic mass.

The stages described above are shown graphically in Figure 31.

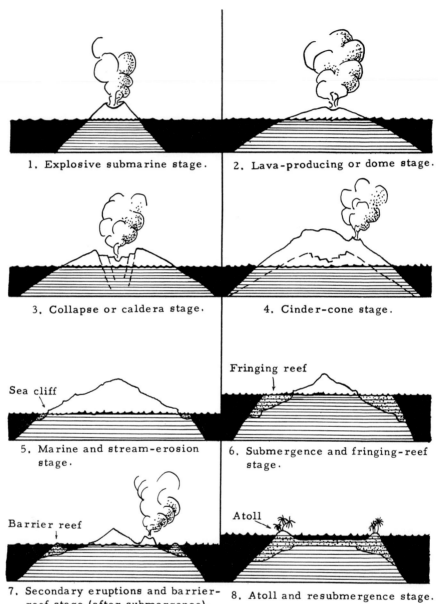

1. Explosive submarine stage.

2. Lava-producing or dome stage.

3. Collapse or caldera stage.

4. Cinder-cone stage.

Sea cliff

5. Marine and stream-erosion
stage.

Fringing reef

6. Submergence and fringing-reef
stage.

Barrier reef

7. Secondary eruptions and barrier-
reef stage (after submergence).

Atoll

8. Atoll and resubmergence stage.

FIGURE 31. Stages in the history of a volcanic island in the central Pacific.
After Stearns (1946).

The Island of Hawaii, or the "Big Island," as stated previously, consists of five great lava domes or shield volcanoes which have coalesced to form the island. Two of the volcanoes, Mauna Loa and Kilauea, are still active and are continuing to add to the bulk of the island. These two volcanoes, the craters of which are included in the area of the Hawaii National Park, are among the most active volcanoes in the world, and they attract thousands of visitors each year. Further, they are the type examples of the Hawaiian type of eruption as described in the classification of volcanoes. A rather detailed description of these two volcanoes seems justified because of the importance of this type of eruption and in view of the fact that many people have an opportunity to visit the Hawaiian volcanoes.

Mauna Loa Volcano

Size, general appearance, and location

Mauna Loa is an oval-shaped lava dome (Fig. 30) about sixty miles long and thirty miles wide, rising from a base 15,000 feet below sea level to 13,680 feet above sea level, making it truly the "Monarch of Mountains." It is the world's largest active volcano and probably the largest single mountain of any sort on earth. Its volume is of the order of ten thousand cubic miles, as compared to eighty cubic miles for the big cone of Mount Shasta in California. This huge bulk has been formed almost entirely by the accumulation of thousands of thin flows of lava, the separate flows averaging only about ten feet in thickness. The broad, flat dome shape, which has given rise to the name "shield" volcano for this type, nowhere has slopes steeper than 12°, and near the top of the slope is as little as 4°. Similar slopes extend outward beneath the water to the sea floor.

At the summit of Mauna Loa is an oval-shaped depression, called Mokuaweoweo, three miles long, one and one-half miles wide, and as much as six hundred feet deep. This depression, commonly called a "crater" but more properly termed a "caldera," was formed by collapse of the summit of the mountain. At the northern and southern ends Mokuaweoweo coalesces with adjacent pit craters formed in a similar manner. The depth of the crater at any particular time is dependent on

Mauna Loa

Volcano Observatory

Kilauea Caldera

PLATE 18. Mauna Loa (shield volcano) in profile with Kilauea caldera in foreground.

PLATE 19. Summit caldera (Mokuaweoweo) of Mauna Loa. The eruption shown in Plate 22 was along the line of steam vents on the far side of the caldera floor.   Photo by author, 1939.

the ratio between subsidence and filling by outpourings of lava. In the hundred years prior to 1942 lava accumulated on the floor in excess of subsidence to the amount of 192 feet, which in effect reduced the depth of the crater by that amount.

Mauna Loa is located on a well-defined rift zone which trends in a northeast-southwest direction (Pl. 21). This rift zone is approximately at right angles to the main fissure over which the Hawaiian Archipelago is located, and, as suggested previously, the intersection of the two zones may be responsible for the location of the volcanic vent. The rift zone on Mauna Loa is identified at the surface by many open fissures and an alignment of cinder and spatter cones formed by lava fountains along the fissure.

A typical eruption

A typical eruption of Mauna Loa is signaled by a series of earth-quakes which accompany the splitting of the mountain, or the opening of

PLATE 20. Detail of the floor of Mokuaweoweo showing pahoehoe (center left) and aa (center right) lava of the 1935 eruption.

a new fracture along the rift zone. The eruptions usually begin in Mokuaweoweo as lava fountains on the floor of the caldera and then extend down one of the rift zones. The summit activity is usually short-lived but several days may elapse before the flank outbreak occurs. Sometimes eruptions occur in the summit caldera without any accompanying flank outbreak.

The eruption begins with a great eruption cloud rising from the crater and with lava fountains from many points along the fissure playing to heights of five hundred feet or more, producing a veritable "curtain of fire." Great volumes of lava are poured out during the first few days. The rivers of lava, only two or three feet thick at the source, flow with high velocities which reach ten to twenty-five miles per hour, slowing down and becoming thicker on the lower slopes. Generally the bulk of the gas is released in a few days and the lava fountains die down, building a chain of spatter and cinder cones along the fissure. During the prolonged eruptions the rivers of pahoehoe lava crust over to form tubes,

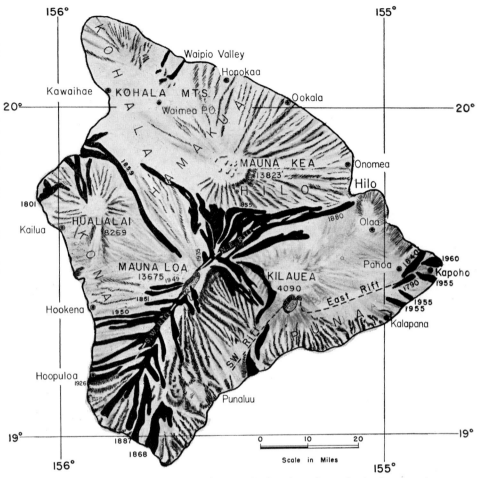

PLATE 21. Map of the Island of Hawaii showing the principal volcanic mountains and the general pattern of lava flows.

and thus insulated beneath the crust the flow may continue with only slight loss of heat for many miles down the mountain side. Division of a lava flow occurs frequently as a result of irregularities on the surface, leaving small "islands" surrounded but not covered by the new lava. In Hawaii such islands are known as *kipukas*. On the lower slopes of Mauna Loa the *kipukas* are marked by clumps of large trees, such as Kipuka Puaula, where Bird Park in Hawaii National Park is located. The longest

PLATE 22. The 1940 eruption (curtain of fire) within the caldera of Mauna Loa.   From a kodachrome, courtesy of Gunnar Fagerlund.

flow in historic times was that of 1859, which continued for ten months and reached the coast thirty-three miles away and continued its flow an unknown distance under the sea. The 1881 flow stopped in the outskirts of Hilo after flowing twenty-nine miles. Submarine flows sometimes issue from the seaward extension of the southwest rift zone.

Volume of lava flows

Historic eruptions have produced from one to five million tons of lava per hour during their earlier phases. Since 1831 flank flows have added three-fifths of a cubic mile to the mass of Mauna Loa. At this rate the portion of Mauna Loa above sea level would have required 270,000 years to accumulate. This figure should not be taken too seriously, but it is an indication of the magnitude of the age of Mauna Loa. Also, it does point up the fact that Mauna Loa is one of the most prolific lava producers on earth.

PLATE 23. The 1940 eruption of Mauna Loa from Hawaiian Volcano Observatory, twenty-five miles away. The outline of the "shield" volcano is silhouetted against the "curtain of fire."
From a kodachrome, courtesy of Merel Sager.

Periodicity in eruptions of Mauna Loa

During the period from the first recorded eruption in 1832 to the end of 1950, Mauna Loa has averaged an eruption every 3.6 years and has been active approximately 6.2 percent of the time. To some extent there is an alternation of summit and flank eruptions, but it should be remembered that even flank eruptions usually begin with a few hours of activity at the summit. Most of the eruptions last less than a month, but a few have lasted two months, and one continued for more than a year. A summit eruption followed in two or three years by a flank eruption is the typical short-term cycle on Mauna Loa, but variations from this pattern are common.[2]

[2] A further discussion of this topic is included in Chapter 12.

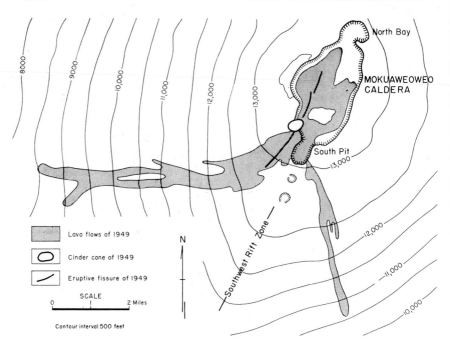

FIGURE 32. The 1949 summit eruption of Mauna Loa.
After Macdonald and Finch (1949).

Eruption of January, 1949

The January, 1949, eruption of Mauna Loa is typical of the summit eruptions. After a period of repose lasting six years and eight months, Mauna Loa resumed eruptive activity on January 6, 1949. The eruption, described by Macdonald and Finch (1949), was confined to the summit caldera, Mokuaweoweo, and to the uppermost part of the southwest rift zone. Following the flank eruption of 1942 on the northeast rift zone, it thus continued the alternation of summit and flank eruptions which has existed since 1926. Heavy rumblings were heard at the Volcano Observatory, twenty miles from the summit of Mauna Loa, at 4:15 P.M. on January 6, and it is believed that lava reached the surface at that time. The lava broke out along a fissure which extended south-southwesterly across the floor of Mokuaweoweo Caldera from a point north of its center over the rim of the caldera, and on about 1.7 miles down the southwest side of the mountain (Fig. 32). In the initial stage lava fountaining was nearly, if not completely, continuous along this crack, a distance of about three miles. Activity on the southwest side outside the caldera lasted only a few hours, and thereafter the activity was confined to the caldera area. Some very copious outpourings of lava came from the vents outside the caldera during the first few hours of the eruption. One flow which moved westward covered a distance of six miles in twenty-four hours. By the afternoon of January 7, after less than twenty-four hours of activity, more than two-thirds of the caldera floor had been flooded with pahoehoe lava. The chain of lava fountains along the fissure on the caldera floor continued for about ten days, although they were variable in size and shifted position frequently. On January 19 two lava fountains near the caldera wall became extremely vigorous, sending up sprays of lava in which some bursts reached heights of eight hundred feet. The high fountains produced an exceptionally large amount of pumice, building a cone which was banked against the caldera wall and eventually projected approximately one hundred feet above the rim and rested partly on the outer slope of the mountain. By January 25 South Pit, which had been filled by lava from the caldera, began to overflow on its southeastern rim.

The lava stream moved southeasterly, and by the evening of January 26 it was two miles below South Pit, or three miles from its source at the lava fountains in the caldera. Later, new branches of lava broke out near South Pit and advanced downslope alongside the earlier flow, finally reaching some four miles beyond South Pit. The eruption ceased on February 5, having lasted just thirty days.

Eruption of June, 1950

The June, 1950, eruption of Mauna Loa is typical of the flank eruptions. A notable lack of westward tilting of the ground at Kilauea Crater after the 1949 summit eruption of Mauna Loa suggested that the magmatic pressure under Mauna Loa remained high. This, together with continued light fuming in Mokuaweoweo Caldera, indicated that the column of molten magma was standing at a high level in the conduit. On the basis of past history it was expected that the summit eruption would be followed by a flank eruption, probably within two years, but with the magma column in such a high position the interval might be shorter. Strong earthquakes on Mauna Loa in May, 1950, indicated that the eruption might be soon, and the location of the earthquakes indicated an outbreak on the southwest rift.

The eruption began on the evening of June 1, 1950 (Macdonald and Finch, 1950). Tremors started recording on the Volcano Observatory seismograph at 9:04 P.M., indicating that lava probably reached the surface at that time. A red glow was first observed from Volcano House at 9:25 P.M. Deep rumblings, probably emanating from the lava fountains, were heard at Naalehu, twenty-three miles from the point of the outbreak, at 9:10 P.M. The outbreak occurred along the upper portion of the southwest rift zone. A fissure two and one-half miles long opened from about 12,600 feet to 11,250 feet altitude, and from this fissure poured great volumes of fumes rising in relatively narrow columns to a height of about two miles then spreading laterally to form mushroom-shaped clouds brightly illuminated by the glare of the incandescent lava below. A flood of very fluid lava poured from the fissure and down the mountain side, most of it going westward toward the Kona District. The longest of these flows extended downslope about five miles to an altitude of 9,000 feet.

The outbreak at the upper source lasted only a few hours, and by 1:30 A.M. on June 2 the activity was greatly diminished and may have already ceased. However, as the activity at the vent diminished, a new outbreak occurred with the opening of a fissure about seven miles long which extended from the 10,500-foot level down to the 8,000-foot level. Floods of lava, accompanied by many lava fountains, poured from this fissure. During the first few hours of the eruption two very rapid flows poured from the fissure near the 10,000-foot level. One of these (No. 5, Fig. 33) advanced south-southeastward in the general direction of Punaluu, and by the morning of June 2 it had covered a distance of ten miles, reaching an altitude of 5,500 feet. The other flow (No. 3, Fig. 33) moved westward into the Kona District. This flow crossed the highway at 12:30 A.M., destroyed Hookena Post Office, several houses and a filling station, and reached the sea at 1:05 A.M., having covered its fifteen-mile course down the mountain at an average rate of 5.8

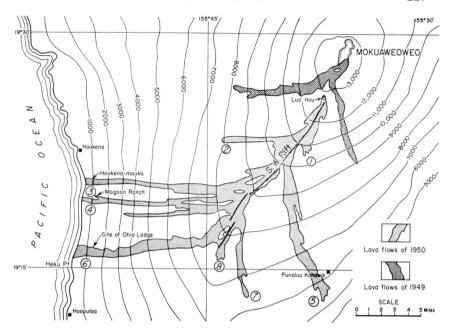

FIGURE 33. Map of a portion of the southwest rift of Mauna Loa showing the 1949 and the 1950 lava flows.   After Macdonald and Finch (1950).

miles per hour. Early on June 2 another flow (No. 4, Fig. 33) poured westward from the fissure between the 8,500- and 9,000-foot levels, and it reached the sea at 12:04 A.M. Some movement continued in this flow until the afternoon of June 3.

What proved to be the principal flow of the eruption originated at the lower end of the fissure between the 7,800- and 8,800-foot levels late on June 1 or early on June 2. This flow (No. 6, Fig. 33), known as the Kaapuna Flow, plunged into the ocean at 3:30 P.M. on June 2 over a sea cliff fifty to seventy-five feet high, sending up a great billowing cloud of steam but without violent explosions. Close to shore and directly over the flow the water was boiling, and a semicircular area of hot turbulent water extended for a mile offshore. The cloud of steam which formed as the flow entered the sea blew inland, and condensation caused heavy rains beneath it. The flow continued until June 13.

The initial outpouring of lava from the entire length of the fissure ended on the morning of June 2, and thereafter the outpourings of lava were largely concentrated in a zone about two and one-half miles long between the 8,100- and 8,800-foot levels. Most of the lava moved westward, feeding the Kaapuna Flow. The eruption ended on June 23.

The total volume of lava erupted is estimated at about 600 million cubic yards of which 100 million cubic yards flowed into the ocean and is not now visible. This ranks as the largest volume of lava produced in a historic eruption, being comparable to the eruption of 1859, which was the largest previous historic eruption. An interesting observation on this eruption was that between one-half and two-thirds of the total volume of lava poured out during the first thirty-six hours of the eruption.

Kilauea Volcano
Location and general appearance

Kilauea Volcano is located on the southeast slope of Mauna Loa about ten thousand feet below the summit. It creates the impression of being a crater on the side of the higher mountain, although in reality it is a separate lava dome (shield volcano) approximately fifty miles long and fourteen miles wide, built against the side of Mauna Loa. Although small compared to Mauna Loa, its summit (elevation 4,090 feet) rises nearly twenty thousand feet above the surrounding ocean floor.

Kilauea has been built largely by eruptions from two rift zones, extending eastward and southwestward from the summit caldera. The row of pit craters along the Chain of Craters road is on the east rift. Noteworthy among the fissures on the southwest rift is the "Great Crack," continuous for more than ten miles, from which issued the 1823 lava flow of Kilauea. During most of the nineteenth century and the first quarter of the twentieth Kilauea was famous among volcanoes because of the presence of a lake of liquid lava in its crater. This unique feature was doubtless one of the reasons for the selection of Kilauea as the site for the Volcano Observatory established at Kilauea in 1912. Later the Hawaii National Park was established to include the crater areas of both Kilauea and Mauna Loa. Connected by paved road with the port of

Hilo, Kilauea is the headquarters of the Hawaii National Park and offers hotel facilities and many recreational opportunities as well as the view of an active volcano.

The caldera

The summit caldera (crater) of Kilauea is an oval-shaped depression two and one-half miles long by two miles wide, the lava-covered floor of which is about four hundred feet below the vertical cliffs which nearly encircle it. At its northern edge, below Volcano House (hotel), and its western edge below the Observatory, the walls of the caldera consist of steplike fault blocks (Fig. 34). On the floor of the caldera, near the southwestern edge, is the "fire pit," known as "Halemaumau" (House of Everlasting Fire), which from time to time has contained a lake of boiling lava. Halemaumau is a circular, pitlike depression which has varied from two thousand to thirty-five hundred feet or more in diameter and up to thirteen hundred feet in depth. Its dimensions vary from time to time, since lava flows fill it from the bottom, and since the diameter is enlarged by avalanching from the walls. Halemaumau is the focus of Kilauea's eruptive activity and the traditional home of Madam Pele, Hawaiian goddess of volcanoes. According to tradition, Madam Pele, taking the form of a poor old woman, always appears before an eruption.

The lava lake in Halemaumau

For a hundred years preceding 1924 the most spectacular feature of Kilauea was the lava lake in Halemaumau. The surface of the lake rises and falls, much as a column of mercury in a barometer, sometimes overflowing and spreading lava over the floor of the caldera. Again, as in 1924, the lake may disappear altogether, and occasionally Halemaumau may be enlarged by the collapse of its walls into the pit. Halemaumau appears to be the point where the principal lava conduit of Kilauea reaches the surface. A true lava lake, such as Halemaumau, is distinguished from a pond of lava in a depression by a convectionlike circulation which connects the lake magma with the magma column at depth. During much of the period prior to 1924, the upper end of the

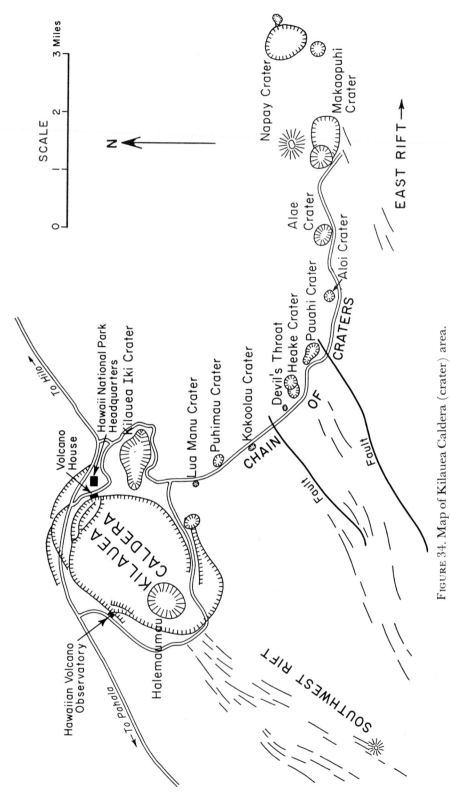

FIGURE 34. Map of Kilauea Caldera (crater) area. After Stearns and Macdonald (1946).

conduit contained a plug of semisolid lava known as "epimagma." Liquid lava, rising from below through fissures in the plug, formed a surface pool of lava about fifty feet deep on top of the epimagma. This thin, freely flowing lava, termed "pyromagma," congealed to form typical pahoehoe lava. A constant circulation was set up by the rise of the pyromagma through source wells and its descent, convectionlike, through sinkholes. Crusts which formed continuously on the surface of the lake were dragged into heaps resembling piles of rope, or broken into cakes which tilted on edge and sank in the lava. Both the epimagma and the pyromagma were free to move up or down in the conduit, either independently or together. Because of its greater fluidity the pyromagma generally sank or rose more rapidly than the epimagma, and sometimes pieces of epimagma would project through the pyromagma as island-like masses which gave the false appearance of islands floating on the lake. At times the pyromagma drained away, leaving exposed the glowing epimagma at the bottom of the lake; at other times both pyromagma and epimagma sank, sometimes as much as several hundred feet in a single day.

There has been much speculation regarding the means by which the high temperature is maintained for long periods of time in the lava lake. Temperature measurements at the lake showed that the surface is substantially hotter than at a depth of three feet, suggesting that the heat, in part at least, is due to reaction of the volcanic gases with atmospheric gases (i.e., exothermic reactions). A temperature of 1,175° C. was measured at a depth of forty feet with a decrease to 860° C. at a depth of three feet, followed by a rise to 1,000° C. at the lake surface. Higher temperatures, up to 1,350° C., were recorded in the blasts of blowing cones where the gases had free access to atmospheric oxygen. Temperatures at depth were measured by means of Seger cones, bits of ceramic material constructed to melt at various temperatures, which were placed in pipes inserted to various levels in the lava lake.

The typical Kilauea eruption

Typical eruptions of Kilauea consist of lava flows forming lava lakes in Halemaumau or of short-lived lava flows within the crater and flank flows from fissures along the rift zones on which Kilauea is situated. Paroxysmal eruptions, due to the entrance of ground water into the zone of heated rocks, are rare, but explosions of this type occurred in 1790 and again in 1924. Eruptions of this type are known as "phreatic eruptions." The explosive eruption of 1924 was preceded by the abrupt disappearance of the lava lake in Halemaumau and strong fissuring of the rocks both around the lava lake and in the Puna area to the southeast. The walls of Halemaumau Pit began to collapse on April 28, 1924, with great avalanches from the sides, each sending up a tremendous cloud of dust. These avalanches continued, and on May 11, 1924, the first steam blasts began to throw rocks up through the dust cloud. The steam blast came in pulsations every few hours like geyser eruptions, reaching a climax on May 18, when the explosion cloud reached a height of four miles. Tremendous blocks of lava from the debris avalanching into the pit were blown out and scattered over the surrounding area. One boulder weighing eight tons was blown nearly three-quarters of a mile from the pit. The steam blasts continued for sixteen days, and the pit of Halemaumau was enlarged from two thousand feet to thirty-five hundred feet in diameter and was left thirteen hundred feet in depth. Red-hot walls were revealed near the base, but no molten lava was visible.

Flank lava flows, which issue from the rift zone to the east and the southwest of the crater, yield the greatest volume of lava. The flank eruptions are frequently far removed from the central crater and even occur as submarine eruptions. Flank flows have always followed increased activity and a rising stage in the lava lake in Halemaumau. After a flank outbreak the lava lake subsides rapidly and commonly disappears entirely, and the pit is enlarged by engulfment. The subsidence of the magma column, which is followed by engulfment, may result from lava discharges on the flanks, either above or below sea level; intrusion of magma into the underground area as sills or dikes; or possibly a recession of the magma into the magma reservoir. Whether an explosive eruption accompanies the collapse is purely a matter of accident, depending on whether the magma column recedes sufficiently to permit ground water to gain access to the zone of heated rocks.

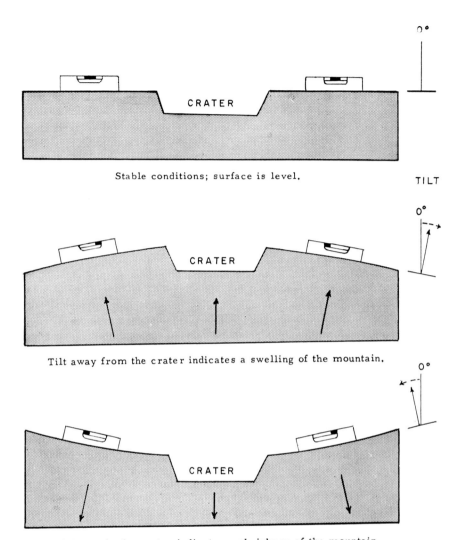

CRATER

Stable conditions; surface is level.

TILT

CRATER

Tilt away from the crater indicates a swelling of the mountain.

CRATER

Tilt towards the crater indicates a shrinkage of the mountain.

FIGURE 35. Diagrammatic illustration of the significance of tilt, using a carpenter's spirit level to indicate direction of movement.

For several decades following a collapse lava flows may enter the pit through cracks in the floor or from cracks high on the walls, and slowly the pit fills. A lava lake may form and be kept hot and in motion for months, or years, by convection circulation and exothermic chemical reactions at the surface. The lake may be present only a few months during a ten-year interval, as between 1895 and 1905, or it may be nearly constantly present, as between 1851 and 1894, when it was absent only a few months in a forty-three–year period. The level of the lake may rise and fall within the pit, or it may slowly fill the pit and overflow onto the caldera floor, as it did in 1921 and at other times in the past. All of these features are characteristic of rising magma beneath Kilauea, which causes the mountain to actually "swell-up" by an amount of increase (described as "tumescence") which can be measured by special instruments known as "tilt meters." The Hawaiian Volcano Observatory is located nearly north of Halemaumau, the volcanic center of Kilauea and nearly east of Mauna Loa. Hence, as measured at the Observatory, tumescence of Kilauea produces a northward tilt while tumescence of Mauna Loa gives an eastward tilt (Fig. 35).

An eruption of either volcano is accompanied by a reversal of the direction of tilt, indicating a shrinkage of the mountain. During the period of gradually rising magma levels at Kilauea between 1912 and 1921, a point near the Observatory was elevated about two feet, and by 1927, following the collapse and explosive eruption of 1924, the same point had subsided three and one-half feet. Measurements of this type appear to be one of the most promising methods of predicting eruptions.

The eruptive cycle at Kilauea Volcano develops through two stages: (1) a period of increasing pressure accompanied by rising of the magma column with lava flows in the crater and on the flanks, and (2) a collapse, indicating decreasing pressure as the magma column recedes. After collapse the lava slowly returns to the crater, gradually building it up again for another eruption and subsequent collapse.

Since the explosive eruption of 1924, there have been ten periods of activity at Kilauea. Nine of these were limited to activity within Halemaumau Pit, and one, the 1955 eruption, was a flank outbreak. The dates and duration of the eruptions during this range of years are shown in the following table:

ERUPTIONS AT KILAUEA SINCE MAY, 1924*

Date	Duration in Days
July, 1924	12.0
July, 1927	14.0
February, 1929	2.0
July, 1929	4.0
November–December, 1930	18.0
December, 1931–January, 1932	13.0
September–October, 1934	33.0
June–November, 1952	136.0
May–June, 1954	3.5
February–May, 1955	90.0
November, 1959–February, 1960[3]	97.0

* Adapted from R. H. Finch, "The Inactive Periods of Kilauea," Volcano Letter No. 497, 1947.

For the period covered by the preceding table Kilauea was in eruption 422.5 days, or 3 percent of the time. During the 125 years preceding the 1924 explosive eruption Kilauea had been active about 73 percent of the time. It is obvious that an explosive eruption such as that of 1924 marks a turning point in the behavior of Kilauea.[4]

Some recent eruptions

A brief description of three of the more recent eruptions of Kilauea will be of interest as examples of the type of activity of Kilauea Volcano.[5]

THE ERUPTION OF 1952. The eruption of Kilauea on June 27, 1952, ended a quiescence which had lasted since October 9, 1934, nearly eighteen years. This is the longest inactive period for Kilauea on record; in fact, prior to 1924 the longest inactive period was only eleven months. The 1952 eruption (Macdonald, 1952) began with huge lava fountains breaking out on the floor of Halemaumau Pit at 11:40 P.M., June 27. In the initial stage the lava fountains were visible above the rim of Halemaumau Pit, which at that time was 800 feet deep. Liquid lava soon covered the floor of the pit and quickly crusted over, but movement

[3] The period of the eruption is considered to extend from the first outflow of lava on November 14, 1959, to the last outpouring of lava on February 19, 1960.
[4] This topic is discussed in Chapter 12.
[5] The eruptive cycle of Kilauea is discussed in Chapter 12.

of the underlying liquid tore the crust apart, revealing the red-hot lava beneath. Lava fountains continued to play at several points, some reaching a height of 300 feet. The development of several sinkholes indicated that a convection circulation had been established. As the lava streamed from all directions toward a sinkhole the crust was broken and torn apart, and as the fragments reached the sink, they tilted on edge and plunged beneath the surface. The eruption continued with varying degrees of intensity until November 10, 1952. The lava fill in the pit averaged 310 feet in depth, leaving the bottom of the pit now 460 feet below the rim in the visitors' observation area.

THE ERUPTION OF 1954. No reversal in tilt, suggesting a release of pressure beneath the volcano, followed the eruption of 1952. On the contrary, during 1953 twelve seconds of northward tilt accumulated on the northeastern rim of Kilauea Caldera, suggesting an actual increase in pressure due to tumescence of Kilauea Volcano. Although there was no basis for predicting an outbreak at a specific time, the conditions were such that an eruption was imminent. The eruption (Macdonald and Eaton, 1954) began shortly after 4:00 A.M. on May 31, 1954, after a dormancy of about eighteen months. A giant lava fountain, partly obscured by a dense column of fume, played to a height of about 100 feet above the rim of Halemaumau. Rising from 460 feet below the rim, its height was between 550 and 600 feet. Lava quickly flooded the floor of the pit. One spectacular feature of the eruption was a cascade of brilliant, orange-yellow lava that poured from a fissure 300 feet above the floor, on the northeastern wall of the pit. Plunging down the wall, this incandescent stream joined the turbulent lava on the floor. The first rapid outflow of lava, during the first eight hours of the eruption, filled the pit of Halemaumau with about 63 feet of new lava, most of which was extruded during the first two hours. About noon on May 31, eight hours after the eruption started, a rapid sinking of the lava level began over the entire floor of the pit, leaving a band of congealed lava on the wall marking the former level. By the end of the eruption the level had dropped 32 feet, resulting in a net gain of 31 feet in the floor level. Ponded lava commonly shrinks as much as 20 percent in volume as a result of gas escape and of shrinkage from cooling. However, the decrease in volume of the new lava in Halemaumau was approximately

THE HAWAIIAN TYPE OF VOLCANIC ERUPTION

52 percent. Since this proportion appears to be far too great to have re-sulted from shrinkage due to cooling and loss of gases, it appears that some of the new lava must have drained back into the fissure through which it had previously risen. The eruption lasted three and one-half days.

THE ERUPTION OF 1955. The 1955 eruption on the east rift zone of Kilauea in the eastern part of the Puna District was the first flank erup-tion since 1923 and the first eruption in eastern Puna since 1840. It was unusual in that the opening of the eruptive fissures progressed in part up-slope toward the central crater of Kilauea while normally they begin high on the slope and progress away from the central vent. Also unusual was the irregular manner in which activity shifted from one vent to an-other.

The first indications of the eruption (Macdonald and Eaton, 1955) were two strong earthquakes centered in eastern Puna on March 30, 1954. The earthquakes came from a focus twelve miles deep and nearly south of Pahoa, between the surface trace of the east rift zone and the coast. Throughout the year many earthquakes originated at centers along the east rift zone and in the caldera area. At the same time tilting of the surface at Kilauea Caldera indicated a swelling of the mountain, apparently from an increase of volcanic pressure beneath it. Further, the brief eruption on May 31, 1954, which has been described, had scarcely any effect on the tilting of the surface or the sequence of earthquakes, for both continued uninterrupted through the remainder of the year. Finally, in late February earthquake activity increased greatly, and since it was centered in Puna it was thought that the outbreak would occur in that area.

The initial outbreak occurred just before 8:00 A.M. on February 28 in the area where the strongest earthquakes had been felt the preceding days (Vent A, Fig. 36). Small lava fountains played from a number of fissures which were arranged *en échelon,* with the most easterly fissure offset slightly to the north. The lava fountains were from 50 to 150 feet high, and from them a rather sluggish lava flow spread southward. By noon of March 1, activity at Vents A, B, and C (Fig 36) had ceased. However, new vents opened to the northeast in the direction of Kapoho. These vents (labeled J, G, and E on Fig. 36) were longer-lived than

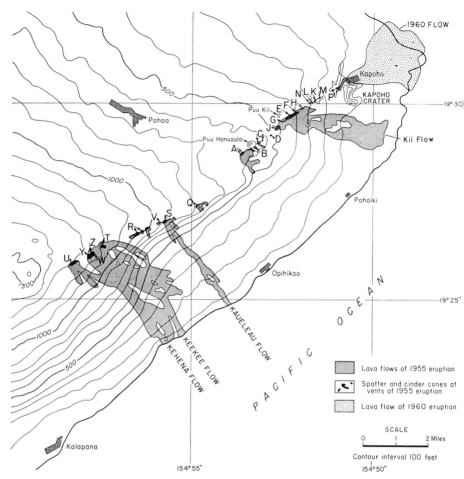

FIGURE 36. Map of the southeastern part of the Island of Hawaii, showing the lava flows of the 1955 and the 1960 eruptions of Kilauea. Letters indicate the location of the 1955 vents mentioned in the text in the order of their outbreak.   After Macdonald and Eaton (1955) and Parsons (1960).

some of the other vents, and they fed a very active lava flow, the Kii Flow. By 9:30 P.M. on March 3 the activity had reached the outskirts of the village of Kapoho, and lava fountains issued from a line of fissures in the outskirts of the town. However, a low ridge turned the lava flow northward, away from the main part of the village. A few houses were destroyed, but the main part of the village was unharmed. As a

precaution, the village had been evacuated the previous day. By 8:00
A.M. on March 4 the activity at the Kapoho vents was over. After a lull
of nearly a week, during which time it appeared that the eruption might
be over, a new vent (Q, Fig. 36) opened on March 12 to the southwest
of the original outbreak. It was here that volcanologists from the Hawaiian Volcano Observatory observed the actual development of a new
volcanic vent, which they described as follows (Macdonald and Eaton,
1955, p. 6):

First, hairline cracks opened in the ground, gradually widening to 2 or
3 inches. Then from the crack there poured out a cloud of white choking
sulfur dioxide fume. This was followed a few minutes later by the ejection
of scattered tiny fragments of red hot lava, and then the appearance at the
surface of a small bulb of viscous molten lava. The bulb gradually
swelled to a diameter of 1 to 1.5 feet, and started to spread laterally to form
a lava flow. From the top of the bulb there developed a fountain of molten
lava which gradually built around itself a cone of solidified spatter. The
same general sequence was observed at three separate points during the day.

During the remainder of March as activity ceased at one vent a new
one developed elsewhere. The activity in general migrated to the southwest along the rift zone, although there were some exceptions to this
pattern as is shown on Figure 36.

One of the most active vents was the one marked "T" on Figure 36,
where on March 20 the lava fountains reached a height of 600 to 750
feet. A spatter cone 1,000 feet across and 100 feet high was built around
the larger of the fountains. The extensive lava flow from Vent T entered the head of a small valley that led directly to a small plantation
camp. With a bulldozer the owner hurriedly threw up an earthen dam
1,000 feet long and about 10 feet high in an effort to protect the camp.
During the afternoon the flow reached the barrier and was deflected by
it, but advanced along it only about 50 feet before this particular eruption ceased and the flow stopped! Activity continued in this general area,
and on April 2 a tongue of lava (Kehena Flow) entered the ocean. On
April 7 all lava activity ceased, and for more than two weeks no sign of
activity appeared except clouds of white sulphurous fume and steam
rising from the vents.

On April 24 moderate lava fountaining was resumed at Vent T, but in a few days the activity shifted to Vents Y and Z, and here it continued with renewed vigor until the end of the eruption. Large volumes of lava poured out. As it ponded in depressions and began to spill over into adjacent valleys some spectacular lava cascades were formed. Velocities up to thirty miles per hour were attained by the lava in some of the cascades. On May 26 lava fountaining ceased, and by the morning of May 27 all movement in the lava flows had stopped. The eruption was over.

The total volume of material extruded was about 120 million cubic yards. This is about twice the volume of material extruded in the 1952 eruption in Kilauea Caldera, but only about one-fifth that extruded in the 1950 eruption of Mauna Loa.

The statement was made in a previous paragraph that the "eruption was over." It will be of interest to inquire into the basis for this conclusion. The answer lies in the action of the tilt meters and seismographs. During the eruption the inclination of the earth's surface (tilt) was recorded at Pahoa, about two and one-half miles northwest of the initial outbreak, and at Kilauea Caldera. Northward tilt at the Pahoa station, resulting from a swelling of the rift zone to the southeast, was recorded for a week preceding the initial outbreak. Swarms of earthquakes occur when new fissures are being opened, but while the eruption is in progress and lava is flowing freely at the surface very few earthquakes are recorded. As long as new vents were being opened, seismic activity continued to be high, but after the last new section of the rift was opened on March 26 seismic activity in Puna dropped to a low level, where it remained for the duration of the eruption. A southward tilt (i.e., a subsidence of the rift zone) was underway at Pahoa by March 7; however, this was temporarily reversed on March 8, and for the next two weeks there was an oscillation of swelling and sinking. At Kilauea Caldera subsidence began on March 7 and continued, with two brief interruptions, until the end of the year. The amount of the sinking in the area of Kilauea Caldera between February 20 and April 10 has been calculated to be equivalent to about 216 million cubic yards, which interestingly is of the same order of magnitude as the volume of lava extruded in the Puna District during the same interval. Thus, with a collapse due to a decrease in pressure under the volcano it could be confidently stated that the "eruption is over."

THE ERUPTION OF 1959–1960. This eruption (Parsons, 1960) began on November 14, 1959, in Kilauea Iki Crater, which is immediately adjacent to Kilauea Caldera (Fig. 34). In the initial stage lava fountains erupted from a fissure about one-half mile long on the south wall of Kilauea Iki, but within twenty-four hours the activity was restricted to a single fountain at the west end of the crater. This phase of the eruption continued intermittently through December 19. At one time Kilauea Iki crater contained a lava lake 414 feet deep, but part of this lava drained back into the vent after the eruption ceased so the crater filling was reduced to 382 feet above the previous floor.

Although the eruptions at Kilauea-Iki ceased on December 19, seismic activity continued, suggesting that the lava was moving underground. In early January numerous small earthquakes were felt in the Puna District, twenty-eight miles east of Kilauea Caldera. These became progressively more severe, and on January 13 some fairly strong shocks were felt at Kapoho and several cracks opened in the ground in the central part of the town. At 7:41 P.M. that evening lava began flowing from an east-west fissure about one-third mile north of Kapoho. At first lava fountains played from the entire five-eighths–mile–long fracture but it was soon restricted to the central section of the fracture which became the main vent. In two days the lava flow reached the sea, three miles away, and as it poured into the sea great billowing clouds of steam rose thousands of feet into the air. When the eruption ended the shore line had been extended, in places up to one-half mile (Fig. 36). As the eruption continued and the valley became filled with lava, the flow widened and presented a real threat to the village of Kapoho as well as to the Kapoho School, the lighthouse, and other developments in the area. Earthen embankments were hastily constructed in a vain effort to protect some of the structures from the lava. They were ineffective and in the end the village of Kapoho, the school, and other developments in the area were destroyed. The outflow of lava ceased on February 19. The eruption was over, having lasted ninety-seven days, including the eruptions at Kilauea Iki and the interval between the end of the eruptions at Kilauea Iki and the outbreak at Kapoho.

The typical pattern or cycle of Kilauea is well illustrated by the 1959–1960 eruption. Tilt-meter and seismograph studies by the staff of the Hawaiian Volcano Observatory indicated that a swelling of the entire summit area of Kilauea began in 1957 and continued until the outbreak of lava in Kilauea Iki and Kapoho eruptions. Seismograph records indicated that during the swelling period the lava was rising from depths of around twenty-five miles. After the eruption the entire summit area of Kilauea settled and in a few months it was back to its 1957 level.

Fires that shook me once, but now to
  silent ashes fall'n away.
Cold upon the dead volcano sleeps the
  gleam of dying day.

TENNYSON

II. THE ICELANDIC TYPE OF VOLCANIC ERUPTION

Fissure Eruptions

THE GREAT LAVA PLATEAUS of the world, such as the Columbia River Plateau of northwestern United States, are believed to have been derived from outpourings of lava from fissures. The Columbia River Plateau and the adjacent Snake River Plateau were built up by innumerable lava flows which spread over parts of Washington, Oregon, and Idaho, covering an area of over 200,000 square miles. The combined thickness of the flows reaches a maximum of over three thousand feet; yet individual flows rarely exceed thirty to one hundred feet in thickness. The volume of the Columbia and

FIGURE 37. Columbia River and Snake River lava plateaus.

Snake River plateau flows is estimated to be sixty thousand cubic miles. Similar areas, perhaps even larger, are the Deccan Plateau in India and the Paraná region of South America. Other vast areas which have been flooded by basalt occur in Mongolia, in Siberia, in many parts of Africa, and in Australia. In a fissure eruption the flows spread out from the fissure, and when the eruption is over the sheet of lava conceals the eruptive vent (Fig. 38). The individual lava flows are relatively flat-lying, and the vents from which the lava issued must have shifted location widely from time to time to permit the lava to cover such an extensive area.

A fissure eruption differs from the usual volcanic eruption in that the material issues from a long crack, or fissure, rather than from a central vent. Most volcanic eruptions are, in a limited sense, fissure eruptions in that the lava issues from a crack or fissure and the cone is built over a fissure. What distinguishes the type of eruption which is called "fissure" eruption is the extended length of the fissure through which the magma issues. In the fissure eruptions of Iceland lava rises from a fissure or a zone of fissures several miles in length and flows as great sheets for long distances to either side of the fissure. Sometimes the outpouring is in the form of numerous tongues of lava, issuing at many points along the fissure. Small spatter cones may be formed by mild explosive activity along the fissure, but in general no main cone is formed. Indeed, in some of the prehistoric fissure eruptions the upwelling lava has sealed the fissure, leaving no indication of the location from which the lava issued.

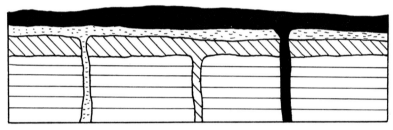

FIGURE 38. Icelandic type of eruption. Shifts in location of fissure result in a series of superimposed lava flows, forming a lava plateau.

The Icelandic type of eruption has many features in common with the Hawaiian type. The lava in both cases is primary basalt (i.e., not differentiated), and the eruptions are quite similar. In the Hawaiian type the lava piles up in great dome-shaped masses (shield volcanoes) while in the Icelandic type the lava flows form plateaus with nearly flat-lying layers. The volume of lava involved in individual plateau building and in dome making is not greatly different. In dome making the system of fissures that supplies magma, under the domes, has remained open in the same place for long periods of time, whereas in plateau building the activity shifts frequently from one fissure system to another.

The only modern examples of fissure eruptions such as are believed to have produced the great lava plateaus have been in Iceland, and eruptions of this type may appropriately be termed the "Icelandic"

FIGURE 39. Iceland and the Mid-Atlantic Ridge.

type. A description of these eruptions will be helpful in understanding this type of activity.

Significance of Location of Iceland

The island of Iceland, with an area of 103,000 square kilometers, is roughly the size of the state of Georgia. It is the exposed part of the northernmost extension of the Mid-Atlantic Ridge. Only a few of the peaks on the Mid-Atlantic Ridge, all of which are volcanic, emerge to form islands. Among these are the Azores, Ascension, and Tristan da Cunha, the latter in the far South Atlantic (Fig. 39). Iceland is five hundred miles west of Norway and two hundred miles east of Greenland, and its northern shore touches the Arctic Circle. Lying in the Mid-

Atlantic, Iceland has long served as a stepping stone between Europe and America. The Norse Viking, Eric the Red, sailed from Iceland to Greenland in A.D. 982 and was thus the first white man to set foot on North America. His son, Leiv Eriksson, sailed from Iceland to the American continent in A.D. 1000, and settlements were established in Vinland (New England) and in Greenland, with regular trade between the colonies and Iceland. Since Iceland was a treeless country, regular trips were made to Labrador for timber. The settlements in New England were all abandoned many years before the arrival of Columbus.

Iceland is a mountainous country with its highest peak, Oraefa Jökull (glacier), rising to 6,952 feet above sea level. About 13 percent of the total area of Iceland is now covered by glaciers, shrunken remnants of the great continental ice sheets which covered much of the Northern Hemisphere during the Ice Age. The glaciers, the largest of which is about twice the size of Rhode Island, are known as "ice caps." Broad, low plains border the southern coast.

Iceland consists entirely of volcanic material, largely successive outpourings of basaltic lava, which rises from the ocean floor along the Mid-Atlantic Ridge, here between three thousand and five thousand feet below sea level, to nearly seven thousand feet above sea level. Depths on either side of the Mid-Atlantic Ridge in the North Atlantic range from nine to ten thousand feet. The origin of the Mid-Atlantic Ridge is not known, and a discussion of the various theories explaining it is beyond the scope of this work.

Early Volcanic History of Iceland

The volcanic history of Iceland began in early Tertiary (Eocene) time with the outpouring of great floods of basalt which piled up to thicknesses in excess of ten thousand feet. The upbuilding to such heights in the latitude of Iceland would certainly result in glaciers, and since no evidence of glaciation is found during this period it is assumed that the area was sinking to compensate for the upbuilding. The early Tertiary vulcanism in Iceland was related to the enormous flood basalts that were spread from Ireland and Scotland on the south to Greenland on the north. At that time vulcanism in Iceland was not unique as it is today. This early and widespread vulcanism was from great fissure eruptions,

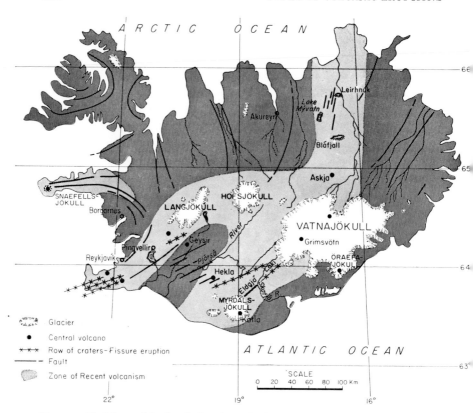

FIGURE 40. Map of Iceland showing glaciers and major volcanic features. After Barth (1950) and others.

but today Iceland is the only place where such eruptions are still continuing. Following a long period of repose, lasting many millions of years (Middle and Upper Tertiary), modern vulcanism began in Iceland in Pleistocene time (Ice Age) and has continued uninterrupted to the present. The modern vulcanism is much more restricted than the earlier vulcanism, being limited to a zone crossing the island in a NE-SW direction (Fig. 40).

During the geologically recent Great Ice Age, Iceland was completely covered by a continental ice sheet; consequently the volcanic eruptions during this period took place under a covering of thousands of feet of ice. The deposits of volcanic material under such conditions are of a peculiar type, similar to deposits from eruptions under water. In Iceland such deposits are known as "palagonite." Since subglacial eruptions have occurred in Iceland in modern times, it has been possible to observe the manner in which palagonite deposits are formed.

Subglacial Eruptions

The two most famous subglacial eruptions are from Volcano Katla in the Mýrdalsjökull (jökull, [Eng. jokul] glacier) and Volcano Grimsvötn in the Vatnajökull, both in southern Iceland (Fig. 40). When a subglacial volcano erupts, the surrounding ice melts, and large quantities of water form. If the heat is not sufficient to melt the entire thickness of ice above the volcano, the trapped water will seep out along the base, and the surface of the glacier will collapse into large sinks, often several miles in diameter. If the entire ice cap around the volcano melts, a lake will form. In time the huge accumulation of water will break through the ice dam which confines it, and water and icebergs in unbelievable volume will sweep over the countryside, destroying everything in their path. Such floods are known in Iceland as jökulhlaups which translated literally means "glacier runs." No words can express the violence of a jökulhlaup. The maximum discharge of water during the eruption of Volcano Grimsvötn in Vatnajökull in 1934 and again in 1938, each of which lasted about one week, was about 50,000 cubic meters per second. In 1918 Katla Volcano, in an eruption which lasted only two days, discharged 200,000 cubic meters per second. The magnitude of these floods can be appreciated when they are compared to the 10,000-cubic-meters-per-second discharge of the Amazon, the world's largest river. Tremendous amounts of mud, stones, sand, and debris are carried by the floods and washed into the sea. In fact, the entire contour of the south-coastal section of Iceland has been altered by these deposits since the early settlements in Iceland, about a thousand years ago. While features similar to the Icelandic jökulhlaup are known in other parts of the world, especially in the high Andes of South America, where volcanoes and glaciers are associated, nothing on a comparable scale is known.

Icelandic Areas of Fissure Eruptions in Historic Times

In Iceland the fissure eruptions of historic times have occurred in two areas, which are described below.

The Bláfjall-Leírhnúk fissure system

This area, in the northern part of Iceland, was the site of a series of fissure eruptions during the five-year period from 1724 to 1729 (Fig. 40). The fissure zone extended about thirty-five kilometers and consisted of individual fissures from one to two kilometers in length arranged *en échelon*. In some cases open fissures more than six hundred feet in depth were formed without producing any lava. Severe earthquakes accompanied the opening of fissures, and the lava flows were generally accompanied by explosions which threw out ash, lapilli, and bombs, building cones and spatter craters aligned along the fissure. This area is unique in the great concentration of small craters, or explosion vents. The shores of Lake Mývatn are thickly studded with craters, and it is doubtful that any other place on earth has such a concentration of craters in so small an area.

The total volume of lava ($10^9 m^3$) extruded in the Bláfjall-Leirhnúk fissure eruptions was small compared to that from the great Laki eruption described below. The sequence of events in a fissure eruption has been studied in this area by a number of investigators, including Rittmann (1939) and Barth (1950). All agree on the general sequence of events, although they differ concerning some details. The fissure eruption is preceded by severe earthquakes which accompany the opening of the fissures. The decrease in pressure as the magma rises in the fissures causes it to "foam" and boil over, and then to pour out in floods of liquid lava. Explosive activity accompanying the outpouring may build a row of spatter or ash cones along the line of the fissure. As the lava continues to flow from the fissure the newly formed cones may be destroyed, in part, by floods of lava breaching them. When the outpouring lava ceases, the surface frequently collapses over large areas.

Laki Fissure (eruption of Skaptar Jökull)

Mount Skaptar is located in southern Iceland, about eighty miles east of Mount Hekla and two hundred miles east of Reykjavík. The eruption in 1783 was the first historic eruption of Mount Skaptar. Preceded by eight days of severe earthquakes, the actual outbreak began on June 8, 1783, with tremendous explosions accompanied by vast ash clouds which rained ash over a wide area, in sufficient quantities in Scotland and Norway to damage crops. On June 11, floods of lava issued from twenty-two vents along a ten-mile-long fissure and flowed in a southwesterly direction. On reaching the Skaftá River, the lava filled the valley, which was four hundred to six hundred feet deep, overflowing onto the surrounding plains. Repeated outflows occurred until the middle of July, adding to the lava in the Skaftá Valley. The lava flow which flooded the Skaftá Valley was fifty miles long and in the lowland area spread to a maximum width of twelve to fifteen miles, with an average thickness of about one hundred feet. In the deeper points of the valley, of course, its thickness exceeded six hundred feet. On August 3, 1783, the valley of the Hverfisfljot River, a stream parallel to the Skaftá, was invaded and, like the Skaftá, was filled, the lava overflowing the adjoining open country. This flow was forty miles long with a maximum width of seven miles. The volume[1] of lava from the Laki Fissure is estimated to be $12 \times 10^9 m^3$. (A figure of $12\frac{1}{4}$ cu. km. is given by Thoroddsen.)

Rivers flooded by the melting of the glaciers and the damming of the lava-blocked streams, destroyed many farms and much livestock. Although the lava flows caused great damage, even more serious was the bluish haze (probably containing SO_2) that lay over the country during the summer of 1783. It stunted the grass growth, causing a disastrous famine, still referred to as the Haze Famine. Hunger and disease following the catastrophe took their toll of human life. As a result of the eruption, Iceland lost one-fifth of its population, about three-fourths of its sheep and horses, and one-half of its cattle (230,000 head). It was a national disaster from which it took years for the country to recover.

---

[1] For describing large volumes, distances, etc., it is convenient to use the *powers of ten*. Thus, 10^1 (10 with an exponent of 1) is equal to 10. The exponent indicates the number of zeroes following 1. Thus, 10^3 is one with three zeroes or 1,000, and 10^6 is 1,000,000.

The Eldgjá Fissure eruption of A.D. 950

This fissure, in the same area and a short distance to the south-west of the Laki Fissure, erupted in the early days of the settlement of Iceland in 950. The volume of lava produced is estimated at $9 \times 10^9 m^3$, somewhat smaller than that from Laki, yet a tremendous volume of lava.

Mount Hekla

Mount Hekla is the most famous volcano in Iceland. It is located in the southern part of the country, 110 kilometers east of Reykjavík and 55 kilometers from the southern coast. It is an elongate ridge 27 kilometers long and from 2 to 5 kilometers wide, fissured in the direction of its length with a row of craters along the fissure. It is built of successive sheets of lava and ash with a maximum height of 4,747 feet above sea level and 3,280 feet above the lava plateau on which it is situated. It is regarded by some as a strato-type volcano, but to others it seems more closely related to the "shield" volcanoes of the Hawaiian type, although Hekla produces more ash than is generally true for typical "shield-type" volcanoes. The activity at Hekla is a modification of the typical fissure eruption of Iceland, in which successive outpourings of lava and ash-forming explosions have occurred along a fissure but in a restricted area, piling up the present mass of Hekla.

The first historic eruption of Hekla was in 1104, about two hundred years after the settlement of the country. Since that time there have been twenty major eruptions, the last in 1947–1948, with an average interval of about forty years between eruptions. However, in recent centuries the intervals between eruptions have been much longer than the earlier ones. Eruptions were recorded in the following years:

1104	1300	1545	1725
1158	1341	1597	1728
1206	1389	1619	1766
1222	1434	1636	1845[3]
1294	1510	1693[2]	1947–1948[4]

[2] One of the most violent eruptions on record.

[3] After 77 years of quiescence this eruption produced a large volume of lava.

[4] After 102 years of quiescence this eruption produced a large volume of lava.

Most of the damage from an eruption of Hekla is due to the heavy ash falls. Ash from the great eruption of 1300 is conspicuous in the soil profiles in Iceland. The latest eruption of Hekla, which occurred in 1947, has been described by Thorarinsson (1950, 1956). A brief résumé, based on his account, will be of interest.

On the morning of March 30, 1947, about 6:00 A.M., a farmer near Mount Hekla was looking at the mountain, which at that time was covered with snow. He observed a yellow-brown cloud growing rapidly in size to a height of 100–200 meters. Several severe earthquakes were felt at about this same time. Shortly later the Hekla Ridge was split lengthwise by a fissure 5 kilometers in length, from which issued throughout its entire length clouds of ash-laden gases and outpourings of lava. As the snow melted huge volumes of water flooded the Ytri Rangá River. By 7:00 A.M. the ash-laden cloud had reached the astonishing height of 90,000 feet! The surrounding area was enveloped in darkness and covered by pumice and ash which, 30 kilometers south of Reykjavík, reached a thickness of 10 centimeters. Forty hours after the eruption began, ash falls occurred in Finland. The main ash discharge took place during the first two hours of the eruption, and this initial phase might properly be termed a "Plinian" phase, but it was soon replaced by outpourings of lava. Activity decreased markedly after the first day. During the first day lava flowed from the whole length of the fissure; on the second day activity was concentrated at the summit crater and at points on either side; and on the third day lava flowed mainly from the ends of the rift at an elevation of about 830 meters. After that the activity occurred almost exclusively at the "Lava Crater" at the southwest end of the fissure. Here the flow continued until April 25, 1948, ending a period of almost thirteen months. The lava at the vent had a temperature of from 1,020° C. to 1,040° C. In the initial phase the silica content of the lava (as well as of the ash) was 59.6 percent, but later this dropped to 57–58 percent. Thus, as has been true of previous eruptions of Hekla, the lavas are more acidic than typical flood basalts. The total volume of lava from the eruption is estimated at 1 cubic kilometer ($10^9 m^3$) while the clastic ejectamenta is estimated at 220 million cubic meters. This lava output is the greatest in Iceland since the Laki eruption of 1783, and ranks among the greatest in the world for the present century.

When lava stopped flowing in late April, 1948, escaping CO_2, on calm quiet nights, accumulated up to six feet in depth in surface depressions. About twenty sheep and numerous other animals were killed when they wandered into these depressions. Although the reasons for the gas are not clear, it appears that when the CO_2 emerged it had the same temperature as the ground water, and it was taken into solution under pressure and then escaped as the pressure decreased on reaching the surface. In addition to the animals killed by CO_2 poisoning, some animals were killed by fluorine poisoning. This phase of activity lasted only a few weeks, but the streams originating on the slope of Hekla still contain dissolved CO_2 and precipitate calcium carbonate when they issue at the surface. On the whole, little damage was caused by the eruption.

Eruptions of the Icelandic type have occurred throughout geologic time in many parts of the world, although the only historic eruptions of this type have been in Iceland. We are indeed fortunate that eye-witness accounts of these eruptions are available, for without them it would be difficult to explain how some of the great lava plateaus of the world were formed.

PART THREE: *Theory, Cycles, and Utilization of Volcanoes*

A theory is a tool—not a creed.

J. J. THOMSON

12. VOLCANIC CYCLES

AS A CONSEQUENCE of the earth's yearly trip around
the sun and its daily spinning on its axis, there are the
seasons, day and night, tides, and other features which
reoccur with mathematical regularity. Orderliness prevails in the physical universe, from the atom with its
nucleus, about which the electrons revolve, to the sun,
about which the planets revolve, and finally to the great
galaxies of stars all fitting into their respective orbits,
the whole going we know not where, but perfectly
adjusted and intermeshing like the delicate mechanism
of a watch. The rhythmic or cyclic recurrence of many
earth phenomena is well established and a basic prin-
ciple in geology.

Although accepted as commonplace today, we have achieved the ability to accomplish what would have seemed a miracle once—the prediction of the occurrence of the different seasons at any point on the earth—because the laws which govern the seasons are known. There is a clear relationship of cause and effect, and there is the possibility, even probability, that all recurring aspects of the earth are governed by definite laws of causal relationships. It is the province of science to discover these laws and then to predict the occurrence of phenomena which they govern. Once the pattern of activity is established, the possibility of control can be considered.

The weather may be taken as an example to illustrate this point. After long years of careful observation and scientific study, the weather can be predicted from day to day, or even for longer periods. The factors, at least in part, which control the weather are known, and their effect at any given place can be predicted. Knowing these factors, the next logical step is control of the weather, and attempts are being made in this direction. The climate as a whole, however, appears to follow a cyclic pattern in which at intervals there are excessively dry years followed by wet years. Many believe that the weather and in fact almost all earth activities are related to sunspot cycles. Sunspots are great eruptive areas on the sun, and they may well be considered the "Volcanoes of the sun." These solar disturbances, actual atomic explosions, send out a stream of electrified particles which so heavily ionize (make capable of conducting an electrical charge) the upper atmosphere as to cause discharges in the rarefied air, producing the glow of the familiar "Northern Lights." This change in the electron density of the upper atmosphere also alters the intensity of the earth's magnetism, causing the so-called "magnetic storms" which interfere seriously with radio communication. Sunspots vary in size, number, and position on the sun from time to time, as was noted even before 1612, when Galileo trained his telescope on the sun and was able to observe them in detail. Since 1750 sunspots have been observed on a regular basis, and today the sunspot "number" is determined daily by observatories throughout the world. From the daily number is obtained a yearly average, which is an index to sunspot activity. Over the years there has been a regular repetition of sunspot activity, the individual cycle varying from 9 to 13 years, with an over-all average of 11.2 years between successive maxima. Sunspot maxima have occurred recently in 1928, 1937, 1947, and 1958.

Volcanic Cycles

Volcanic cycles are said to coincide with sunspot cycles, although there is wide disagreement on this subject. The causal relationship, if it exists, is obscure. Some of the evidence used to support the relationship between sunspots and volcanic cycles will be presented in the following pages.

Volcanic cycles are even less firmly established than sunspot cycles and are certainly as controversial. Most investigators will agree that volcanic activity is cyclic, but only in a few cases can they give even an approximation as to the nature and the length of the eruptive cycle. A volcanic cycle is likely to span a great many years, in some cases hundreds, and there are records for only a few volcanoes for a sufficient length of time to detect in the activity the repetition which must be observed before a cycle can be recognized. Each volcano has its own individual pattern of activity. Therefore it is impossible to formulate a cycle pattern which will apply to all volcanoes. In order to reduce the eruptive activity of each volcano to a cycle it is necessary to have detailed records for each volcano for many years. Such records are available for Vesuvius and Mount Etna in Italy, and, to a limited extent, for the Hawaiian volcanoes. The eruptive cycle for each of these volcanoes will be described in order to show the nature of a cycle and to acquaint the reader with the type of information revealed by such studies.

Cycle of Kilauea

The two active volcanoes of the Hawaiian Islands, Kilauea and Mauna Loa, have been described in some detail in Chapter 10, and at this point only the cyclic pattern of the eruptions of Kilauea will be considered.

Summary of the eruptive cycle

The eruptive cycle at Kilauea begins with an explosion which forms a pit (Halemaumau) on the floor of the crater. Concurrent and subsequent collapse widens the pit, as happened after the explosive eruptions in 1790 and 1924. Then for several decades eruptions separated by quiescent intervals of several months or several years break out in the floor or wall of the pit and slowly fill it up. These eruptions produce cinder and spatter cones and lava lakes. Slowly the pit fills, and finally it may overflow the rim and flood the crater floor. All of these features are characteristics of rising magma beneath Kilauea and cause the mountain to actually "swell up" by an amount which can be measured by special instruments known as "tilt meters." Flank flows may occur, causing the level of the lava lake to sink to the level of the flank outflow. Flank outflows are usually of brief duration, lasting only a few days and in most cases less than one month. The phase of upbuilding is finally terminated by another collapse, which may engulf most of the crater floor and which marks the end of the cycle.

The subsidence of the magma column, which results in engulfment, may result from lava discharges on the flanks, either above or below sea level; intrusions of magma into the underground area as sills or dikes; or possibly from a recession of the magma into the magma reservoir. Whether an explosive eruption accompanies the collapse is purely a matter of accident, depending on whether the magma column recedes sufficiently to permit ground water to gain access to the zone of heated rocks. In summary, then, there are essentially two stages in the cycle: (1) a period of increasing pressure accompanied by rising of the lava column with lava flows in the crater and on the flanks, and (2) a collapse, indicating decreasing pressure as the magma column recedes. Following collapse, the lava slowly returns to the crater, gradually building it up again for another collapse.

Periodicity of the eruptive cycle

Dr. Thomas A. Jaggar, who spent a lifetime studying Kilauea and Mauna Loa, was firmly convinced that the activity was rhythmic, with its basis on an 11-year cycle. He further believed that the 11-year cycles were superimposed on a 132-year supercycle, made up of two parts of 66 years each. In considering what constitutes a cycle, Dr. Jaggar concluded, in common with most students of volcanoes, that the most distinctive feature of a volcanic cycle is the short repose period. It is only in volcanoes where the magma is visible most of the time, such as

Kilauea, that the repose period is striking. His adoption of an 11-year cycle was first based on the repose periods of 1913 and 1924. Then, when this theory was applied to the entire period of 1790 to 1924, he found that no figure fits the repose periods as well as an 11-year interval. Further, he observed that if the entire period of 1790 to 1924 is divided into twelve cycles, the average length of each cycle is 11.1 years, or the same as the sunspot cycle. The supercycle of 132 years was the period between the two paroxysmal eruptions of Kilauea, in 1790 and in 1924. In justifying his 11-year cycle, Dr. Jaggar pointed out that in the 1902–1913 interval both Mauna Loa and Kilauea were in complete repose at the beginning and end of the cycle and that both erupted lava during the cycle.

In his tabulation of the 11-year cycle the repose (low-pressure) periods correspond with sunspot minima while the active discharge of lavas (high-pressure periods) correlate with sunspot maxima. Dr. Jaggar (1931) was unable to account for this relationship between sunspots and the volcanic cycle, but he felt that:

If the earth magnetism and electricity are in some way associated with gravity, volcanism may be affected. If heat by earth's radioactivity affects volcanism, the sun may in turn affect the earth's radiations. Finally, if volcanic emanations on the earth are a last remnant of solar processes here, these processes by unknown means may be sympathetic with the sun.

Recently Stearns and Macdonald (1946) have evaluated the data on cycles in the eruptions of Kilauea and concluded that the evidence does not warrant the conclusions drawn by Dr. Jaggar. They point out that the 1790 explosive eruption, a key point in Dr. Jaggar's supercycle, is a "volcanic accident" and is not significant in the cyclic behavior of the volcano. The important feature is the subsidence of the magma column, and the explosion is more or less accidental. Likewise they are unable to relate the activity of Kilauea to an 11-year cycle or to see any close correlation between its activity and the sunspot cycle. The closest correlation between sunspots and eruptive periods was with Mauna Loa, which erupted during six of the nine years of sunspot minima and whose eruptions for two of the remaining three years were only one year removed from sunspot minima.

PLATE 24. Mount Etna, Sicily, from Taormina.

Such conflicting conclusions point up the fact that the 150 years of reliable observations is far too brief a period of observation for establishing an eruptive pattern for the volcano. Nevertheless, the facts do indicate that a cyclic repetition in the type of activity exists and that past performance is a reliable guide to future activity. It seems reasonable to conclude that this activity will fit into some rhythmic sequence, but whether it is Dr. Jaggar's 11-year cycle or some other pattern remains to be determined.

Cycle of Mount Etna

Eruptional history of Mount Etna

Mount Etna, on the island of Sicily, is one of the large volcanoes of the world and the highest in Europe, rising 10,625 feet above sea level. Its enormous cone, made up of many superimposed lava flows, is surmounted by literally hundreds of minor (parasitic) cinder cones which dot its flanks. More than two hundred of these secondary cones occur

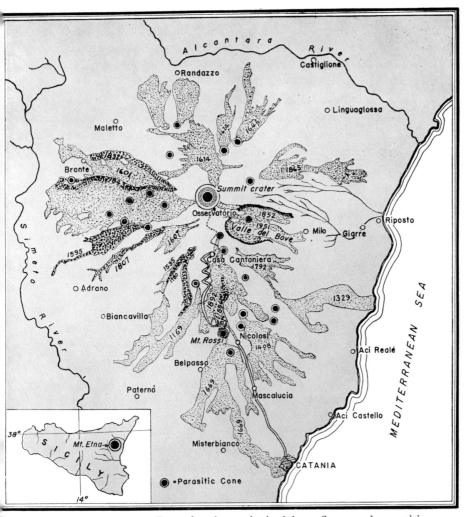

Map labels (clockwise/around):

Alcantara River

o Randazzo   Castiglione

Maletto o   o Linguaglossa

Bronte   1614

1832   1865

1595   Summit crater

1807   Osservatorio   1852
                Valle del Bove   o Milo   o Riposto
o Adrano   Casa Cantoniera   Giarre
                1792
o Biancavilla   1329

          Mt. Rossi   Nicolosi   o Aci Realé
          1498
Belpasso o

Paterno o   Mascalucia   o Aci Castello

          Misterbianco o   CATANIA

          ⊚ =Parasitic Cone

Simeto River

MEDITERRANEAN SEA

Inset map: 38° — SICILY — Mt. Etna →⊚ — 14°

FIGURE 41. Map of Mount Etna showing principal lava flows and parasitic cones.

within a radius of twenty miles from the summit crater. Some of these cones, such as Mount Rossi, 450 feet above its base and two miles in circumference, are quite prominent volcanoes in their own right.

Mount Etna has had a long eruptional history, and, unlike Vesuvius, was known from the earliest time to be volcanic in nature. Homer makes reference to Mount Etna in about 800 B.C., and Virgil (70 B.C.–A.D. 19) in the *Aeneid* describes an eruption of Mount Etna. According to Diodorus Siculus, a lava flow from Mount Etna in 396 B.C., twenty-four miles long and two miles wide, stopped the advance of the Carthaginian army. The absence of records during the Dark Ages makes it impossible to compile a complete list of the eruptions of Mount Etna. Disastrous eruptions are known to have occurred in 1169, 1329, 1536, and 1669. The eruption of 1669, which is well described, was the most violent on record. The summit cone was practically destroyed, and an enormous lava flow, sixteen kilometers long, destroyed the city of Catania and flowed into the sea, blocking the harbor. The eruption of 1669 initiated for Mount Etna a new phase of activity which has continued to the present time.

Professor G. Imbo (1928), now director of the Vesuvian Volcano Observatory, but previously stationed at Catania, made a study of the cyclic nature of the eruptions of Mount Etna from the year 1669 to 1928. In this period thirty-three eruptions occurred, with an average interval of slightly over eight years between eruptions. The period from 1669 to 1755 is open to some question because of poor records. During the period from 1755 to 1928, in which eruptions occurred at intervals of about $6\frac{1}{2}$ years, Imbo recognizes three major cycles:

> 1755 to 1809—54-year cycle; 9-year interval between eruptions
> 1809 to 1865—56-year cycle; 6-year interval between eruptions
> 1865 to 1908—43-year cycle; 7-year interval between eruptions

Pattern of the cycle

A typical eruption on Mount Etna is a "lateral eruption" in which lava issues from a fracture on the side of the cone. Generally, the lava issues from the lower part of the fracture while explosive eruptions build cinder cones along the upper part of the fissure. In succeeding eruptions lava issues from higher points along the fracture until its entire extent is sealed. The formation of a fracture and the outflow of lava from progressively higher points along the fracture until it is sealed, constitutes a cycle. Occasionally the lava flows begin at the top and proceed downward, but this is the exception. Normally the interval between an eruption closing a cycle and that initiating a new cycle is longer than the interval between eruptions within a single cycle. It requires more pressure (and time for it to accumulate) to split the cone to initiate a new cycle than to force lava out along an already existing break. The initiation of a new cycle is usually accompanied by vigorous earthquakes.

Future eruptions

On the basis of Professor Imbo's cycles, we may expect that the present cycle will end in 1963, assuming a cycle length of fifty-five years. Until that time, eruptions should occur along the existing fracture at intervals of about seven years. The last two lava flows from Etna were in 1951 and 1958.

We know also the direction along which the fractures will most likely occur. Of 262 eruptive centers plotted, the great majority were aligned in a general north-south direction, corresponding to the trend of a major fracture line in eastern Sicily. Thus, since geologists can predict the probable time as well as the direction along which the eruptions will occur, the element of surprise in an eruption of Mount Etna is largely eliminated.

Cycle of Vesuvius

The geologic setting as well as the history of Vesuvius is described in Chapter 8. The first to recognize the cyclic nature of the eruptions of Vesuvius was Professor L. Palmieri (1873), who, following his study of the great eruption of 1872, announced that paroxysmal eruptions, such as that of 1872, always follow a long period of constructive activity and that a repose period follows the paroxysmal eruption. The eruptive cycle of Vesuvius, following the general pattern recognized by Palmieri, has been described by Mercalli (1907), Perret (1924), Friedlander and Alfano (1928), and Bullard (1954a).

Stages in the cycle

The various stages in the Vesuvian cycle, as interpreted by the writer, are illustrated by a series of sketches in Figure 42, to which the following explanations refer. After a grand eruption, such as in 1872, 1906, or 1944, in which large outflows of lava occurred and the upper part of the cone was destroyed and the crater enlarged, Vesuvius lapses into a period of repose which, on the average, has lasted about seven

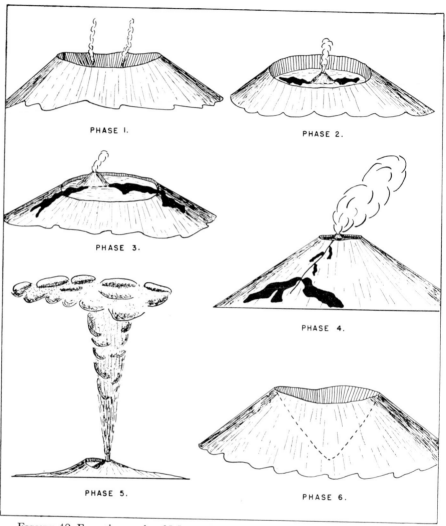

PHASE 1.

PHASE 2.

PHASE 3.

PHASE 4.

PHASE 5.

PHASE 6.

FIGURE 42. Eruptive cycle of Mount Vesuvius.

years (Phase 1, Fig. 42). The renewal of activity begins with explosions forming a cinder cone in the bottom of the crater. As the intracrater cone grows in size (Phase 2, Fig. 42) outflows of lava may fill the space between it and the outer crater walls, forming a crater platform which becomes higher and higher, until it finally fills the summit crater (Phase 3, Fig. 42). Some of the lava flows may spill over the crater rim or issue from fissures near the top of the crater but such flows are of small volume and cause little damage. In other cases the explosive activity may throw out scoria and incandescent lava in an amount equal to a lava flow. The cone building in the summit crater, or the spilling of lava over the rim, constitutes a moderate type of activity which is normal for Vesuvius and which may continue for twenty-five or thirty years. When the rebuilding of the summit cone is complete, that is, when the summit crater is filled, the stage is set for the culminating eruption. The column of lava now standing at a high level in the throat of the volcano is under tremendous pressure and is saturated with gas. Finally, accompanied by sharp earthquakes and strong explosions, the cone splits frequently from crater rim to the base (Phase 4, Fig. 42). This fracture taps the lava in the conduit at a lower level, and, saturated with gases and under pressure of the lava column, it issues in great floods and flows rapidly down the side of the cone, destroying everything in its path. This is the grand eruption which signals the end of a cycle. Such an eruption is of short duration, lasting only a few weeks at most.

The fissures, from which the lava issues, usually open on the side of the main cone of Vesuvius, but three times in the last two centuries (1760, 1794, and 1861) the fissures opened on the outer slope of Mount Somma, indicating a deep connection with the volcanic conduit. The lava level in the conduit sinks as the lava drains out, reducing the pressure on the upper walls of the summit cone, and large-scale avalanching enlarges the crater and reduces the height of the cone. Finally, as the pressure is reduced on the lava column by the rapid outflows, a tremendous "gas blowoff" takes place, forming a gigantic eruption cloud miles in height (Phase 5, Fig. 42). Perret (1924), who first recognized this phase in the 1906 eruption, emphasizes the continuity of the phenomenon. It is not an explosion but a continuous emission of gas under tremendous pressure, like a huge locomotive "blowing off" steam. This phase, in its most vigorous aspect, lasts only a matter of hours, and it marks the end of the eruption as well as the end of the cycle. The volcano then lapses into a period of repose, during which time the magma is again becoming gas-saturated and developing enough pressure to force an opening to the surface and initiate a new cycle. In summary then, the eruptive cycle of Vesuvius may be divided into three main stages: (1) repose period, (2) moderate activity, and (3) paroxysmal eruption.

Recurrence of cycles

Nearly all studies of the Vesuvian cycle begin with the great eruption of 1631, which initiated a new era in the activity of Vesuvius. Since that time it has been in an almost constant state of activity and its eruptions have followed a cyclic pattern. Investigators do not agree on the number or length of the various cycles but these differences relate to details rather than basic principles. Mercalli (1907) recognizes twelve eruptive cycles since 1700, each culminating with a paroxysmal eruption followed by a repose period. The length of the cycles is variable, ranging from a minimum of five years (1850–1855) to a maximum of thirty-eight years. The last two cycles, from 1872 to 1906 and from 1906 to 1944, were thirty-four and thirty-eight years respectively. Further details on the cycles of Vesuvius, including a description of several of the paroxysmal eruptions which ended cycles, is given in the section on the eruptive history of Vesuvius, pp. 133–150, 156–168.

Current status

The latest grand eruption of Vesuvius, which ended a cycle, was in March, 1944 (Chapter 8, pp. 165–168), when lava flows destroyed the towns of Massa and San Sebastiano. Vesuvius then lapsed into a period of repose which marks the beginning of a new cycle. It has now been in repose for more than twice the average length of this period, and it is apparent that a renewal of eruptive activity is long overdue. If it follows the normal pattern, the activity will begin with explosions forming a cinder cone on the floor of the crater and will continue with cone building and outpourings of lava, which will gradually fill the crater. After some thirty years (more or less) of this type of activity, a paroxysmal eruption will end the cycle.

The fact that volcanic eruptions are cyclic seems well established. However, the length and the sequence of events in a cycle, even with the best-known volcanoes, is somewhat in doubt. Volcanic observations so far, with few exceptions, have been limited to the periods of

Plate 25. The 1805 eruption of Mount Vesuvius. Lava is issuing from several points along a fracture which extends from the rim of the crater to the base of the cone. From an old painting.

spectacular eruptions. In order to determine the eruptive cycle of a volcano continuous observations are necessary. If such observations were carried on at all of the active vents of the earth, with use of the new equipment now available to scientists, it seems likely that a significant "break-through" would soon be made. With the establishment of the details of the eruptive cycle of a volcano, the next step would be prediction and control, including the possibility of utilizing the natural energy being released for the benefit of mankind. It is a goal worthy of our best efforts.

The present is the key to the past.

Sir A. Geike

13. BIRTH OF NEW VOLCANOES

THE BIRTH OF A NEW VOLCANO in historic times is indeed a rare event. The development of a parasitic cone on the side of an older, active volcano is a fairly common occurrence, but these should not be considered to be "new" volcanoes. Mount Etna has more than two hundred parasitic cones, several of which have formed in historic time. Some of these cones are miles from the main crater and several hundred feet in height. Many of them would form impressive cones if they were on a plain where they were not dwarfed by the great mass of Mount Etna. The distinction between a new volcano and a parasitic cone is frequently difficult. Parasitic cones are related to a pre-existing vent, while a new volcano must open its own connection with the magma chamber. Thus an eruption removed from other volcanoes must be presumed to be a new vent. If, as is often the case, the eruption is near, but not a part of, an older volcano the relationship may be uncertain. It is even more difficult if the older volcano has had no eruptions in historic time and appears to be extinct. In such a case the weight of evidence would favor classifying the eruption as a new volcano.

Only two new volcanoes, both in western Mexico, have been born in North America in historic times. The first was Jorullo in 1759, and the second was Parícutin in 1943; both are described in the following pages. It is quite possible that some of the submarine eruptions described as "new" volcanoes may, in fact, be parasitic cones in which the relationships cannot be determined.

Parícutin Volcano, Mexico[1]

Significance of Parícutin

Without a doubt the best known of the "new" volcanoes is Parícutin, born in the state of Michoacán, Mexico, on February 20, 1943. Described as having been born in a cornfield while the owner was looking at it, it was featured in many popular magazines and has been the subject of numerous books and scientific articles. Dr. Ezequiel Ordóñez, distinguished Mexican geologist, arrived on the scene on the third day of its activity. From that time until its activity ceased, nine years later, the volcano was under almost constant observation by a team of scientists organized as a Committee of the U. S. National Research Council. As a member of that Committee the writer participated in its work throughout the life of the volcano. The writer first visited Parícutin when it was two and one-half months old, but this was only the first of many trips to observe the volcano during its nine years of activity.

[1] This material was first prepared by the author for the Twentieth International Geologic Congress excursion to Parícutin Volcano in 1956. It was published (in Spanish) under the title: Resumen de la historia del Volcán Parícutin, Michoacán, México. Guide Book Excursion A-15. It is presented here with some minor revisions.

In the second year of its life, which was one of its most active periods, the writer carried on an independent research study of Parícutin under a grant from the Geological Society of America and the University of Texas Research Institute. During the period of this study, from late July to December, 1944, the writer lived in a small observation cabin built by the National University of Mexico. The cabin, located about one kilometer from the base of the cone, afforded an unsurpassed view of the dramatic spectacle of a volcano in action, which may truly be called "the greatest show on earth." The cone was frequently covered with red-hot bombs of scoria ejected by tremendous explosions from the crater. Numerous lava flows poured from vents, some of which were near enough to the cabin to be observed from the doorstep. In one case a lava flow came to within thirty feet of the cabin before it stopped! When the cabin was eventually isolated by lava, the writer was forced to cross the still hot (but cooling) lava flows to get in and out of the area. Later the "island" on which the cabin stood was buried by lava, although it had been abandoned some time before in anticipation of such a catastrophe.

It will be understandable, then, because of the writer's personal experience with Parícutin, that more space is devoted to it than might otherwise be the case. This seems justifiable, furthermore, because, since Parícutin is the first volcano which has been observed in detail throughout its entire active cycle, it has provided much valuable information on many aspects of volcanic activity hitherto unknown or unexplained.

Named "Parícutin" for a small Tarascan Indian village (population five hundred at the time of the eruption) 3 kilometers from the vent, it is 320 kilometers due west of Mexico City. It can be reached by air, rail, or paved highway from Mexico City to Uruapan, and thence by 32 kilometers of paved and dirt road to Angahuan, 8 kilometers to the northeast of the cone.

Birth of the volcano

Parícutin Volcano was born on February 20, 1943, about 183 years after the birth of Jorullo, 72 kilometers to the southeast. Although literally hundreds of cinder cones similar to Parícutin abound in the

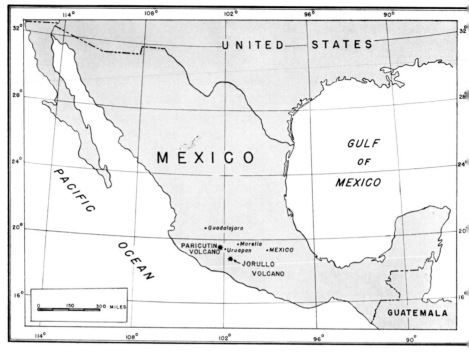

FIGURE 43. Map showing location of Parícutin and Jorullo volcanoes.

general region, no eruptions had occurred previously (other than at Jorullo), and the Indians had no legends of any volcanic activity in the area.

The stories of the beginning of the volcano are varied. Fortunately, two trained scientists (R. González and W. F. Foshag, 1947) investigated the various accounts, interviewed the eyewitnesses and many local officials, and prepared a record of the birth of Parícutin while it was still fresh in the memory of the local inhabitants.

One of the most fertile portions of this section of the state of Michoacán was the municipality of San Juan Parangaricutiro, which included also the villages of Parícutin, Anaghuan, Zirosto, Zacan, and others. It consists of small, rich valleys between volcanic ridges and cones. The region is inhabited by the Tarascan Indians, who have maintained their own language and customs. As is customary in this section of Michoacán the tillable lands are privately owned, but the owners live in the villages and travel each day with their oxen and tools to the fields, returning to their homes in the evening. Three kilometers south of San Juan de Parangaricutiro and two kilometers southeast of Parícutin lay the valley of Rancho Tepacua. It is on the southeast slope of Cerros de Tancítaro (3,845 m.), the highest point in Michoacán.

In the valley of Rancho Tepacua a dweller in Parícutin Village, Dionisio Pulido, owned a parcel of land of about nine acres, on which a small hole had existed for many years. One of the older inhabitants recalled that as a small child, more than fifty years before, she had played about this small pit, where she frequently heard underground noises like falling rocks, and felt emerging from it "a pleasant warmth."

The first indications of the eruption were a series of earthquakes on February 5, 1943. For two weeks they increased in number and intensity, and on February 19 no less than three hundred were felt (Trask, 1943).

On the morning of February 20 Dionisio Pulido left his village to prepare his farm for planting. He was accompanied by his wife, Paula, his son, and a neighbor, Demetrio Toral. There were, then, four eyewitnesses who saw the birth of Parícutin Volcano at close range.

As reported by González and Foshag (1947, p. 226), it was about 4:00 P.M. when Dionisio Pulido noticed a fissure which, at first only a half meter in depth, extended northwest-southeast through the hole previously mentioned. Almost immediately there was a thunder; the trees trembled; the ground swelled two to two and one-half meters; a smoke or fine ash-gray dust began to rise from portions of the fissure. More smoke, accompanied by a loud and continuous hissing and the odor of sulphur, followed. "Sparks" also were coming out of the fissure, and pine trees thirty meters from the opening began to burn. At this point all eyewitnesses hurriedly left the scene. By 5:00 P.M., from the plaza in Parangaricutiro, a thin column of smoke could be seen rising, and many people gathered to discuss the phenomenon. It was decided that a group would go to investigate. Going on horseback, they soon arrived at the scene. They reported a fissure at the southern end of which was a hole a half meter across, from which issued smoke and red-hot stones. As they watched, the hole increased to two meters in breadth, and the volume of smoke increased.

The observers described the opening as pear-shaped. They saw this cavity erupting a fine, gray, dustlike ash with "sparks," and stones, which were thrown out without much force to a height of five meters. In the opening the sand was "boiling" with a gurgling noise; a choking odor pervaded the area. Although the ash was very hot, the observers collected some, as well as two of the hot stones, to take back to Parangaricutiro. The ground seemed to them to be "jumping up and down," but not with the swaying motion they had experienced in Parangaricutiro (González and Foshag, 1947, p. 320). In the early evening the volcano began to throw out larger stones, sufficient in size to be seen from Parangaricutiro, although there was little noise accompanying the outbursts. Around midnight huge incandescent bombs were hurled into the air with a roar, and lightning flashes appeared in the heavy ash column. When Dionisio Pulido arrived at the scene at 8:00 A.M. the next morning, February 21, he saw a cone about ten meters high emitting smoke and rocks with great violence. During the morning of the twenty-first the activity increased, and by midday the cone was thirty to fifty meters high, growing rapidly from the accumulation of great quantities of incandescent material being ejected. The amount of ash was relatively small, and the eruptive column much smaller than in later periods. The first lava issued on the second day, from the northeastern base of the new cone, spreading as a slaglike mass of black, jagged blocks about five meters in thickness over Sr. Pulido's farm, and moving approximately five meters per hour (Ordóñez, 1943, p. 65). Then, on the evening of February 22, Dr. Ezequiel Ordóñez, veteran Mexican geologist, reached Parícutin. He describes the eruption, (Ordóñez, 1943) as he first observed it, as follows:

Amid the almost continuous explosions I could see many tons of incandescent rocks being hurled high into the darkness of the night, and the flames attending each explosion brightly illuminated the big column of vapor and gas that were issuing from the huge vent.

The first year

In its early stages the cone grew with startling rapidity. At the end of the first week it was 140 meters high, and its explosive activity

PLATE 26. Parícutin Volcano, Michoacán, Mexico.
Courtesy Tad Nichols, photo February 23, 1944.

had increased to an awesome thunderous bombardment, in which immense quantities of viscous lava were hurled continuously into the air. The noise of the explosions could be heard throughout the State of Michoacán and even in Guanajuato, 350 kilometers to the northeast (González and Foshag, 1947, p. 233). Every few seconds showers of glowing ejecta were thrown six hundred to a thousand meters above the crater rim, and, as they reached their zenith, they seemed to stop before beginning to fall. Then they shattered over the cone like a giant skyrocket, leaving a trail of fire as they cascaded down the sides. So abundant were these fragments that frequently the entire cone was covered with interlacing fiery trails (Bullard, 1947a). Most of the bombs were from one-third meter to a meter in diameter and were smashed into fragments when they struck the ground. Occasionally they were fluid enough to flatten when they landed. Mixed with these clots of new magma were fragments of old andesite and plutonic rock torn from the wall of the conduit.

In late March the first lava flow stopped and the emission of ash greatly increased. The great ash-filled eruptive column, frequently rising to a height of six thousand meters or more, scattered ash widely over the countryside. Heavy ash showers were frequent in Uruapan, and on April 8, 9, and 10 fine ash falls occurred in Mexico City, 320 kilometers away.

In mid-April lava began to issue from the southwestern base of the cone, almost directly opposite the first flow. On June 10 a section of the upper part of the cone collapsed, and lava began to flow from the lower part of the break at a point some one hundred meters below the crater rim. Spectacular lava fountains developed, and a flow cascaded down the side of the cone, carrying huge masses of the slumped cone and fragments of earlier flows as erratics on its surface. At no other time in the history of Parícutin did lava flow from the crater; all other flows issued from *bocas* at or near the base on the northeast and southwest sides. The writer's first visit to Parícutin, at the time of this spectacular activity, marked the beginning of an association with Parícutin which included a visit of a few weeks to several months at the volcano during each year for the next seven years.

The most violent period in the life of Parícutin was probably that of July and August of 1943, when lava stood higher in the central crater than at any subsequent period. On June 19 Trask (1943, p. 504) reported lava to be only fifteen meters below the rim. In general, the explosive activity at the central crater was greatest preceding the outbreak of a new lava flow. While the lava was flowing freely, the explosive activity was somewhat diminished.

On October 19, 1943, a parasitic vent named "Sapichu" opened at the northeastern base of the cone. It erupted with intense explosive activity, throwing out spectacular fountains of lava. Within a few weeks it attained a height of more than a hundred meters, resembling in all respects the main cone. Shortly, a lava flow began to issue from Sapichu, carrying a wide section of the cone with it. This horseshoe-shaped, or "breached," cone (Pl. 27) was a familiar landmark at Parícutin until the summer of 1946, when it was finally buried by a succession of lava

PLATE 27. Parícutin Volcano, October 9, 1944, showing the "breached" cone of Sapichu.

PLATE 28. Only the towers of the church project above the lava flow from Parícutin Volcano which destroyed the town of San Juan de Parangaricutiro in June, 1944.   Courtesy Tad Nichols, photo, July, 1945.

flows. While Sapichu was active the main cone was dormant, but as soon as Sapichu subsided the parent cone renewed its violent activity.

By the end of the first year Parícutin had reached a height of 325 meters above the cornfield where it started. It was during this period that cone building was the dominant process. Thereafter effusion of lava was the dominant process, and the growth of the cone was slight. Its maximum height up to February 21, 1950, was 397 meters in comparison with 360 meters on the same day in 1947 and 336 meters on that day in 1944 (Fries and Gutiérrez, 1951, p. 219). When the eruptions ceased in 1952 the cone was 410 meters above the original surface of Sr. Pulido's cornfield (Fries and Gutiérrez, 1954, p. 490), although it had attained greater heights at various stages in its history only to lose it by explosion or collapse.

PLATE 29. *Boca* of Parícutin lava flow of September, 1944.   Photo by author, October 6, 1944.

The second year

In early 1944 the lava activity shifted to the southwest side of the cone, or the side opposite Sapichu, and for the next three years, or until January 19, 1947, lava emerged from closely spaced *bocas* on this side. The area of lava vents became known as the "Mesa de los Hornitos" (Tableland of Little Ovens) and hardly did one flow stop before another broke out from a new *boca* nearby. These flows were hotter, more fluid, and larger than the earlier flows.

The most extensive and voluminous flow from Parícutin was the flow which covered San Juan Parangaricutiro. It began in January, 1944, from a *boca* in the Mesa de los Hornitos, and continued until August, 1944. It flowed eastward around the cone and then to the southeast until it reached a stream valley, which it followed in a northwesterly direction. The town of San Juan Parangaricutiro, located in this valley, was largely covered during June and July, and the lava continued for about two and one-half kilometers beyond the town. The flow stopped early in August, having attained a total length of ten kilometers.

The characteristics of the lava flows from Mesa de los Hornitos are well illustrated by the flow which covered the village of Parícutin in 1944. The flow began on September 27, 1944, while the writer was living in a small observation cabin about one kilometer from the south base of the cone. The following is a description of this flow (Bullard, 1947, p. 439).[2]

"The first definite evidence that this *boca* was active was noted on the evening of September 27, when a strong red glow appeared on the southwest side of the cone. Since the *boca* is nearly directly back of the cone with respect to the *casita* (position of observation), some of the peculiar red glow observed about midnight on September 26 may have been associated with its development. The lava flow was first observed on the morning of September 28, when the lava front was approximately three-fourths of a mile from its source. It is perhaps worth noting that on the evening of September 27 the writer made the following entry: 'There does not seem to be the red glow over the crater, such as

[2] With slight editorial changes.

PLATE 30. Close view of *boca* shown in Plate 29.   Photo by author, October 6, 1944.

has been present for several nights.' This strongly suggests that the lava in the crater drained out as the new *boca* became active.

"The *boca* was located on the southwest side of the cone about four hundred feet from the base and in the general vicinity of the source of the San Juan flow. The most striking feature at the *boca* was a large graben with one side at the Hornitos (actually cutting through the center of the most prominent one) and the other side about two hundred yards to the northwest. The lava was issuing from a fault marking the west side of the graben. The displacement of the down-dropped block was about thirty feet.

"On a trip to this area about a month before the outbreak of the flow, a large fracture cutting through the most prominent hornito was mapped and photographed. This fracture proved to be the east side of the graben. On this same trip many fractures were noted along the west side of the graben area, but their location could not be established with certainty. That these fractures were evident at least a month before the outbreak of the lava is proof that a close study of such features is essential.

"The *boca* was about seventy-five feet in width, and the lava, rising along the fault marking the west side of the graben, was flowing at the rate of fifty feet per minute. In addition to the *boca*, there was a lake of lava, which at first appeared to be a whirlpool, but which was actually the lava welling up at either end of a circular pool and flowing to the center, where the two streams joined and disappeared together in a crevasse. The line of juncture of the two currents shifted from one side to the other, possibly in response to variations in volume and velocity of the lava streams from the two sides. Such a convection system is characteristic of lava lakes and indicates a direct connection with the underlying magma. The cooler, heavier surface lava sinks and is replaced by the hotter, lighter material from below. Convection systems of this type are common features in the fire pit of Halemaumau at Kilauea Volcano, Hawaii.

"Intrusive lava was present in the southward extension of the fractures along which the lava lake and the *boca* were located. Comparatively little gas was present in the lava as it issued from the *boca*. Occasionally a blister would form, and gas would escape with a hissing

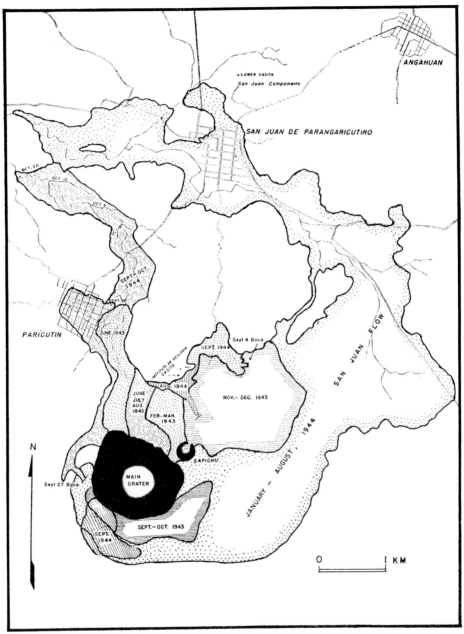

FIGURE 44. Lava flow from Parícutin Volcano during first two years, 1943 and 1944.   From Bullard (1947).

noise, but there were no explosions such as were observed in the September 4 flow.

"The lava flowed westward from the *boca*, carrying, in the early stages, many erratics of the San Juan flow with it. About a quarter of a mile from the *boca* the lava stream plunged into a deep ravine. This ravine was about seventy-five feet deep, and as the stream of lava plunged over the side it produced a most spectacular lava cascade. The flow followed the ravine, which was along the margin of the June, 1943, flow, and on reaching the end of this flow, near the village of Parícutin, it spread out, covering most of the site of the village of Parícutin, which had escaped the earlier flow. Continuing beyond the village of Parícutin, the flow reached a stream valley, which it followed to the northwest.

"When the *boca* area was investigated on October 6, the lava lake was crusted over, and the surface was covered with many active gas vents. The gas vents were small chimneylike elevations, three to five feet high, and from the red-hot interior gas was escaping with a roar like the exhaust of steam from a locomotive. Dozens of these 'exhausts' produced a noise that could be heard for more than half a mile. Deposits of ferrous chloride covered the entire area, and hydrochloric acid fumes made it difficult to approach the area, except under favorable wind conditions.

"When the rate of advance of the flow was first measured (11:00 A.M., September 28) the lava front was due west of the *casita*, along the west margin of the June, 1943, flow. The rate of advance at this time was sixty feet per hour. Later, on September 29, the most rapid lobe was moving about forty feet per hour. The lobe which covered the site of the village of Parícutin was advancing twenty feet per hour when it crossed the main east-west street at 5:00 P.M., on September 29. This flow joined the San Juan flow on October 17 and continued its forward movement until about November 1."

Activity from 1945 to 1952

The general outline of the Parícutin lava field was defined by the end of 1944 (Fig. 44). Subsequent flows, which were superimposed on

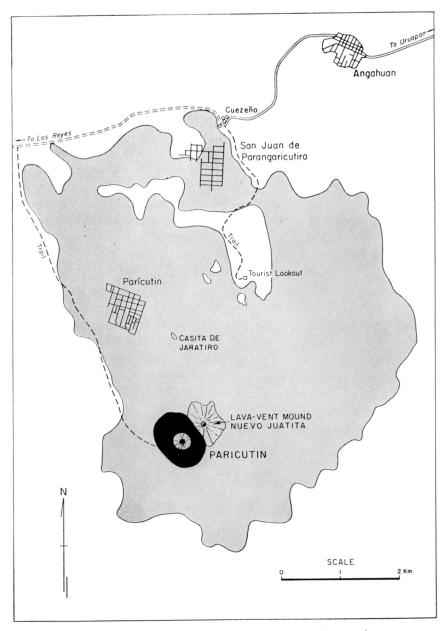

FIGURE 45. Lava fields of Parícutin Volcano at the end of the eruption.
After Fries, from Bullard (1956).

earlier flows or injected sill-like into earlier flows, did not enlarge the lava area appreciably (Fig. 45). Lava continued to issue from various vents at the southwest base of the cone throughout 1945 and 1946.

On January 19, 1947, a new *boca* opened at the northeastern base of the cone not far from the former site of Sapichu and about one hundred meters lower than the vents on the southwestern side. An interesting change in the surface of the cone accompanied the opening of this new vent. On December 4, 1946, two sets of steam cracks were observed on the southwestern flank of the cone. On January 15 the segment of the cone between the cracks slumped, leaving scarps two meters in height extending down the side of the cone, and a new lava vent opened at the base of the slumped segment. Additional slumping of this segment in the ensuing weeks depressed the southwestern rim a total of about ten meters. Diametrically opposite, a segment of the northeastern cone slumped on January 13, the fractures first appearing at the top of the cone and extending farther down the flank from day to day. On January 19 a portion of the base of the slumped segment, exactly in line with the old Sapichu vent, was pushed outward to form the new *boca*, later named the "Juatito" (Wilcox, 1947, pp. 729–730). The development of the slumped block, or graben, directly in alignment with the fracture on which the northeastern and southwestern vents were situated, seems significant. On September 1, 1947, the old Ahuan vent on the southeastern side became active and continued to emit large quantities of lava until the end of 1947. It may be noted that the lava from the revived Ahuan vent tended to pile up around the vent and spread in lobes of much greater thickness than the previous flows. This may be due in part to the smaller gradients in the direction of flow and in part to the greater viscosity of the lava, which had by this time reached a silica content of over 58 percent (Wilcox, 1954, p. 288).

On February 7, 1948, the vents at the northeastern base of the cone reopened, and shortly afterwards the Ahuan vent closed. Thereafter, up to the final cessation of lava activity on February 25, 1952, lava continued to flow from the northeastern vents (Fries and Gutiérrez, 1950; 1950a; 1951; 1951a; 1952; 1952a; 1954).

The final activity

The cessation of activity came abruptly, rather than by a gradual decline, as might have been expected. As described by Fries and Gutiérrez (1954) the continued activity at the northeastern side had formed a lava-vent mound down which the lava flows cascaded from time to time. On February 8, 1952, a new cascade formed on this mound, and the lava continued to flow in large volume until February 22, when the flow became sluggish on the surface. During the evening the emission declined abruptly, and on the morning of February 25 it ceased altogether. The cessation of lava emission also marked the cessation of continuous eruptions in the crater. Fries and Gutiérrez (1954, p. 489) reported that the strong detonations characteristic of the last two years of the eruptive history continued to increase in frequency, some 305 detonations occurring between February 1 and 25, 1952, when the strong eruptions ceased abruptly. This frequency compares with a total of about 400 such detonations for the last six months of 1951. Coarse pyroclastic material expelled by these intense explosions was so abundant that it frequently obscured the cone from view. Blocks of lava weighing more than a hundred tons were hurled from the crater and fell beyond the base of the cone.

As reported by Fries and Gutiérrez (1954, p. 489) the final explosive activity developed as follows:

Beginning on January 1, 1952 both crater vents were active and of nearly equal eruptive intensity. At times the eruptions were simultaneous in the two vents and at other times they showed no relationship from one vent to the other. On January 23 the eruptions alternated from white vapor to black ash-laden vapors, but at other times such an alternation was not observed. In addition to ordinary explosions every 5 to 15 seconds, intense detonations occurred at irregular intervals of 15 minutes to four hours, without exhibiting any recognizable periodicity.

On February 24, the last day of strong continuous eruptive activity, the ash eruption was of the type that first began on March 18, 1943, and ash rained down over the countryside in large quantities, especially northeast of the cone, where a gray curtain extended several kilometers from the Volcano. This eruption was apparently the final spasm of activity, for during that same night continuous activity came to a halt. Except for a few intense explosions the following day, eruptions occurred only intermittently until March 4, when activity ceased entirely.

Thus, after nine years and twelve days the active period in the life of Parícutin Volcano came to an end.

Notes on the eruptive products

VOLUME OF EJECTA. The total area covered by lava from Parícutin is 24.8 square kilometers (Fries and Gutiérrez, 1954). As pointed out previously, the surface extent of the lava field did not increase a great deal after the second year, but the thickness, especially near the cone, increased markedly. On the northeastern side, where flows issued almost continuously from early 1944 to early 1947, the lava attained a thickness of about 245 meters and a similar condition obtained on the southeastern side. As a result of the flows' burying the lower part of the cone, the height above the lava field decreased, and the cone appeared to be smaller. The total volume of rock material erupted, including both lava and pyroclastics, was computed by Fries (1953, p. 611) to be equal to 1.4 cubic kilometers in the magma chamber. Fries calculated this to be 3,596 million metric tons, or an average of 1.1 million metric tons of solids (i.e., lava and pyroclastics) per day during the entire life of the volcano. Lava constituted about 27 percent of the total, with pyroclastic material making up the remainder. The determination of the gases, including water vapor, was less satisfactory, and in the calculation made by Fries only the year of 1945 was used. During this period Fries calculated that the daily emission of water amounted to about 13,600 metric tons, and this amounted to about 1.1 percent of the total magma reaching the surface during this period.

COMPOSITION OF THE LAVA. The lavas of 1943 were olivine-bearing andesites (basic andesite) with a silica content of 55 percent. Wilcox (1954) showed that the lava became progressively more acidic (i.e., containing a higher percentage of SiO_2) throughout the life of the volcano, with 1952 lavas containing 60 percent silica. In the first-year lavas a few phenocrysts (crystals which can be seen with the unaided eye or a simple land lens) of olivine and plagioclase occur in a fine ground mass. In later flows the plagioclase phenocrysts disappeared and the olivine phenocrysts became scarce. The lavas are classified as orthopyroxene andesites.

DISTRIBUTION OF PYROCLASTICS. This topic is discussed in Chapter 5 on "What Comes Out of a Volcano," pp. 48–50.

Geologic setting of Paricutin Volcano

The oldest rocks exposed in the region surrounding Parícutin Volcano are volcanics which Williams (1945, 1950) named the "Zumpinito" formation. These rocks are exposed in deep gorges and canyons where erosion has cut through the cover of recent volcanic material. The Zumpinito formation consists of a variety of material ranging from olivine-rich basalts to rhyolites. In some areas lava predominates while in others tuffaceous sediments are more abundant. No original volcanic forms are preserved, nor is it possible to locate any vents from which the material issued. The Zumpinito formation is usually flat-lying, except locally, as near Uruapan, where it is steeply tilted. Williams (1950) concludes that the formation must cover a considerable span of Tertiary time and that the topmost beds cannot be younger than middle Pliocene.

The oldest volcano of post-Zumpinito age in the area is the great volcanic mass of Cerros de Tancítaro, which lies immediately to the southwest of Parícutin Volcano. Rising to 3,845 meters, it is the highest peak in Michoacán and from a topographic standpoint dominates the region around Parícutin. Although Parícutin Volcano is at the base of Tancítaro, it is not a parasitic cone but belongs to a later period of activity. Williams (1950) describes Tancítaro Volcano as a shield-type cone which has been deeply dissected to the point that it now consists of a series of radiating, sharp-crested spurs separated by deep canyons. The lower part of the cone has been covered by ejecta from the younger volcanoes which dot the area. The eruptions which built Cerros de Tancítaro were the quiet, effusive type consisting largely of prophyritic andesite. The age of Tancítaro is undetermined, but it was formed upon the deeply eroded surface of the Zumpinito formation, and Williams (1950) concludes that the last eruptions of Tancítaro were either in late Pliocene or early Pleistocene time.

After the growth of the large andesitic volcanoes, such as Tancítaro, the centers of volcanic activity in the Parícutin region became more numerous, and the lavas ejected were dominantly olivine basalts and olivine-bearing basaltic andesites. These younger volcanoes, of which there are literally dozens in the general area, show little effects of erosion and certainly must be post glacial (Recent) in age. Parícutin Volcano belongs in this group and is unique only in the fact that it was the last one to have formed.

Jorullo Volcano

The volcano Jorullo was born on September 29, 1759, in the midst of an area that was being cultivated at the time. Alexander von Humboldt visited Jorullo in 1803 and was enchanted with the notion of having found in Jorullo an example of the crater-elevation theory of his good friend, Baron von Buch. Since Humboldt's time nearly every geologic textbook has used Jorullo either as an example of the crater-elevation theory or as evidence to disprove it. It is certainly one of the best known of the volcanoes born in historic time.

Location

Jorullo is located in western Mexico in the state of Michoacán, about 150 miles west of Mexico City and some 50 miles southeast of Parícutin Volcano (Fig. 43). It is on the Pacific slope of the Mexican plateau and in an area containing a number of young basaltic cones. The general elevation is about twenty-five hundred feet, and the climate is tropical. The region is relatively inaccessible but can be reached by a truck road south from Pátzcuaro, through Ario de Rosales to La Playa and La Huacana. The nearest settlements are La Playa, about 3 miles to the east of the cone, and La Huacana, about 7 miles to the southwest. La Playa contains the ruins of a once rather elaborate hacienda which the writer was fortunate in being able to use as headquarters on two trips to Jorullo.

At the time of the eruption the Hacienda de Jorullo was one of three farms operated in the general area for the production of sugar and cattle. Because of the fertility of the soil and the tropical climate, the area was known as Jorullo, which in the language of the Tarascan Indians means "Paradise."

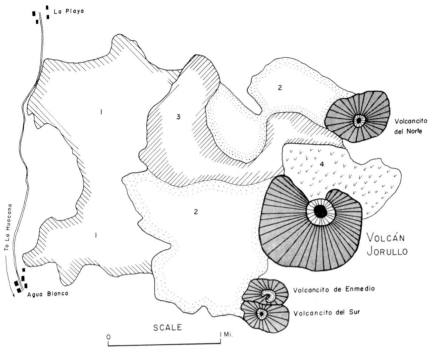

FIGURE 46. Sketch map of Volcán Jorullo and subsidiary cones. Lava flows are numbered from oldest (No. 1) to youngest (No. 4). After Ordóñez (1906).

Records of eruptive history

Accounts of the early stages of the eruption are contained in two diarylike reports by D. Manuel Roman Sáyago, administrator-in-chief of the haciendas, to the governor of Michoacán and through him to the viceroy of New Spain. Two other brief accounts by eyewitnesses, which unfortunately add little to Sáyago's reports, are contained in letters of Joaquin de Anzagorri, priest at La Huacana, to his bishop at Morelia and to the Abbé Clavigero, the latter published in Italian but later translated into Spanish and English. Other than the accounts mentioned, which cover only the first months, no records of the eruptive history of Jorullo by eyewitnesses have been found. The next account is a report by Antonio de Riaño, governor of Michoacán, who in company with Franz Fischer, a German mining expert, visited Jorullo in 1789, thirty years after the initial eruption. With information he could obtain from the natives Riaño attempted to reconstruct some of the details of the eruption. However, in the twenty-odd years which had elapsed and without any written records, many of the details he obtained were hazy and uncertain. The area surrounding the volcano was abandoned, and quite likely very few, if any, of the Indians had been close enough to see what was actually going on at the volcano.

Since Humboldt's visit in 1803 many geologists have visited Jorullo, although they have written comparatively little on it. An excursion of the Tenth International Geologic Congress, held in Mexico City in 1907, visited Jorullo. The guidebook for the excursion, written in French and prepared by Ezequiel Ordóñez with the help of Andres Villafaña, is still the standard reference on Jorullo. Dr. Hans Gadow, biologist from the University of Cambridge, visited Jorullo in 1908 in order to study the reintroduction of plants and animals to the region following their destruction by the eruption. Gadow's book, published posthumously in 1930, contains, in addition to information on the plant and animal life, an excellent review of the historical material on Jorullo, which the author has used freely in the preparation of this topic. The writer made two trips to Jorullo, one in 1945 and another in 1950.

Eruptions of Jorullo

Near the end of June, 1759, the people living at the Hacienda de Jorullo were alarmed by subterranean noises which, accompanied by mild earthquakes, continued until September 17. At this time the noises became much louder, being compared to cannon fire, and the earthquakes were strong enough to seriously damage the chapel. The frightened people fled to the surrounding hills for safety. There was a rumor that on St. Michael's Day, September 29, Jorullo would be destroyed. The administrator sent to Pátzcuaro for a priest to celebrate Mass in order to appease the divine ire. The priest arrived on September 20, and on the twenty-first he began a nine-day Mass, during which time the noises and earthquakes continued until the twenty-seventh, when there was a brief lull. At 3:00 A.M. on September 29, about a mile to

PLATE 31. Volcán Jorullo, Mexico. The last lava flow, which issued from the crater (No. 4, Fig. 46), is the dark mass on the left of the cone. Courtesy Dr. Donald Brand.

the southeast of the Hacienda in a ravine known as Cuitinga Creek, a very dark and dense steam cloud rose, accompanied by sharp earth tremors and loud explosions, and soon flames burst through the cloud, which was becoming thicker and denser. The terrified people gathered in the chapel. While Mass was being heard a rain of mud covered the roof and the ground, and as the tremendous explosions continued a strong odor of sulphur permeated the air. It seemed indeed that the predictions for St. Michael's Day were coming true! For two days the volcano threw out masses of "sand [cinders], fire and thunder without one minute cessation." On October 1 a mass of "sand so hot it set fire to whatever it fell upon" rose from the outlet of the volcano, which was little more than a cleft, and flowed for nearly a mile down Cuitinga Creek. The steam bed was filled for the first half mile, and as the water underneath was converted into steam it exploded in geyserlike eruptions at many places. All of the neighboring streams became flooded, and many of the domestic animals were drowned in trying to escape. The flood of water associated with the eruption is one of the controversial points in Administrator Sáyago's account. He mentions that the floods were produced "not only by the rain from the sky, but by springs which opened from all the hills around." In fact, the volume of water was so great that he feared "that all the valleys of Jorullo, the Presentación [another one of the farms five miles to the west of Jorullo], and the village of La Huacana may be turned into one big lake."

The heavy rains accompanying volcanic eruptions have been noted in many cases, and, also, the origin of floods of water which do not appear to be directly related to rains. It is interesting to note that the same problem is raised at Jorullo. It may be recalled, in this connection, that the outpouring of hot gases and the tremendous quantities of steam produce what is the equivalent of a thunderstorm, but unlike the customary thunderstorm which moves across the country, this one is stationary over the volcano.

By October 6 ash and cinders had destroyed the Presentación farm, as well as the village of La Huacana, two miles beyond, and the natives had fled to the neighboring hills. Administrator Sáyago makes special note of the fact that on October 8 began a new phase of activity, in which "the volcano threw up a great lot of stones which fell as far as half a league from its mouth, and which, as was found later on, were very soft and as if overbaked or glassy." This clearly indicates that the first scoria bombs were ejected at this time. Administrator Sáyago's first report ends with October 8, and his second and last report continues the account up to November 13.

From his second report we learn that "since this day [October 9] fell moreover great masses of rocks from the clouds, some of them as large as the body of an ox, which after having been shot up like a bullet, fell around the mouth of the volcano, and smaller pieces, thrown up higher, came down at longer distance and in such numbers that scattering in the cloud they looked in the daytime like a flock of crows and in the night like a crowd of stars."

On Friday, October 12, a new vent opened, six hundred yards from the main crater. This is one of the three satellite cones which are aligned in a general N-S direction with the main vent at Jorullo. The dates for the origin of the others are in doubt, but it is interesting to have confirmation on at least one of them.

The vigorous ash eruptions continued throughout the period covered by the second report, spreading destruction over a wide area in all directions from the volcano, and "the cattle could find nothing to eat, the trees and shrubs being destroyed and the leaves covered with ashes; and nothing to drink during all this time the water was rendered unfit by mud and sulphurous matter." Similar conditions were reported for a distance of ten to twelve leagues (thirty to forty miles) west of the volcano. This distance, however, seemed to be somewhat exaggerated.

No lava flows were reported from the volcano during the period covered by Sáyago's first report. From his second report we learn that the governor was interested in this particular aspect and that on November 13 (the last day covered by his report), "I went down [from the hills] for a new look at Jorullo to find out whether that pitch or lava has run, about which his Excellency has asked in particular." To which Administrator Sáyago, showing wisdom which all will envy, replied, "Please let his Excellency know in answer to his special question, that I neither have any knowledge of so-called lava, nor have I anyone to tell me what stuff it may be; but whatever it may be here does not run or flow."

Here Administrator Sáyago's diary ends with a note that the cone is now three hundred varas (820 feet) in height; that it began not from the top of a hill but in the deepest and level part of the Cuitinga Valley; and finally that no lives were lost in the eruption. It is certainly regretable that so accurate an observer as Sáyago could not have provided a complete record of the activity of Jorullo. However, since the land had been ruined for cultivation, he was ordered to move the inhabitants elsewhere, and we hear no more from him.

There are no written records covering the remainder of the active period of Jorullo. Oral tradition, compiled years later, indicates that violent eruptions continued until February, 1760, and with decreasing intensity until about 1775, making the total life of Jorullo's activity about fifteen years. The outpouring of lava consisted of at least four separate flows forming a great malpais which covered nine square kilometers to depths up to a hundred meters. They are believed to have appeared in 1764, considered to be the year of maximum activity. The first three flows are covered with ash and cinders, indicating that these materials were still being ejected after the outpourings of lava. However, the last flow, which issued from a breach on the north rim of the crater and flowed as a great cascade down the north side of the cone, is free of any ash or cinder cover. This "frozen" cascade of black lava is still quite "new" and "fresh" looking and is one of the striking features of Jorullo. It seems likely that this was the end of the explosive activity of the volcano and that thereafter it was in a fumarolic state. The three satellite cones, one on the north and two on the south of Jorullo, were present in 1766. It appears, therefore, that the general aspects of the eruption were completed during the first seven years of its activity and that only minor activity continued for the next eight years.

Posteruptive appearance

A reliable description of Jorullo, thirty years after the eruption began, is given by Antonio de Riaño, governor of Michoacán, who visited the volcano in 1789 in company with Franz Fischer, a German mining expert and Ramón Espelde, a local Spaniard who was living at La Playa. Espelde had made an ascent of Jorullo in 1780 and was familiar with the area. From Riaño's account it is learned that the "hill of the

volcano is bare and only here and there some small trees . . . and patches
of grass are beginning to take root." Also, that there were still numerous
fumaroles, especially from the "hornitos" on the lava flows, and on
"some spots the inner fire is strong enough to scorch the feet and one
cannot hold his hand to the holes of these chimneys on account of the
moist heat [steam]."

Riaño apparently was familiar with von Buch's crater-elevation
theory, probably through Franz Fischer, and he points out that "on the
day of the frightful event it was observed that the surface of the ground
rose perpendicularly, more or less bulging up and forming huge bladders, the largest of which is today the hill of the volcano. These swell-
ings, big bladders or cones of various sizes and shapes, burst and threw
out of their mouths boiling mud . . . and stones."

Alexander von Humboldt[3] spent two days at Jorullo on September
18 and 19, 1803, forty-four years after the initial eruption. He had
Riaño's description, published in 1789, and he was accompanied by
Ramón Espelde, who had also accompanied Riaño. Humboldt was an
enthusiastic supporter of von Buch's crater-elevation theory, and he was
so eager to find support for it at Jorullo that he was unable to see any
other possibility. Humboldt described the malpais, an area of nine
square kilometers, which he did not recognize as a lava flow, as rising
like a bladder:

the original limits of this elevation may still be recognized by broken strata
at the edge . . . the convexity of the elevated area increases progressively
towards the center to a height of 160 meters. . . . In the middle of the
pushed up area, on a crack running NNE to SSW came six large hills, all
elevated from 400 to 500 meters above the ancient plain.

The writer, along with Ordóñez and others, was able to count only
three satellite cones in addition to the main cone of Jorullo; so Humboldt has included two additional ones. It seems incredible that von
Humboldt did not recognize the true nature of the malpais as a lava
flow, since its nature is so apparent. As late as 1848, after Lyell, Scrope,

[3] A. von Humboldt, Essai politique sur le royaume de la Nouvelle-Espagne;
also, Essai geognostique sur le gisement des roches. A more complete account is
found in his Kosmos, Book 4.

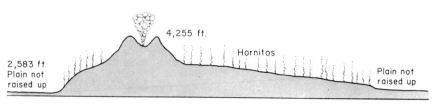

FIGURE 47. Section of Volcán Jorullo and malpais, as interpreted by Daubeny (1848).

and others had shown conclusively that volcanic cones were the result of accumulation of ejected material, Daubeny, in an exhaustive work on volcanoes (1848, p. 480), follows Humboldt and thus describes Jorullo: "a tract of ground from three to four square miles in extent rose up in the shape of a bladder." He includes a sketch (Fig. 47) to show the nature of the phenomenon. Daubeny, in a footnote, recognizes that "Mr. Lyell and Mr. Paulett Scrope and others have questioned the correctness of the representation which Humboldt has given of the above phenomena, but without, as I conceive, being able to substitute a more plausible hypothesis."

On the surface of the malpais at Jorullo were numerous small dome-like protuberances from which hot gases escaped. These are known as "hornitos" from the Spanish word for "little oven." Although somewhat of a mystery at Jorullo, they have since been observed on many active lava flows and are now a commonplace feature. At the time of Humboldt's visit to Jorullo many of the hornitos were still giving off hot gases to the extent that the air temperature over the malpais was somewhat higher than that of the surrounding area. However, when Burkart visited Jorullo in 1827 he found only a few of the hornitos on the malpais giving off any heat, although there were numerous steam vents in the crater. When Schleiden visited Jorullo in 1846 he noted that there were only two fumaroles on the malpais proper, but he counted more than a hundred at other places, mostly at the southern edge of the lava flow which cascaded from the crater and from the crater rim.

The most recent material published on Jorullo is a brief note contained in a report on erosion studies at Parícutin Volcano by Segerstrom (1950). A topographic map was made of the immediate area, and this map, which is probably the first accurate map of the volcano, is an important part of the report. The maximum height of Jorullo is 1,330 meters, although the average elevation of the crater rim is 1,300 meters. The cone rises 380 meters above its west base and 230 meters above its east base. The crater is an oval-shaped depression with a diameter at the rim of 400 meters by 500 meters. Its depth is 150 meters below the highest point, or about 120 meters below the average rim level. The bottom of the crater appears to have collapsed since its last eruptive activity, and the bottom is filled with rubble which has fallen from the sides. On the northwestern side of the crater, a little nearer the rim than the bottom, there is an area of perhaps one-half acre of "hot rocks." This area, which has been exposed by avalanching from the crater walls, contains a series of fissures a foot or more in width and parallel to the rim of the crater. They appear to have been caused by the collapse of the crater floor. These fissures are filled with rubble through which the hot gases rise. The rubble is oxidized to a red color and encrusted in many places with deposits of green ferrous chloride and white ammonium chloride. Some of the vents give off steam, but others emit what appears to be only heated air. In some spots there is a disagreeable odor of chlorine. At a depth of a foot or so below the rubble the heat was too intense for the hand but not sufficient to brown a piece of paper or to make water "hiss." However, the fact that Jorullo is continuing to give off heat as well as gases after two hundred years is in itself remarkable.

The cone of Jorullo is covered with trees, some of which are large enough that they have been cut for lumber. Several large trees grow in the lowest part of the crater. The malpais is also covered with vegetation, except that the last flow, which cascades from the crater, remains "new" in appearance and is barren of vegetation. In the short period of two hundred years Jorullo has taken on the appearance of the other cinder cones in the surrounding area, for which there are no records of any historic activity.

Monte Nuovo

A well-known "new volcano" of historic time was born on September 28, 1538, near Pozzuoli, a port on the Bay of Baia, about six miles west of Naples, Italy, in the Phlegraean Fields. Named "Monte Nuovo" (New Mountain), it is partly on the site of Lake Lucrine, famous resort during the time of the Roman Empire.

The Phlegraean Fields

The Phlegraean Fields, a unique volcanic area,[4] contains nineteen separate craters concentrated in an area of about twenty-five square miles. The craters are so closely spaced that in a number of cases they overlap, the older cone being partly destroyed when the younger one formed. Although the volcanic activity in the Phlegraean Fields is older than that at Vesuvius, it appears to have been dormant throughout historic time with the exception of an eruption of Solfatara Volcano in 1198 and the eruption of Monte Nuovo in 1538. However, gaseous emanations from several of the craters, as well as numerous hot springs, clearly indicate that the volcanic forces are not exhausted. Several of the craters in the Phlegraean Fields contain beautiful lakes, of which Lake Avernus is perhaps the best known because of its connection with classical mythology.

Birth of the Volcano

Knowledge of the 1538 eruption of Monte Nuovo is based on four separate accounts contained in letters of eyewitnesses of the event. From these letters, parts of which are reproduced below, some helpful facts have been established.

For two years prior to the outbreak the region was disturbed by earthquakes which reached a climax in September, 1538. On September 27 and 28 the shocks were said to have been felt almost continuously day and night. About 8:00 A.M. on September 29 a depression of the ground occurred, and from this depression water began to issue, at first cold and later tepid. Four hours later the ground was seen to swell up and open, forming a gaping fissure within which incandescent matter

---

[4] Described elsewhere in this work. See Chapter 8.

was visible. From this fissure numerous masses of stones, some of them "as large as an ox," with vast quantities of pumice and mud, were thrown to a great height, and these, falling upon the sides of the opening, formed a mound. This violent ejection of material, continuing for two days and nights, by the third day had formed a cone of considerable size. Since some of the eyewitnesses at this time climbed the cone, we may assume that there was a lull in activity. When the eruptions continued the next day many persons who had ventured onto the hill were injured, and several were killed by falling stones. Thereafter the eruptions decreased in violence, ceasing on the seventh or eighth day after the outbreak. Thus the greater bulk of Monte Nuovo was ejected during the first two days.

Monte Nuovo is a cone, rising 440 feet above the shore, with a cup-shaped crater, the bottom of which is only 19 feet above the level of the sea. It is composed entirely of ash, lapilli, and scoria, and differs in no way from the other cones in the Phlegraean Fields, except that it came into existence much later. The cone, which is about one and one-half miles in circumference at its base, stands partly on the site of Lake Lucrine. Lake Lucrine, occupying the breached crater of an old volcano adjoining the Bay of Baia, was a favorite resort during the period of the Roman Empire, and its shores were lined with fashionable villas, among which was one belonging to Cicero. The superior flavor of the oysters obtained from the Lake was another of its attractions. At this time, as today, it was separated from the Mediterranean by a narrow bar. By means of a canal the lake was accessible as a protected anchorage for the galleys of the Roman fleet. The building of the cone of Monte Nuovo largely filled Lake Lucrine, leaving only a narrow segment of the original Lake.

Significance of the record of the eruption

The historical record of the birth of Monte Nuovo is of more importance than the mere story of the origin of a new volcano. It will be recalled from the discussion of the development of the science of volcanology (Chapter 3) that during the close of the eighteenth century and the early part of the nineteenth geologists developed a heated con-

troversy as to the manner in which volcanic cones were formed, a dispute between supporters of Baron von Buch's craters-of-elevation theory,
which held that volcanic cones were formed by upheaval, like a blister
on the earth's surface, and supporters of the opposing idea, ably advocated by Charles Lyell, which held that the cones were the result of the
accumulation of ejected material. Today it seems strange that the
crater-elevation theory would have been taken seriously, but it was the
widely held orthodox view of the time. The controversy was centered
in Western Europe, where the science of geology developed; and since
Monte Nuovo was the only "new" volcano in this region, it is quite natural that each side would seek to find in the origin of Monte Nuovo
evidence to support its views. As a result, the records were carefully
searched for any eyewitness accounts which might throw light on the
problem.

Fortunately, Sir William Hamilton, English ambassador to the Court
of Naples for thirty-six years (1764–1800), was an ardent student of
volcanoes and fully aware of the controversy. Through his efforts two
narrative accounts of the birth of Monte Nuovo by contemporary wit-
nesses of credit were discovered and preserved. These accounts, consisting of two letters written a few months after the event, were bound
in a volume, with Hamilton's translation, and presented to the British
Museum. The first letter was an account by Marco Antonio delli Falconi, and the second was a report by Pietro Giacomo di Toledo. Two
other accounts of the eruption have been preserved. One, by Simon
Porizo, an eminent physician and Neapolitan scholar, is contained in a
letter to the viceroy of Naples, Don Pedro di Toledo. This was published, along with other writings by S. Porzio, in 1551. An English
translation was first published by Lobley (1889). A fourth manuscript,
written immediately after the eruption by Francesco del Nero, was discovered in 1846 and published in German. An English translation was
published in 1847.[5]

Because of the historical interest surrounding these letters, as well as
the colorful descriptions of the eruption which they afford, several ex-
cerpts are included here.

[5] Quarterly Journal Geol. Soc. for 1847, Vol. 3, p. 20.

LETTER BY MARCO ANTONIO DELLI FALCONI. From this letter[6] the following is extracted:

It is now two years that there have been frequent earthquakes at Pozzuoli, Naples, and the neighboring ports; on the day and in the night preceding the eruption above 20 shocks, great and small, were felt at the above mentioned places. The eruption made its appearance on the 29th of September, 1538; . . . it was on a Sunday, about an hour in the night; and I have been informed they began on that spot between the hot baths . . . and Tripergola . . . in a short time the fire increased to such a degree that it burst open the earth at this place, and threw up so great a quantity of ashes and pumice stone mixed with water as covered the whole country; and in Naples a shower of these ashes and water fell the greater part of the night.

Next morning, which was Monday, the poor inhabitants of Pozzuoli, struck with so horrible a sight, quitted their habitations . . . some with children in their arms, some with sacks full of goods; . . . others carrying quantities of birds that had fallen dead at the time the eruption began, others with fish that they had found, and were to meet with in plenty upon the shore, the sea having been at that time considerably dried up. . . . The sea towards Baia had retired a considerable way, although from the quantity of ashes and broken pumice stone thrown up by the eruption it appeared almost dry. . . . Turning towards the place of the eruption, you saw mountains of smoke, part of which was very black and part very white, rising up to a great height; and in the midst of the smoke, at times, deep colored flames burst forth with huge stones and ashes, and you heard a noise like the discharge of a number of artillery. . . . After the stones and ashes, with clouds of thick smoke, had been sent up by the impulse of the fire and windy exhalations into the middle region of the air, overcome by their own natural weight, . . . you saw them fall, . . . raining ashes with water and stones of different sizes according to the distance from the place; then by degrees with the same noise and smoke it threw out stones and ashes again, and so on by fits this continued two days and nights, when the smoke and the force of the fire began to abate. The fourth day, which was Thursday, at 22 o'clock there was so great an eruption . . . and the quantity of ashes and stones and smoke seemed as if they would cover the whole earth and sea. . . .

[6] From Sir William Hamilton's translation, as quoted by J. Phillips (1868), Vesuvius, p. 220.

Then Friday and Saturday nothing but a little smoke appeared; so many taking courage went upon the spot, and say that with the ashes and stones thrown up a mountain has been formed; . . . a thing almost incredible to those who have not seen it, that in so short a time so considerable a mountain could have been formed. On its summit there is a mouth in the form of a cup, which may be a quarter of a mile in circumference. . . .

The Sunday following which was the 6th of October, many people going to see the performance, and some having ascended half the mountain, others more, about 22 o'clock there happened so great and horrible eruption with so great a smoke, that many of the people were stifled, some of which could never be found. I have been told that the number of the dead or lost amounted to 24. . . .

LETTER BY PIETRO GIACOMO DI TOLEDO. From this letter[7] the following is extracted:

It is now more than two years that the province of Campagna has been afflicted with earthquakes, the country about Pozzuoli much more than any other parts; but the 27th and 28th of the month of September, last, the earthquakes did not cease day or night, in the above mentioned city of Pozzuoli. . . . At last, on the 29th . . . about two hours in the night the earth opened near the lake and discovered a horrid mouth, from which was vomited, furiously, smoke, fire, stones, and mud composed of ashes; making at the time of its opening a noise like loud thunder. The fire that issued from the mouth went towards the walls of the unfortunate city; the smoke was partly black and partly white, . . . the stones that followed were by the devouring flames converted to pumice, the size of which (of some I say) were much larger than an ox.

The stones went about as high as a cross bow can carry, and then fell down, sometimes on the edge, sometimes in the mouth itself. . . . The mud was of the color of ashes, and at first very liquid, then by degrees less so; and in such quantity that in less than 12 hours, with the help of the above mentioned stones, a mountain was raised of 1000 paces height. . . .

Now this eruption lasted two days and two nights without intermission, though, it is true, not always with the same force, but more or less; when it was at its greatest height, even at Naples you heard a noise like heavy

[7] Sir William Hamilton's translation, as quoted by J. Phillips (1868), Vesuvius, p. 225.

artillery when two armies are engaged. The third day the eruption ceased, so that the mountain made its appearance uncovered, to the no small astonishment of everyone who saw it. On this day I went up with many people to the top of the mountain, I saw down into its mouth, which was a round concavity about one-fourth mile in circumference [at present about one-fourth mile in diameter] in the middle of which the stones that had fallen were boiling up, just as in a great cauldron of water that boils on the fire. The fourth day it began to throw up again, and the 7th much more, but still with less violence than on the first night. It was at this time that many people who were unfortunately on the mountain were either suddenly covered with ashes, smothered with smoke, or knocked down by stones, burnt by flame, and left dead on the spot. The smoke continues to this day, and you often see in the night time fire in the midst of it. . . .

LETTER OF FRANCESCO DEL NERO. Del Nero mentions the drying up of the bed of the sea near Pozzuoli, which enabled the inhabitants of the town to carry away loads of fish. He then continues:

At about 8:00 in the morning of the 29th of September the earth sank down about 14 feet in that place where the volcanic orifice now appears. . . . At noon on the same day the earth began to swell up in the spot where it had sunk down 14 feet, so as to form a hill. About this time fire issued forth . . . and I, who was standing in my garden, was seized with terror. Forty minutes afterwards, although unwell, I got upon a neighboring height, from which I saw all that took place, and by my troth it was a splendid fire that threw up a long time much earth and many stones which fell back again all around the gulf, in a semi-circle of from one to three bow-shots in diameter, and, filling up part of the sea, formed a hill nearly of the height of Monte Morello. Masses of earth and stone, as large as an ox, were shot up from the fiery gulf into the air to a height which I estimate at a mile and a half. When they descended, some were dry, others in a soft muddy state. . . .

Notwithstanding this overwhelming testimony in support of the craters-of-accumulation theory, Baron von Buch and others continued to hold to the crater-of-elevation explanation, even for Monte Nuovo. Lyell (1875, Vol. 1, p. 611), in reviewing the problem, quotes von Buch who in 1836 wrote as follows:

It is an error to imagine that this hill was formed by eruption, or by ejection of pumice, scoria, and other incoherent matter; for the solid beds of upraised tuff are visible all around the crater, and it is merely the superficial covering of the cone which is made up of ejected scoria.

Since this natal eruption, Monte Nuovo has not renewed activity, and today, clothed with vegetation, it is indistinguishable from the prehistoric craters in the Phlegraean Fields.

Submarine Eruptions and "New" Island Volcanoes

Extent of submarine volcanic action

With three-fourths of the earth's surface beneath the sea, it is apparent that submarine eruptions must constitute an important part of the earth's volcanism. The average depth of the oceans is about 13,000 feet, and submarine eruptions of lava and fragmental products must have taken place on a stupendous scale in order to build up from the ocean depth foundations of the numerous large volcanic islands. In the Hawaiian Islands, for example, volcanic outpourings not only reach sea level but have piled up material to a height (Mauna Loa) of more than 13,000 feet above sea level! Eruptions of this type are characterized by basaltic (basic) lavas, and the activity must continue for many thousands of years to produce the extensive archipelagoes such as those of Hawaii, Samoa, and Tonga, to name only a few Pacific examples.

Unless the submarine eruption piles up enough material to form an island, the chances of a passing vessel's notice of it are remote. Nevertheless, spots in the sea where the water was discolored and boiling violently, or jets of water and steam erupting from the sea, have been reported from time to time by the crews of passing vessels. Those which erupt basaltic material form cones of scoria and cinders; while those erupting more acid lavas usually have a domelike core of lava. With both types the "new" islands are very susceptible to wave erosion and are frequently destroyed.

A few of the "new" island volcanoes formed by submarine eruptions are described in the following paragraphs.

Graham Island[8]

The most noted of the several submarine eruptions in the Mediterranean occurred in 1831 when a new island, named Graham Island, was formed in water which, according to a survey made a few years earlier, was six hundred feet deep. Graham Island was located about thirty miles southwest of Sciacca, Sicily, or about midway between the port of Sciacca and the island of Pantelleria, sixty miles to the southwest (Fig. 22). The island of Pantelleria, although of volcanic origin, has had no eruptions in historic times.

On June 28, 1831, about two weeks before the eruption was visible, Sir Pulteney Malcolm reported that in passing over the spot in his ship he felt the shock of an earthquake as if his ship had struck a sandbank. At the same time shocks were felt on the west coast of Sicily. On July 10 the captain of a Sicilian vessel, enroute to Agrigento, Sicily, reported that as he passed the place he saw a column of water sixty feet high and eight hundred yards in circumference rising from the sea like a waterspout, followed by dense steam clouds which rose to a height of eighteen hundred feet. On his return trip from Agrigento on July 18 he found a small island, twelve feet high, with a crater from which was being ejected volcanic debris and a huge column of vapor, the sea around being covered with floating cinders and dead fish. He reported the scoria as being of a chocolate color and the water which boiled in the circular basin as a dingy red. The eruption continued with great violence to the end of July, at which time it was visited by several persons, including the German geologist, M. Hoffman. At this time the island was 50 to 90 feet high and three-fourths of a mile in circumference. By August 4 it had reached a height of 200 feet and was three miles in circumference. This was its greatest height, and thereafter it began to diminish in size. By September 3, when carefully measured by Captain Wodehouse, it was only three-fifths of a mile in circumference, and its greatest height was 107 feet.

During the month of August violent agitation of the water on the

[8] A summary of published accounts of the formation of Graham Island is given in Lyell's Principles of Geology, Vol. 2, p. 58.

southwest side of the new island emitted columns of dense white steam, indicating the existence of a second vent, which never reached the level of the sea. Near the end of October the cone had been destroyed by wave action, leaving only a small mound of scoria to mark the site. Two years later no surface vestige of the island remained, but sounding revealed that the center of the cone was marked by a large rocky mass surrounded by loose cinders some eleven feet below sea level and about two hundred feet in diameter. At a distance of about one hundred yards from the rocky mass the depth of the water increased sharply. This rocky mass doubtless was composed of lava which had solidified in the throat of the volcano. If such a remnant were exposed on land it would be a "volcanic neck."

With a height of eight hundred feet at the peak of its growth, three-fourths of which was below sea level, Graham Island was roughly comparable in size to many of the cinder cones found in volcanic regions throughout the world. Graham Island attained its maximum height in about two months, a rate of accumulation similar to that of Parícutin Volcano, which attained a height of about one thousand feet by the end of the second month. A remarkable feature in the record of Graham Island is the short time required for wave action to destroy the exposed portion. The material ejected at Graham Island was basaltic scoria and cinders.

The Azores

These islands, in the mid-Atlantic ocean about twelve hundred miles due west of Lisbon, Portugal, are volcanoes superimposed on the Mid-Atlantic Ridge (p. 246), as are the volcanoes of Iceland. The main structural trend of faulting in the Azores is west-northwest (Agostinho, 1936, p. 124), crossing the trend of the Mid-Atlantic Ridge at a high angle. Thus, as has been noted in other volcanic areas of the world, the intersection of two lines of fissures appears to have determined the location of the volcanic vents. Each of the nine major islands making up the Azores (Fig. 48) is composed of one or more "shield-type" cones with a caldera at the summit. An exception is the symmetrical cone of Pico Volcano, on Pico Island, which has a steep-sided, symmetrical cone.

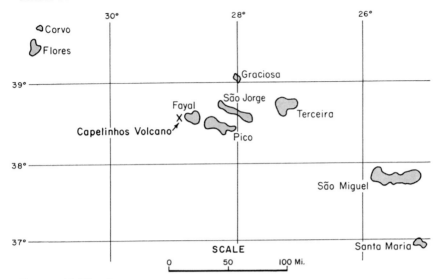

FIGURE 48. The Azores.

Volcanic eruptions have occurred on five of the islands in historic time, with several additional submarine eruptions in the waters surrounding the islands. In 1638, and again in 1811, submarine eruptions near the eastern end of the group formed weak ash and cinder cones which were soon destroyed by wave erosion. The eruption of 1811 formed Sabrina Island, off the coast of São Miguel, in the eastern Azores. It consisted of loose cinders and attained a height of three hundred feet above sea level with a circumference of about one mile. The eruption lasted eight days, but soon thereafter Sabrina was destroyed by wave erosion.

Capelinhos Volcano, Fayal Island

Fayal Island, twelve miles long by eight miles wide, is the top of a large volcano which rises out of the sea to a height of 3,351 feet. Its slopes are gentle, as is typical of Hawaiian-type volcanoes, and at the summit is a caldera about one and one-half miles in diameter and one thousand feet deep. The volcano on Fayal is known as "Caldeira,"[9] from

[9] A Portuguese word for a kettle or a cauldron. The term *caldera,* as used in geology, was adopted from the Portuguese. See p. 72.

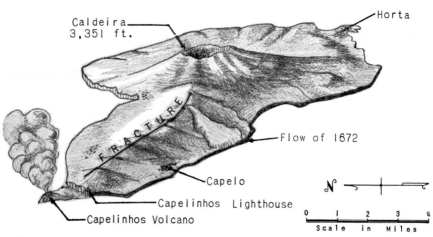

FIGURE 49. Fayal Island, Azores.
Based on Scofield (1958) and Parsons and Mulford (1958).

the huge depression at the summit, which is an example of a caldera as used in volcanology. A line of cinder cones almost due west from the summit caldera to the sea marks the location of a fracture along which repeated volcanic eruptions have occurred in recent geologic time. In 1672 an eruption occurred near the middle of this fracture and lava flows poured into the sea. The new volcano, Capelinhos, came up offshore at the western end of this same fracture (Fig. 49). The events leading up to the submarine outbreak and the early stages of the eruption are described by Richey (1957) in an article in the London *Times Science Review,* on which the following account is based.

From September 16 to 27 earthquakes were felt with increasing frequency near the rocks of Capelinhos, off the western end of Fayal, but they were not of great violence. On September 27 at about 8:00 A.M. the first signs of the eruption were observed on the surface of the sea. The water was boiling at the site; intermittent vapor clouds were observed near the surface of the sea; and the water was discolored or muddy for a half mile or more surrounding the area. On September 29, about 2:00 A.M., explosions began. Cinders were thrown 300 feet or more above the sea, and an eruption cloud rose to more than a mile, but the fall of cinders was not remarkable. During the next few days activity increased, and on October 1 cinders were thrown to 2,000 feet, and the eruption cloud attained a height of 20,000 feet. On the following day the eruption was particularly violent, and cinders fell over a radius of a few miles out to sea. An islet now began to form around the crater. After October 3 the explosions continued to be violent but were less frequent. On October 7 the cone-shaped island was reported to be 200 feet high and 700 yards in diameter, but already its exposed side, to the northwest, was beginning to be destroyed by waves. On October 11 the island was 330 feet high and 800 yards in diameter. It was a horseshoe-shaped cone with the opening to the southwest. The sea flooded the crater through this opening so that the actual vent of the volcano was under water, and for this reason the explosions were extremely violent and the new lava was disrupted into ash and cinders. Explosions continued through October 15, but at the same time the size of the island was being reduced by wave erosion. In the following week the island was cut into two parts, and on the morning of October 30 no portion of either part was visible above the level of the sea. It appeared that the waves had won in the struggle.

However, in early November explosive eruptions were renewed and a second cone was constructed. By mid-November this cone was tied to Fayal Island by a narrow bar of black ash. Explosive eruptions continued throughout the winter of 1957–1958, and by the end of March, 1958, the volcano had built a broad peninsula at the western end of Fayal Island, adding more than a square mile of land area to the island (Scofield, 1958). In April a small lava flow issued from the base of the cone on the seaward side and flowed almost immediately into the sea. Other flows of this type occurred in May and June. On May 14, 1958, scores of severe earthquakes occurred along the fracture zone which connects Capelinhos Volcano with the main caldera at the summit of the Island. It appeared likely that lava was moving underground along the fracture and that there might be an outbreak in the summit caldera. Actually on the floor of the caldera did appear a small fracture, from which eruptions of ash reached a height of 1,000 feet, but no other activity resulted. In July, 1958 (Parsons and Mulford, 1958) the volcano consisted of a broad horseshoe-shaped cinder-cone ring about one-half mile in diameter and, at its highest point, 500 feet above sea level. A typical cinder cone formed on a land surface rises steeply with a rather small crater at the top. However, when such eruptions rise through water, the resulting explosions, due to the meeting of the cold water and the hot lava, pile up the cinders and ash in a wide ring around a large explosion crater. Such cones are sometimes referred to as *phreatic*[10] cones. Diamond Head, a well-known landmark in Honolulu, is an example of such a cone. Inside the phreatic cone of Capelinhos a steep cone of cinders and lava spatter rose 150 to 200 feet. With the vent protected from the sea, showers of incandescent lava were periodically thrown into the air from the inner vent. These Strombolian-type eruptions continued intermittently through the summer of 1958.

Falcon Island[11]

In 1867 a shoal was reported to have developed in the South Pacific thirty miles to the west of Nomuka Island in the Tongas. Ten years later smoke was observed rising from the spot, and in 1885 a volcanic island, named Falcon Island, rose from the sea during a submarine eruption which began on October 14. It was later reported by a passing steamer to be two miles long and 250 feet high. It steadily diminished in size until in the fall of 1892 it was only 25 feet high. By 1898 it had disappeared altogether, leaving only a shoal to mark the site. The composition of the material of Falcon Island is a basic augite-andesite.

Noyöe Volcano[12]

In the early summer of 1783 a new island was formed by a submarine eruption 30 miles southwest from Cape Reykjanes on the west coast of Iceland. It was reported that so much pumice was ejected that it covered the sea for a distance of 150 miles, greatly impeding the progress of ships in the area. The new island, claimed by the Danish government and named Noyöe (or "New"), was destroyed by wave action in less than a year, leaving a submerged reef 5 to 30 fathoms below sea level. The disastrous outbreak of Skaptar Jökull, (Chapter 11)

---

[10] *Phreatic* is the Greek word for "a well" but is also applied to ground water accessible by drilling. A phreatic eruption, as used in volcanology, is an explosion resulting from the mixing of volcanic gases or magma with ground water.

[11] A. Geikie, Textbook of Geology, Vol. 1, p. 334.

[12] C. Lyell, Principles of Geology, Vol. 2, p. 49.

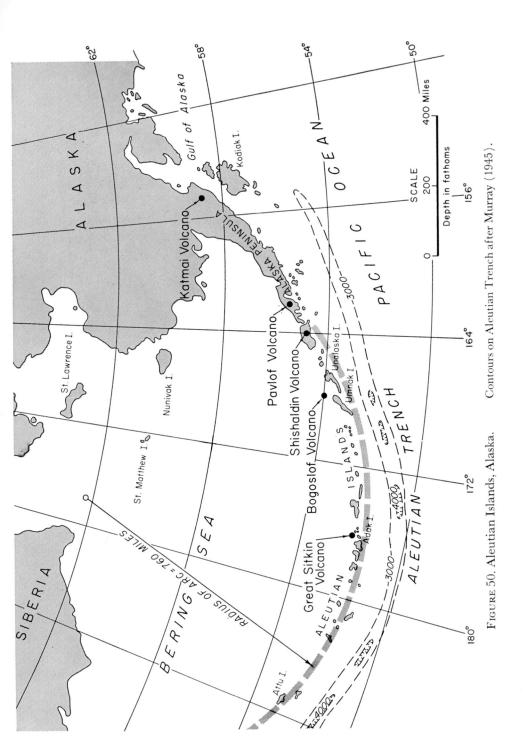

FIGURE 50. Aleutian Islands, Alaska.   Contours on Aleutian Trench after Murray (1945).

located about 200 miles to the east of the submarine vent on the mainland of Iceland, began about a month after this eruption.

Bogoslof Volcano

The most famous volcano in the Aleutian Islands of Alaska is the "disappearing" island of Bogoslof, which has appeared and disappeared several times since it was first sighted in 1768.

Bogoslof is the top of a nearly submerged volcano which rises about six thousand feet above the ocean floor. The strange antics of this volcano are caused by eruptions which form islands that are promptly destroyed by wave erosion or shattered by explosive activity.

Bogoslof Volcano is located about midway in the Aleutian chain of islands, which extends for fifteen hundred miles in a broad arc westward from the mainland of Alaska (Fig. 50). About seventy-six major volcanoes are located in this arc, thirty-six of which have been active since 1760, the date of first historic records in this area. Lying to the south of the Aleutian arc is the Aleutian Trench, a deep furrow in the ocean floor with depths in excess of twenty thousand feet. This typical "island arc" structure, consisting of a deep trough on the ocean floor with an arc-shaped chain of islands surmounted by active volcanoes on the continentward side, is a feature characteristic of the margins of the Pacific Ocean. The origin of "island arcs" is discussed in Chapter 15.

About forty miles north of Umnak Island in the Aleutians some rocky pinnacles rise from the ocean in water that on either side drops off to around six thousand feet in depth. These rocks are sometimes connected to form a single island, and at other times they are separated by a channel. This is Bogoslof Volcano. The rocky pinnacles are stiff lava domes which are being squeezed up in the crater of the volcano. The domes are rapidly eroded by vigorous wave action or destroyed by explosions from within the dome. However, new lava domes rise from time to time at other points within the crater. Thus the reports of the disappearance of an island and the appearance of a new one are entirely justified.

The first of the rocky spines which constitute Bogoslof Volcano was reported in 1768 by early navigators who named it "Ship Rock." In 1796 a second peak, called "Castle Rock" rose to the southeast of Ship

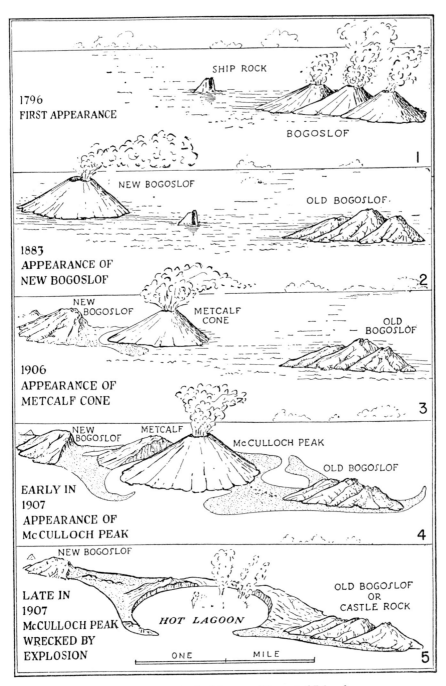

1796
FIRST APPEARANCE

SHIP ROCK

BOGOSLOF

1

1883
APPEARANCE OF
NEW BOGOSLOF

NEW BOGOSLOF

OLD BOGOSLOF

2

1906
APPEARANCE OF
METCALF CONE

NEW
BOGOSLOF

METCALF
CONE

OLD
BOGOSLOF

3

EARLY IN
1907
APPEARANCE OF
McCULLOCH PEAK

NEW
BOGOSLOF

METCALF

McCULLOCH PEAK

OLD BOGOSLOF

4

LATE IN
1907
McCULLOCH PEAK
WRECKED BY
EXPLOSION

NEW BOGOSLOF

HOT LAGOON

OLD BOGOSLOF
OR
CASTLE ROCK

ONE   MILE

5

FIGURE 51. Successive events in the history of Bogoslof Island.
Reproduced by permission from Lobeck's Geomorphology, 1st ed., copyright 1939,
McGraw-Hill Book Company, Inc.

Rock, accompanied by explosions which alarmed the natives on Una-laska Island, fifty miles to the east. When surveyed in 1826, Castle Rock was two miles long, three-fourths of a mile wide and 340 feet high. In 1883 a huge tabular mass of lava rose from the sea more than a mile to the northwest of Castle Rock. This new lava protrusion was named "Grewingk," but more commonly was known as "New Bogos-lof." The bombs and debris from the eruption, added to the products of wave erosion, formed a bar which joined Ship Rock and Castle Rock with the new mass to form a single, elongate island (Fig. 51). A few years later wave erosion had opened a channel, again dividing the mass into two islands.

Two new domes appeared in 1906 and 1907 in the lagoon separat-ing the two older masses. The first of these, Metcalf Cone, four hundred feet high, was a conical mound of talus surrounding a spine of rock, while the other, McCulloch Peak, five hundred feet high, was a typical lava dome (tholoid). However, half of Metcalf Cone was blown away by an explosion before McCulloch dome arose (Fig. 51). Jaggar[13] (1945, p. 83) describes Bogoslof at this time as follows:

> Bogoslof was now [1907] a continuous island 2 miles long, the two active cones were 400 feet and 500 feet high, McCulloch Peak was three-fourths surrounded by steaming salt water at 90° F; it looked like a huge lumpy potato . . . September 1, 1907 a dense black cloud rose from Bogoslof, ash fell at Unalaska mantling everything a quarter inch deep, and there were rain, lightning and distant rumblings. McCulloch Peak had blown itself up. A steaming lagoon was left in its place, the rest of the island was piled high with fallen debris . . . There appeared to be a rhythmic sequence to the events whereby Metcalf Cone built itself up 400 feet high and 2000 feet across, lived 10 months and exploded, then McCulloch Cone was built up 450 feet high and 2000 feet across, lived 10 months and was destroyed. (Fig. 51).

Explosions, erosion, and the occasional appearance of new island lava domes in the lagoon continued to be the pattern for Bogoslof. Eruptions occurred in 1910, 1926, and 1931 but of these only the 1926 eruption gave rise to a new dome. As in previous years, explosions and wave erosion constantly altered the appearance of the islands.

[13] T. A. Jaggar, Volcanoes Declare War, p. 83.

The process of dome formation in the crater of a volcano may be an indication that its eruptive activity is coming to an end. Whether the life of Bogoslof is being prolonged because of its sea-level position, which permits wave erosion to destroy the domes, is, of course, unknown. This seems improbable, however, since the domes are frequently removed by explosive action quite independent of wave erosion.

Myozin-syo Volcano

On September 17, 1952, a Japanese fishing boat, the *Myozin-maru No. 11,* radioed that they had sighted a submarine volcanic eruption at a point about 420 kilometers south of Tokyo. A Maritime Safety Board boat was immediately dispatched to check the exact location. On reaching the site, they found that the eruptions had formed a small island, estimated to be about 150 meters in diameter and 30 meters above sea level. The volcano was erupting every few seconds, throwing out incandescent bombs and ash and a great cloud of gases. It was named the "Myozin-syo,"[14] after the fishing boat which had first reported it. Shortly, however, the eruption pattern changed. The paroxysmal eruptions became more intense but spaced at greater intervals. The small cone was, of course, endangered by wave erosion. With a marked reduction in the amount of new material being ejected and the destructive effects of the strong explosions, the small island vanished from sight on September 21 or 22, only about one week after its birth. However, violent submarine eruptions two or three times a day continued through September and thereafter at longer intervals.

The volcano was in this state of activity when a number of scientists, aboard two ships, went to investigate the eruption. One of the ships was the *Sinyo-maru,* a training ship of the Tokyo Fisheries University; the other was the *Kaiyo-maru No. 5,* from the Hydrographic Office. The *Sinyo-maru* left on September 21 and arrived at the scene in time to observe on September 22 and 23 extraordinary submarine eruptions at close range, but still from a safe distance. The *Kaiyo-maru,* which arrived at the scene on September 24, was apparently directly over the vent when an eruption occurred, and the vessel with its crew

[14] Takeshi Minakami, Report on Volcanic Activities and Volcanological Studies in Japan for the Period from 1951 to 1954, pp. 39–55.

PLATE 32. Submarine eruption of Myozin-syo Volcano on September 23, 1952.   Courtesy Dr. Takeshi Minakami and Asahi Press.

of twenty-two and its seven scientists vanished in the swirling waters. This fantastic catastrophe, although understandable, is believed to have been the first one of this nature on record. Although there were no eye-witnesses to the tragedy, it was established that a strong eruption occurred at 12:30 P.M. on September 24, at which time the vessel was at the site of the volcano. Submarine eruptions produce waves (tsunami) which are recorded on tidal gauges over a wide area, and a study of the tidal-gauge record at the Hatizyo-sima Weather Station 120 kilometers to the north of Myozin-syo Volcano established the fact that a strong eruption had occurred at that time. When the ship did not return as scheduled an intensive search of the area was made with planes and patrol boats, but to no avail. Later, some wrecked material from the

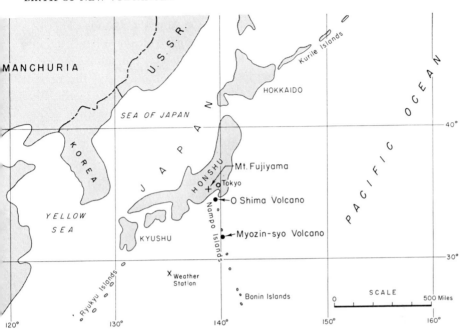

FIGURE 52. Map showing location of Myozin-syo Volcano.

Kaiyo-maru was discovered. Entrapped in the wreckage were numerous pieces of pumice similar to that ejected by Myozin-syo Volcano.

Observations by scientists aboard the *Sinyo-maru* on September 23, the day before the *Kaiyo-maru* catastrophe, reveal clearly the nature of the eruption which trapped the *Kaiyo-maru*. A series of photographs, one of which is reproduced as Plate 32, tells the story vividly. A dome of water forms on the surface of the sea over the submarine crater, and a few seconds later, with a tremendous explosion, the dome is broken, and bombs, ash, and pumice are thrown out in a dense eruption cloud of water and gases. It is obvious that no ship situated over the eruptive area would be able to survive such a blast.

The activity of Myozin-syo Volcano ceased near the end of August, 1953, about one year after it started. A brief renewal of activity was reported to have occurred on November 4, 1954.

The volcanic belt in which Myozin-syo is located extends from Volcano Huzi, near Tokyo, southward to the Mariana Islands (Fig. 52). The belt consists of both active and extinct volcanic islands, among which Myozin-syo is included. Records indicate that submarine eruptions have occurred at Myozin-syo several times during the present century. In 1946 a small island, similar to the one formed by the 1952 eruption, was developed, but it was soon destroyed by wave action.

The birth of a new volcano is, in addition to being an awe-inspiring spectacle, an event of great scientific interest. If the "present is the key to the past," then the study of the birth and subsequent activity of a volcano will provide information to aid in the interpretation of the history of volcanoes long since extinct. It is, in effect, a laboratory where some of the most fundamental geologic processes can be observed in action. The submarine eruptions described in the preceding pages point up the fact that a volcanic cone must attain considerable size before it can project above the level of the sea, and even then it is a struggle between cone building and wave erosion to determine whether the cone will survive. There must be literally thousands of volcanic eruptions on the floor of the ocean which go undetected because they fail to produce a cone which rises above the level of the sea.

There are more things in heaven and earth, Horatio, than are dreamt of in our philosophy. SHAKESPEARE

14. MAN'S USE OF GEOTHERMAL ENERGY

IN ALL VOLCANIC REGIONS, even thousands of years after activity has ceased, numerous hot springs and fumaroles attest the fact that heat is still being contributed to the rocks below the surface. When the pressure in the magma has been exhausted and volcanic activity ceases, the magma continues to cool slowly, giving off hot gases (largely steam but with small amounts also of hydrochloric acid, carbon dioxide, hydrogen, ammonium chloride, etc.) which rise along fissures into the zone of the ground water. The ground water is heated by the volcanic emanations and the mixture issues at the surface as hot springs, geysers, fumaroles, and related phenomena.

In some cases the water is only warm; in others it is so hot that it boils violently; or it may be superheated and issue as steam. Yellowstone National Park is one of the outstanding examples of such an area. Although no volcanic activity has occurred in the Yellowstone area for thousands of years, its three thousand hot springs and related phenomena clearly indicate that the magma is still cooling and that it is close enough to the surface for the emanating gases to heat the ground water. It has been estimated that the hot springs at Mount Lassen in California yield about 10 percent magmatic water, while the amount at Yellowstone is somewhat less. The remainder in each case is, of course, meteoric water, or surface rain water which has seeped into the ground. The fact that hot springs and geysers have existed in Yellowstone for thousands of years is indicated by the association of hot-spring deposits with glacial deposits. The cooling of a magma, even though it is near the surface, is such a slow process that, in terms of human history, it may be considered to supply a source of heat indefinitely.

Some Technical Considerations[1]

An understanding of the types of hydrothermal activity and of some of the technical considerations which enter into the development of natural steam for power production is basic to the utilization of geothermal energy.

In relation to source, natural steam can be classified into two major types. In one, steam is derived from a magma, hence is termed "primary" steam; in the other, it comes from circulating ground water, and is designated as "secondary" steam. Frequently the steam which issues at the surface is a mixture of primary and secondary steam. It is important to recognize the type of steam, or the proportion of each in the mixture, for these factors will govern the method of exploitation as well as the value of the steam as a power source.

Steam derived from magma (primary)

Magmatic water in the form of steam which has reached the surface for the first time plays an interesting role in volcanic eruptions.

[1] Based in part on an article by A. R. McBirney, An Appraisal of the Fumarolic Activity near Ahuachapán, El Salvador, pp. 19–32.

Experiments by Goranson, previously mentioned, show that a granitic melt can hold 9 percent by weight of dissolved water at a pressure corresponding to a depth of seventeen kilometers and a temperature of 900° C., while at a depth of two kilometers, under the same temperature, it can hold only 4 percent dissolved water. This "boiling off" of the excess water as the magma rises toward the surface builds up an ever-increasing pressure in the magma chamber until it finally results in a volcanic eruption. The great gas cloud which rises from an erupting volcano is largely steam. In areas such as Larderello, Italy, where no volcanic eruption has occurred in the immediate area, the steam escapes through fissures into the overlying rocks and on reaching the surface forms steam jets, or *soffioni*. The temperature of the magma is far in excess of the critical temperature of steam (374° C.) and regardless of the pressure the steam will have a high degree of superheat.

As the steam rises along fractures the pressure is determined by the confining rock column, and, since this pressure will exceed the hydrostatic pressure, ground water will be excluded, the only heat loss occurring through conduction to the wall rocks. When the upward-flowing steam reaches permeable formations the pressure is no longer controlled by rock pressure, but by hydrostatic pressure, and the steam comes in contact with ground water. Whether the temperature remains above the boiling point will depend on the amount of ground-water contamination. It may retain enough heat to issue as a steam vent at the surface; or it may completely condense in the permeable horizon, its heat causing an increase in the temperature of the ground water. If an impermeable cap rock is present below the surface the steam may accumulate beneath it without mixing with the ground water. Wells may also be located so as to intersect the steam-bearing fissure at a point below the permeable beds, thus tapping it before ground-water contamination. Thus, a careful study of the geologic structure of an area, especially the position of faults, may be a guide to the location of wells in search of primary steam.

It is possible that a well may yield wet steam at first but later, after a lowering of the ground-water level, produce steam of improved quality, even dry steam, should the ground-water level be lowered sufficiently. In the Wairakei area of New Zealand (p. 347) some wells give a wet steam with a quality exceeding that which comes from the secondary-type, and the excess is believed to represent contribution of primary steam from fissures. From a practical point of view it should be pointed out that superheated, high-pressure steam is more likely to be found within economical reach of surface wells in thermal areas where considerable primary steam is contributed to the system. Surface-heat losses are not a reliable guide to the amount of energy that can be withdrawn in primary-steam areas, as is true of secondary-steam areas.

Steam derived from ground water (secondary)

Ground water heated to above-normal temperature exists in many parts of the world, some of it far removed from any recent volcanic activity. Among the possible sources of heat for abnormally warm water is the normal geothermal gradient of the rocks in the earth's crust. As has been described elsewhere, there is an increase in temperature with depth in the earth. This increase averages about 1° F. for each sixty feet of depth. The geologic structure may cause the water to descend to great depths. In so doing the water will become heated, later rising to the surface and issuing as warm or hot springs, such as Hot Springs, Arkansas,[2] and Warm Springs, Georgia. Heat may be derived also from friction due to slippage along faults and from radioactive materials.

A much more important source of heat is that found in regions of active or recently active volcanoes, where bodies of slowly cooling magma remain hot for thousands of years and heat the surrounding rocks by conduction. Such magmas may not actually contribute steam, or may contribute only a minor amount of steam, such as in Yellowstone National Park, but ground water is heated by coming in contact with the rocks heated by the cooling magma. Water, as a result of heating, becomes lighter and rises through the porous formations to the surface; then as cold water comes in to take its place a convection system is set up. The important characteristics to be recognized in this type of occurrence are the limitation of the heat-carrying capacity of the water, because of the boiling point-pressure relationship, and the absence of

[2] Some hold that the water at Hot Springs, Arkansas, is forced to a sufficient depth that it comes into a zone heated by a cooling magma.

primary magmatic steam in the circulation. The total heat and pressure of steam at any given depth in a thermal system in permeable rocks is controlled by the hydrostatic pressure appropriate to that depth, but in a system confined beneath an impervious cap greater heat and steam pressure may be encountered at a similar depth, since it is not governed by the hydrostatic pressure.

The total internal heat of the water (technically known as "enthalpy") cannot exceed that of a saturated liquid at its boiling point. When the pressure on the water is reduced, thereby reducing its boiling point, a part of this heat is used in partially vaporizing the liquid and a mixture of steam and hot water results. It is, of course, impossible to vaporize the water completely from its internal heat alone. The *quality* (i.e., percent of steam to water) depends on the original temperature and the amount of reduction in pressure. When steam is used for power, a certain minimum input pressure is necessary to drive the machinery. However, as pressure is increased, the quality of the steam is reduced. At depths not exceeding one hundred feet the quality will not exceed 25 percent and if used at seventy psi (4.9 atmospheres) the quality is reduced to 16 percent. Deeper drilling improves the quality but at such a decreasing rate that the added expense of deeper drilling is rarely justified.

If the production exceeds the rate at which the rocks below are heated by conduction, cold water will begin to enter and the quality of the steam will decrease. The total heat available for use is roughly equivalent to the total surface-heat loss through hot springs and fumaroles for the area, and this can be determined by surface measurements.

Drilling for natural steam

Man has used hot springs for bathing and washing since the earliest times. In the days of the Roman Empire the emperor and other important persons maintained elaborate bathhouses at the hot springs in the volcanic areas of Italy, and now large bath houses and health resorts flourish around hot-springs areas. But no serious attempts to develop the heat as a source of energy were made until the early part of the twentieth century.

On the basis of a normal surface temperature of 70° F. (yearly mean temperature) and the average "geothermal gradient," the boiling point of water at the surface would be reached at a depth slightly in excess of one mile. In deep mines, like some of the diamond mines of Africa, elaborate cooling devices such as air-conditioning are installed. Drillers of deep wells, now often in excess of twenty thousand feet, are confronted with the problem of increasing temperatures with increasing depth.

Nevertheless, under normal conditions it is not practical to drill a well to produce "geothermal heat." It was estimated (Bruce and Shorland, 1933) that to obtain a continuous heat yield equivalent to four thousand horse power it would be necessary to drill a hole thirty miles deep and two feet in diameter! Serious attempts to obtain heat by drilling, however, are not unknown. In the September, 1885, issue of the *Geological Magazine,* a distinguished scientific journal, J. Starkie Gardner refers to an attempt then being made to obtain a supply of heat by drilling. He says:

. . . the deepest artesian well in the world is being bored at Pesth, already 951 meters. The work is being done partly at the expense of the city which has granted 40,000 pounds for the purpose, with the intention of obtaining an unlimited supply of warm water for public baths and municipal purposes. The present temperature is 161° F. and they propose to continue until water 178° F. is obtained.

No further mention of this project has been found in the literature.

In regions of recent volcanic activity, however, the heat is close enough to the surface to be tapped and harnessed economically. It might be assumed that sinking tubes into hot soil surrounding volcanoes would provide a useful means of exploiting natural heat, but experience has shown that heat transmission, even from incandescent lava, is exceptionally poor, so that enormous heating surfaces would be required for industrial purposes.

Although thermal activity is widely distributed throughout the world, only four areas have been exploited seriously to harness geothermal heat: Tuscany, Italy; Iceland; New Zealand; and California. The developments in these areas are of considerable interest.

Developments in Italy

The backbone of Italy is made up of the Apennine Mountains, an extension of the Alpine system of southern Europe. In relatively recent geologic time, Italy has experienced a number of uplifts and subsequent sinkings during which the waters of the Mediterranean Sea covered much of the present area of Italy. The most recent of these disturbances was an uplift of the Apennine Mountains accompanied by a sinking of what is now the Tyrrhenian Sea to the west. This uplift began in Pleistocene time (just prior to the Ice Age) a few hundred thousand years ago and is actually still in progress in some areas.

Distribution of volcanoes

The volcanoes of Italy are located along a trend which parallels the Apennine Mountains and the Tyrrhenian coast, following a fracture or series of fractures which resulted from the sinking of the Tyrrhenian Sea and the uplift of the Apennines. Along this fracture, more or less evenly spaced, are located a series of volcanic centers. Beginning at the north, about midway between Florence and Rome (Fig. 22), and extending southward, these volcanic centers are: (1) Vulsini (Lake Bolsena), (2) Cimini (Lake Vico), (3) Sabatini (Lake Bracciano), (4) Alban Hills, (5) Roccamonfina, and (6) the Naples area, including Vesuvius and the Phlegraean Fields. All of these volcanic centers are similar in character, belonging to a type which volcanologists have designated as the Mediterranean type. They are multiple-center volcanic masses with a series of intersecting craters or calderas forming low, flat cones rising only slightly above the surrounding countryside. They are composed essentially of pumiceous material with minor lava flows, except in the southern part of the belt, particularly Vesuvius, which has yielded abundant lava flows in recent eruptions. From the Alban Hills area northward, the craters or calderas are occupied by lakes which lend much charm to the scenery of this part of Italy.

Activity along this belt began at the north and progressively shifted southward until today the only activity along this line is at Vesuvius. While the activity began in the Pleistocene, very recent from a geologic viewpoint, there is no record of any activity in historic time in the centers north of Rome. A slight eruption in the Alban Hills, just south of Rome, is reported as late as 290 B.C., but this is open to some doubt. Activity in the Naples area, of course, has continued until the present time.

Active volcanoes occur in two other areas in Italy today, at Stromboli and Vulcano in the Lipari Islands (north of Sicily) and at Mount Etna in Sicily. The relationship of these areas to the Apennines is not as apparent as it is in the volcanic centers to the north, but the trend of folding represented by the Apennines is continued through Sicily and the Atlas Mountains of North Africa.

Utilization of geothermal steam

Italy has been the pioneer in the utilization of geothermal energy and has served as a laboratory for others interested in this field. Though the broad extent of recent volcanic activity in Italy provides wide distribution of hot springs and fumaroles, only in the Larderello area, in Tuscany, south of Florence, have the natural steam resources been developed. This area alone, in 1952, provided about 6 percent of the total electric power produced in Italy, and the output is being expanded. In addition to producing power this area supports a large chemical industry through recovery of the gases contained in the natural steam. The expansion of the output at Larderello, as well as the development of similar plants elsewhere in Italy, is of the utmost importance to the national economy. This is particularly true in Italy because of the shortage of coal, oil, and gas, the fuels commonly used in power production.

The natural steam vents of Tuscany occur principally in seven groups distributed over an elliptical area of about a hundred square miles, located about fifteen miles south of Volterra and fifty miles south-southwest of Florence. The details of the area are shown in Figure 54. The seven areas which have been exploited are: Larderello, Castelnuovo, Serrazzano, Lustignano, Sasso, Lago, and Monterotondo. The largest development, both for power production and for chemicals, is at Larderello, from which the organization in control of the entire area, Societa Boracifera di Larderello, derives its name. When the writer visited the

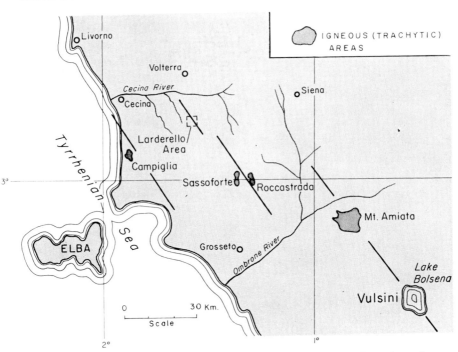

FIGURE 53. Map showing relation of volcanic areas to Larderello and possible northwest-southeast alignment along the volcanic belt.

area in 1952 the only activity of any note, other than at Larderello, was at Castelnuovo.

The natural steam vents, known as *"soffioni,"* and the pools of water formed by the condensation of the steam, called *"lagoni,"* have been known for centuries, but were long regarded as evil by the peasants. In 1777, a pharmacist at the court of Leopold III, Grand Duke of Tuscany, isolated boric acid from the waters of the *lagoni*. Boric acid reacts with soda to form borax, a product which had up to this time been imported from the Orient at great cost. Some early crude attempts were made to produce boric acid, but it was not until 1827 that Count Francesco Larderel, a French exile, conceived the idea of utilizing the steam to concentrate the boric-acid solution, and a profitable industry devel-

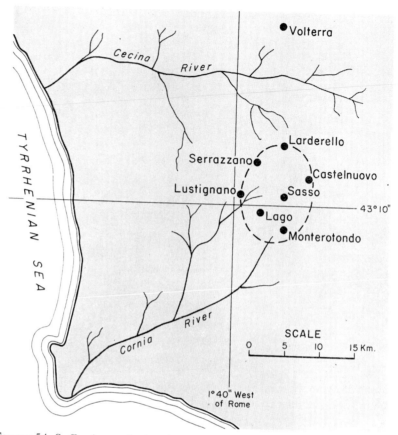

FIGURE 54. *Soffioni* areas in the vicinity of Larderello.
After Keller (1946).

oped.[3] The area was subsequently named in honor of Count Larderel.

Heat from the natural steam was used in various stages of the chemical industry for many years but no attempt was made to use it for generating power until near the end of the nineteenth century. In 1897 the natural steam was used to heat boilers which provided steam to run a reciprocating engine. In 1904 Prince Piero Ginori Conte, then general director of the Larderello works, fed steam directly from a *soffione* into a piston engine used to drive a small dynamo that provided lights for the chemical works. By this time drilling had been undertaken in order to increase the flow of the steam for the boric-acid plant and

[3] Utilization of volcanic steam in Italy. Smithsonian Annual Report for 1925, pp. 519–521, 1925.

PLATE 33. Larderello steam area, Italy.

it was found that higher pressures and steam with superheat could be obtained at depth. The first steam turbine using steam directly from a *soffione* was installed in 1913. It was connected to a 250-kilowatt electric generator. In 1916 three units of 3,000 kilowatts each were added. These did not use the natural steam direct but used steam from pure water heated in boilers by the *soffioni*, thus avoiding the difficulties from corrosion and from the high gas content (4 to 5 percent) of the natural steam.

This procedure was followed until about 1923, when an apparatus for removing about 90 percent of the contaminating gases was devised, and the steam was then fed directly to the turbo-generators so that the intermediate stage was unnecessary. This process, known as the "Bringhenti," after the man who devised the apparatus, is still being used. The wells drilled in the early twenties were usually less than five hundred feet deep and the steam issued at an average pressure of two atmospheres absolute and a temperature varying from 100° C. to 190° C. In 1931 deep drilling tapped steam with higher pressures and higher tempera-

PLATE 34. Condensing towers of chemical plant at Larderello, Italy.

tures. The first large well, Soffionissimo No. 1, drilled in 1931 to a depth of nine hundred feet, yielded 440,000 pounds of steam per hour at a pressure of fifty-two psi and a temperature of 205° C., including 50° C. superheat. At the end of 1944 installations for electric power generation totaled 135,000 kilowatts, and the total electric output in 1943 was 908 million kilowatt hours.

During the retreat of the German Army through Italy in 1945 the installations at Larderello were wrecked and many of the wells destroyed. Since the war the area has been redeveloped, new methods have been introduced, and the output has been expanded. The output in 1952 was 1,840 million kilowatt hours, or about 6 percent of the total electric energy output of Italy for the year. In 1960 the output was 1,914 million kilowatt hours, and while this was about one-third of the thermoelectric power produced in Italy, it was only 3.88 percent of the total power production for the year (Banco di Roma).[4]

[4] Review of Economic Conditions in Italy for 1954. Banco di Roma, Vol. 8, p. 21. Information for 1960 supplied by Banco di Roma in a personal letter.

The steam wells, in most cases, are from five hundred to fifteen hundred feet in depth and are spaced about six hundred feet apart. They are drilled with customary rotary drilling equipment in the same manner used for drilling oil and gas wells. Surface casing is commonly twenty-inch, decreasing to twelve-inch, which is carried to the steam horizon. The deepest well to date is about five thousand feet, but the additional depth did not yield appreciably larger quantities of steam. The steam is carried in insulated lines (about twelve inches in diameter) from the wellhead to the power plant and the condensing towers of the chemical plant.

Composition of the steam

The steam contains an average of 0.06 percent boric acid with a maximum of 0.1 percent, and from 4 to 6 percent by weight of gases, mainly carbon dioxide (over 90 percent) and small quantities of hydrogen sulphide, hydrogen, methane, oxygen, nitrogen, ammonia, argon, and helium. The composition is remarkably constant over the entire area despite the continued drilling.

The following analyses[5] are typical.

One kilogram of vapor contains:

	Grams
H_2O	945.87
CO_2	51.85
H_2S	0.86
H_3BO_3	0.50
NH_3	0.10
CH_4, H_2, etc.	0.40
O_2	0.01
N_2	0.42
Rare gases about 1 cc.	

After condensation of the water vapor and elimination of the boric acid and the ammonia the gases contain:

[5] Manelli, G., The Soffioni of Larderello. Instituta di Chemica, University of Florence. Mimeograph report.

Per 100 liters of gas:

	Liters
CO_2	93.0
H_2S	2.4
H_2	1.8
CH_4	1.8
N_2	1.0

He, Ar, etc. about 3 cc.

The boric acid is concentrated by evaporation in special pans to a solution of about 8 percent. This is cooled and the crude acid, up to 90 percent pure, is crystallized out. The annual pre-World War II production of boric acid was around 8,000 tons and about 4,500 tons of borax. Other chemicals are manufactured at Larderello: carbon dioxide and "dry ice," liquid ammonia, ammonium carbonate, sodium perborate, ammonium chloride, manganese borate, and boron carbide.

Geologic conditions at Larderello

Larderello is located on the northern end of the belt which includes the recently active volcanoes (Fig. 22). The position of deep-seated faults is probably the controlling factor in providing channels along which the steam rises into the surface rocks, but neither the composition nor the age of the surface rocks influences the steam production. The source of the steam at Larderello is unquestionably a relatively shallow (near-the-surface) magma which is still undergoing cooling. The steam, rising along faults, spreads out laterally when the faults intersect permeable beds, and some of it finds its way to the surface through joints and fissures to form the surface steam vents, or *soffioni*. In places the permeable beds are sealed by a resistant horizon of folded limestone beneath which, in domelike structures, the steam has accumulated. High-pressure and superheated steam wells, like the Soffionissimi, are obtained when the steam which has accumulated in the domelike structures beneath the cap rock is tapped. This type of occurrence makes it practicable to apply geologic and geophysical methods, such as are used in oil and gas exploration, in searching for favorable "steam traps."

The Ente Nazionale Idrocarburi, a government organization which operates in all power fields except coal, is in charge of prospecting and exploiting the natural steam resources. An active program of exploration, using all modern techniques, is under way by the E.N.I. The work is closely coordinated with natural gas exploration, which is also under the direction of E.N.I. Prospects indicate that natural steam may be developed at Abano, Acqui, Mount Amiata, Grosseto, and Latial volcanoes; also at Campi Flegrei, Ischia, Vulture, Vulcano, and Sciacca (Sicily).

The magmatic source of the steam is indicated by the abundance of boric acid as well as other "mineralizers" in the emanations. The superheat of the steam, its pressure, and its great volume also argue for a magmatic source. Ground water unquestionably contributes some to the steam but the thermal energy of a magma is the primary source. Keller and Valduga (1946) in speculating on the amount of cooling needed in a magma to account for the steam production at Larderello have provided some interesting figures. Admittedly the figures are pure speculation, but the results are quite interesting. If it is assumed that a granite batholith (the type of magma giving rise to boric acid emanations) lies beneath Tuscany and that it has been cooling (freezing) for a long period of time, the question arises as to how much cooling is necessary to produce the steam output at Larderello. Taking the figure of 6,263,400 tons of steam used for power in 1938 as an approximate minimum, the rate of solidification can be computed if the following assumptions are made: a water-in-solution content of 6 percent in the magma (a figure derived from experimental data); a value of 2.67 for the density of the granite; and a weight of 62.5 pounds per cubic foot for water. Based on these assumptions, 0.008 cubic miles of frozen magma could supply the steam produced in 1938, if the magma's entire water content becomes tapped steam. At this rate, five and one-half cubic miles of granite, a very small part of a mass underlying the hundred-square-mile area, could have furnished the 1938 steam output for the past seven hundred years, the known life of the area. It is quite probable that much more steam was dissipated through the rocks between the *soffioni* than was tapped by wells. The 6 percent figure used for the water content of the magma may not be correct. The results, therefore, provide only a basis for an interesting speculation.

Relation of the Larderello area to volcanic activity

In looking for the source of the steam, one naturally turns his attention to igneous activity which has reached the surface to form volcanic masses in the immediate area. Admittedly, the magma at Larderello has not reached the surface and no volcanic activity has occurred in the immediate vicinity. Perhaps the most favorable localities for natural steam are in such areas. An active vent to the surface, such as a volcano, might be expected to dissipate the steam. Further, geologic conditions must be such that the steam is trapped below the surface, yet shallow enough to be within reach of drilling.

The nearest of the large volcanic craters to Larderello is Vulsini, which is about sixty-five miles to the southeast. It is a multiple-center volcanic mass composed primarily of pumice and ash with the main crater occupied by Lake Bolsena, a body of water about nine miles long and six and a half miles wide. It is the northernmost of several similar volcanic masses which extend to the southeast to beyond Rome (Fig. 53). Lying between Larderello and Lake Bolsena are several volcanic areas, including Mount Amiata, Roccastrada, and Campiglia Marittima, and several other smaller areas (Fig. 53). These groups are aligned in a northwest-southeast zone, a continuation of the volcanic belt which parallels the Tyrrhenian coast to Naples and Vesuvius. The activity, however, in the northern part of this zone, around Mount Amiata, is somewhat different from that in the crater-lake areas to the southeast, where explosive activity has been the rule, with ash and pumice the chief products.

Mount Amiata, the largest of the areas and typical of this group, is a craterless volcanic mass consisting chiefly of superimposed trachytic lava flows, which are believed to have issued from northwest-southeast trending fissures, rather than from explosive centers. The activity is clearly post-Pliocene but is believed to be older than the activity represented by Vulsini and the volcanic centers to the southeast (Preller, 1924, p. 141). The crudely conical mass of Mount Amiata, with slopes of about 9°, rises 1,800 feet above the surrounding area with its summit 5,250 feet above sea level. Mercury mines on the eastern margin have been an important source of mercury for many years.

About eighteen miles northwest from Mount Amiata lies the cluster of trachytic masses of Roccastrada, Sassoforte, and others (Fig. 53). The outcrops of trachytic lava, resting on sedimentary strata, do not represent so many separate centers of eruption but are the result of separation of the original area by erosion. The material and its occurrence are similar to the situation at Mount Amiata.

Another trachytic volcanic mass, Campiglia Marittima, lies about eighteen miles west of the Roccastrada group, near the Tyrrhenian coast. It has an area of fifty square kilometers and attains a height of about two thousand feet above sea level. Like Roccastrada, the material and its occurrence are similar to those at Mount Amiata.

These volcanic centers in the general area of Larderello are ample proof of the presence of a magma in this part of Tuscany in Quaternary (Ice Age) time. It must be assumed, therefore, that a part of this magma, or a separate magma, is cooling at a relatively shallow depth beneath the surface in the Larderello area and is the source of the steam and gases not provided by ground-water contamination.

How to reach Larderello

Larderello is off the main lines of travel and few visitors reach the area. When visited by the writer in November, 1952, the area was approached by car from Florence, on the Siena road as far as Poggibonsi, then Volterra. From Volterra the route was on the Cecina road to a point beyond Salina where a road branches south through Pomarance to Larderello. A small hotel at Larderello, Stazione Termale la Perla, provides adequate accommodations, utilizing natural steam for heating. Two-inch steam pipes, with a series of fins for radiating heat, pass through each room and then the steam is exhausted into the air. The Stazione Termale la Perla was delightfully warm, a decided contrast to most of the Italian hotels at that season. A natural hot spring provides water for baths as well as for a swimming pool in the basement of the hotel. The offices of the Societa Boracifera di Larderello are in Florence, where one should secure a permit if he is interested in visiting the works.

Developments in New Zealand

New Zealand consists of a group of islands in the South Pacific east and slightly south of Australia. Twelve hundred miles from Australia, even farther from the nearest Pacific islands, and over six thousand miles from South America, they are extremely isolated. The two important islands, called "North" and "South," contain 44,131 and 58,120 square miles respectively. North Island is about equal to Pennsylvania in area while South Island compares in size with Georgia.

Geologic Characteristics of New Zealand

Even though North Island is 515 miles long and up to 200 miles in width no point is more than 65 miles from the sea. Its central physical feature is a series of unbroken mountain chains running northeast from Cook Strait to East Cape on the Bay of Plenty. The height is always in excess of three thousand feet but does not reach six thousand feet. To the west of the backbone range is the volcanic plateau, a great triangular area with its base along the Bay of Plenty, and its apex to the south, built up by eruptions which began in late Tertiary time and have continued to the present. It contains the still active cones of Tarawera and Ngauruhoe, as well as a number of extinct or dormant volcanoes. This volcanic area is described in some detail in later paragraphs.

The backbone of South Island is formed by the impressive Southern Alps, which extend the full length of the island. With an average crest elevation of over eight thousand feet and with seventeen peaks over ten thousand feet, they rise steeply from the plains to well above the snow line. With numerous glaciers and spectacular waterfalls, South Island is strikingly similar to many parts of Switzerland. On the west the Southern Alps plunge sheer into the sea along a coast famed for the grandeur of its fiord scenery.

Extending in a north-northeasterly direction from the central part of North Island to the Bay of Plenty is a relatively low-lying belt which includes the basins of Lake Rotorua at the north and Lake Taupo at the southern end. This troughlike belt, known as the White Island Trench (Fig. 55), is regarded by most authors as due to collapse as a result of the ejection of large quantities of volcanic material. The active

North Cape

Whangarei

PACIFIC OCEAN

—36°

AUCKLAND

WHITE ISLAND
VOLCANO

Hamilton

BAY OF PLENTY

East
Cape

Whakatane

—38°

Lake
Rotorua

Rotorua

MT. EDGECUMBE

Waiotapu

MT. TARAWERA

MAUNGAKAKARAMEA

Oraeki Korako

Wairakei

Lake Taupo

Taupo

Gisborne

Tokaanu

MT. TAUHARA

Ketetahi

New Plymouth

MT. NGAURUHOE

MT. TONGARIRO

MT. EGMONT

MT. RUAPEHU

Napier

N O R T H

I S L A N D

—40°

Palmerston
North

C O O K
S T R A I T

Motueka

SCALE

0   100 Miles

WELLINGTON

NELSON

SOUTH

ISLAND

172°

174°

176°

178°

Figure 55. Map of North Island, New Zealand.

and recently active volcanoes of North Island are located along the eastern side of the collapse belt, along a fault, which perhaps should be called a tectonic zone. Along this tectonic zone, called the Whakatane Fault, extending from the Bay of Plenty to Ruapehu, are the active volcanoes of White Island, Tarawera, Ruapehu, and Ngauruhoe, as well as the following dormant or extinct volcanoes: Tongariro, Tauhara, Edgecumbe, and Maungakakaramea. The greatest thermal activity is also along this line. The Whakatane tectonic zone is approximately in line with the Alpine Fault, which extends south-southwesterly along the west margin of South Island. There is no volcanic activity, however, in South Island.

The alignment may be projected northward for a thousand miles through the Kermadec Islands to Tonga and Samoa (Fig. 56). All of these island groups support active or dormant volcanoes. Since 1774 (first historic records) the doubtlessly incomplete record indicates that at least forty-eight volcanic eruptions have occurred along this trend. To the east lies the great Tonga-Kermadec Submarine Trench, which locally attains a depth of 20,000 feet. This trench is believed to represent a major down-warping of the earth's crust which is forming a tectogene (Chap. 15, "Volcanoes in Geologic Perspective").

Volcanic eruptions have occurred along the Whakatane tectonic zone from late Tertiary to the present day. The extent of this activity is indicated by the widespread covering of volcanic debris which mantles much of North Island. A rhyolitic welded tuff (ignimbrite),[6] although largely covered by recent pumice and ash deposits, is present over an area of about five thousand square miles northward from Lake Taupo. The ignimbrite, encountered in steam wells at Wairakei at a depth of around two thousand feet, is estimated to represent the astonishing volume of two hundred cubic miles of material. It was erupted in prehistoric time as a series of incandescent blasts of ash (*nuées ardentes*), probably from longitudinal rifts or from multiple centers along such rifts.

All volcanic eruptions in historic time (i.e., since European settlement in 1839) have been in this zone. Especially noteworthy is the great eruption of Tarawera Volcano in 1886. White Island Volcano,

---

[6] A term applied to all pyroclastic rocks formed by welding of the fragments into a firm, compact rock, which are often mistaken for lava flows.

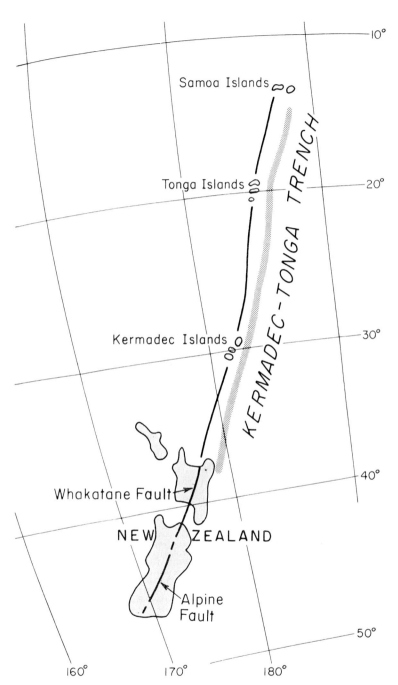

FIGURE 56. Structural trends in the New Zealand region.

in the Bay of Plenty, erupted in 1914 and 1926. Ngauruhoe and Ruapehu volcanoes, south of Lake Taupo in Tongariro National Park, have
erupted in recent years. Eruptions of Ngauruhoe are recorded for 1869
and 1948–1949. Ash eruptions, accompanying the rise of a stiff plug
of lava in the crater of Ruapehu Volcano began in 1945. Ash discharges
again occurred at Ruapehu on June 26, 1950, and March 19, 1951.

Geothermal steam in New Zealand

The thermal region of New Zealand is located on North Island,
extending in a northeasterly trending belt from the central volcanic
district around Ngauruhoe to White Island in the Bay of Plenty. The
more important areas[7] are around Tokaanu and Ketetahi, south of
Lake Taupo (Fig. 55), and Wairakei, Waiotapu, Rotorua, to the
north of Lake Taupo. In none of these areas are the steam emissions
very strong, except at the Karapiti blowhole near Wairakei. The belt
of thermal activity is coincident with the belt of active volcanoes in
North Island.

The Maori people, in the thermal region, have used the hot water
for cooking and washing since ancient times. However, no other use
was made of the thermal resources until very recently. At various times
during the 1930's the possibility of using natural heat from the thermal
areas was suggested. Bruce and Shorland (1932) in the early thirties
suggested the use of water from the hot springs to heat greenhouses for
the growing of out-of-season vegetables, heating homes, evaporation of
sea water for salt recovery, recovery of boric acid and other chemicals,
and for power production.

In 1940 the matter was investigated by the Council of Scientific and
Industrial Research, and, while the investigation revealed that it was
entirely feasible to develop power from the natural steam, the abundance
of water power in North Island did not seem to make it worthwhile.
At Rotorua, where hot ground could be encountered at a shallow depth,
a number of wells were drilled and by 1940 the municipal building, a
theatre, several hotels and schools, and a number of dwellings were
using natural heat. By 1944, fifty wells had been drilled and since then

[7] Based largely on an article by W. M. Hamilton, Geothermal Energy, Cawthorn
Lecture Series.

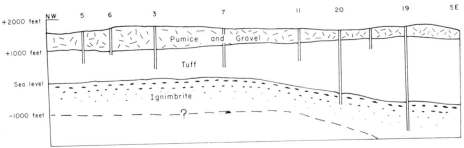

FIGURE 57. Cross section at Wairakei based on exploratory drill holes. Drill holes are identified by number.   After Hamilton (1954).

the number has greatly increased. The possibility of producing "heavy water," used as a moderator in atomic piles, from natural steam was proposed in 1946. This, together with the marked increase in the consumption of electric energy and the awareness that hydroelectric developments could not keep pace with the demand, again directed attention to the thermal areas. The government appointed a volcanologist (in 1945) to undertake a study of the thermal areas with the intention of setting up power plants, should it be feasible to do so. After some preliminary work, a five-year program of simultaneous exploratory drilling and investigation was approved by the government in 1949. Work was started in the Wairakei area, which was considered to be the most promising. Drilling has been limited to a belt one mile wide and about one and one-half miles long, which is known as the "Production Area." Most of the wells range from 1,200 to 1,500 feet in depth, although exploratory wells have been drilled to more than 3,000 feet (Fig. 57).

GEOLOGIC CONDITIONS. Lying to the east of North Island is the great Tonga-Kermadec Trench, in which depths of eighteen thousand to twenty thousand feet are found. Kermadec Ridge, a continuation of East Cape of North Island, separates the Tonga-Kermadec Trench from a shallower depression known as the White Island Trench. The White Island Trench extends southwestward across North Island and includes the thermal and volcanic belt (Fig. 58). This belt is also a zone of deep-focus (200 to 300 km.) earthquakes. Although the structure is con-

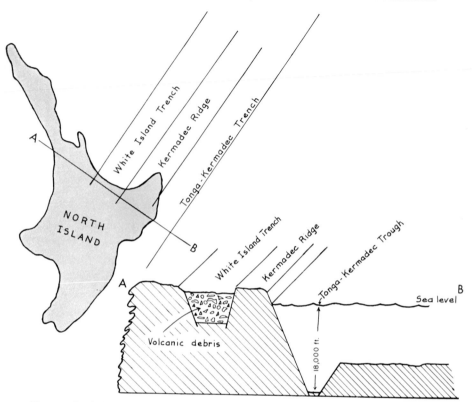

FIGURE 58. Major structural features of North Island, New Zealand.

cealed by volcanic debris which has filled the trench (graben), geophysical data indicates that its floor is about seven thousand feet below sea level. The filling of this great trough with volcanic ash, cinders, and other debris must have extended over a long period of time. From radio carbon studies it is known that many volcanic eruptions occurred in this area during the last nine thousand years. One of the most recent, about seventeen hundred years ago, spread five cubic miles of ash over an area of 8,800 square miles. Another eruption occurred at Tarawera about seven hundred years ago, and of course, the great eruption of Tarawera in 1886 is a matter of record. The thermal activity in the Wairakei-Taupo area is doubtless related to the cooling of the magmas responsible for these eruptions. As the intruded magma cools it releases steam (with other gases) which finds its way to the surface along faults in the basement rocks.

In the thermal area around Wairakei, the top 120 feet consists of loose gravel and pumice. This rests on rhyolitic tuff (a consolidated ash) to about 2,000 feet, underneath which is an ignimbrite which appears to be widespread and of unknown thickness. A slight domed structure in the ignimbrite appears to produce water of the hottest temperature and highest percentage of magmatic steam. Geophysical evidence indicates that greywacke lies about 8,000 feet below the surface (7,000 ft. below sea level) and is probably similar to the rocks exposed in the hills around Wellington.

The steam is believed to rise along fissures in the basement rocks into the permeable volcanics filling the trench. The permeable surface rocks are saturated with circulating ground water, which is heated by rising steam and gases. The hottest areas appear to be associated with northeast trending faults. If it is assumed that 2,000 feet of permeable rocks are saturated with circulating ground water, the boiling point at 2,000 feet would be raised to 265° C. by the increased pressure. At 1,000 feet it would be approximately 230° C. In most wells the temperature at the bottom is slightly less than the corresponding value on the boiling-point curve; near the surface it is considerably less. Temperatures above the boiling point, giving dry steam, are encountered in narrow zones, the result of impermeable beds impeding circulation. The temperature and average steam content at various depths are approximately as follows:

Depth in Feet	Temperature in C.	% Steam at Atmospheric Pressure
0	100°	0
130	150°	9
540	200°	19
1000	230°	25
1500	250°	30
1800	260°	32
2150	270°	34

At Larderello, in Italy, the magmatic steam, trapped under an impermeable cap, is dry and often considerably superheated. When wells are drilled at such places ground temperatures are low until the cap is penetrated. At Wairakei the temperature approaches the boiling point for the depth throughout the permeable beds. The small lenses which trap dry steam are not large enough to be significant. It is possible, of course, that the ignimbrite sheet extending two thousand feet below may serve as a cap rock. It is increasingly apparent that anticlinal structures with a suitable cap rock are as important in steam production as they are in oil and gas production. Thus far, the New Zealand steam production has been obtained only from the permeable surface layers of volcanic material.

DRILLING STEAM WELLS. Drilling in hot ground and against high pressures introduces many of the problems encountered by the oil industry and requires employment of the same techniques. The wells are drilled with a rotary-type rig and the pressure is controlled by circulation of drilling mud, which also keeps the drill bit cool. A column of water two thousand feet deep would exert a pressure of about one thousand psi at the bottom, and since the mud used has a somewhat higher density it would withstand a somewhat higher pressure. The circulating mud is also viscous enough to carry out the drill cuttings from the hole. Generally, surface casing of ten inches in diameter is set into position for the first fifty to one hundred feet. Drilling is continued inside the surface casing and eight-inch casing is set on the top of the steam horizon. This casing is fitted with a special valve to stop the flow of water and steam through the casing until it has been cemented into place. The casing is cemented into position by placing a precalculated amount of cement in the lower part of the casing and then forcing the cement, by water pressure, to rise around the outside. The bottom valve and any cement remaining in the bottom of the hole are removed by drilling. A master valve, in conjunction with a gate valve for reducing the size of the bore, is fitted to the top of the casing as a master control. When large steam wells are initially opened, water and steam issue in a plume rising two hundred to five hundred feet, accompanied by considerable quantities of rock fragments. After the debris is discharged the steam and water are usually discharged horizontally into a silencer to reduce the noise.

The ratio of steam to water from a well depends on the extent to which the well is "throttled" down to give increased pressure. The quantity of steam varies inversely with the wellhead pressure. In New Zealand the maximum power is obtained on four-inch and six-inch bores at about 70 psi. Ten such wells are capable of generating 16,600 kilowatts. The best of the four-inch wells produce about 21,000 pounds of steam per hour at 70 psi. A six-inch well will produce about 61,000 pounds at the same wellhead pressure. An eight-inch well will probably produce about twice as much as a six-inch well. A good eight-inch well will discharge four tons of a steam-and-water mixture per minute. The noise from such a well is tremendous and the need for a silencer is obvious. The large eight-inch wells give a shut-in pressure as high as 430 psi but 200 to 350 psi is more common. No relationship between depth and steam production is apparent. Instead, production appears to be controlled by the permeability of the rocks, irrespective of depth.

About 90 percent of the water in the steam-water mixture discharged by the wells can be removed by passing the discharge over a 180° bend centrifuge separator; the remaining 10 percent must be removed in a cyclone separator. Since most of the corrosive impurities are in the water fraction, a good separation is essential.

COMPOSITION OF THE STEAM-AND-WATER MIXTURE. The gas content of the steam is low, rarely exceeding 0.05 percent. The proportion of gases varies from well to well, but usually runs around 90 percent CO_2, with small quantities of hydrogen, nitrogen, hydrogen sulphide, methane, and ethane. The water contains principally sodium chloride, with minor amounts of metaboric acid (HBO_2), potassium, lithium, fluoride, ammonium, etc. A typical analysis, as given by Hamilton, is as follows:

	Parts per million
Sodium	820.00
Potassium	57.00
Lithium	3.00
Ammonium	2.30
Chloride	1254.00
Fluoride	4.00
Sulphate	9.20
Bicarbonate	35.00
Metaboric acid	71.00
Hydrogen sulphide	.01

Corrosion is definitely greater in geothermal steam than in typical boiler-plant steam but by careful selection of materials and design it can be adequately controlled for the life of the equipment.

POWER RESOURCES OF THE AREA. It is estimated that full development of the Wairakei area would yield 134,600 kilowatts of electric power. This estimate is based on utilization of the permeable layers near the surface. If drier steam is obtained at greater depth this figure would be substantially increased. In an effort to compare the potential of other areas in New Zealand with the Wairakei area, careful estimates of the natural heat escape in the various areas have been made. These furnish a comparison of the possibilities as far as they can be ascertained without drilling.

	Heat escape in millions Btu per hour relative to 0° C.
Wairakei	2150
Waiotapu	1400
Oraeki Korako	1000
Rotokaua	750

Several other areas with smaller figures are not included above.

USE OF STEAM FOR PRODUCTION OF HEAVY WATER.[8] Heavy water occurs in small amounts in all water, its concentration being about 1 part in 5,400 parts by weight of ordinary water. The production of heavy water is important because it is used as a moderator in atomic piles, particularly those designed for power generation.

A gallon of water weighs ten pounds while a gallon of heavy water weighs eleven pounds, hence the name. Heavy water has a boiling point of 101.42° C. as compared to 100° C. for ordinary water, a fact making possible the recovery of heavy water by fractional distillation. The tremendous quantities of water which must be boiled away to recover heavy water make the expense prohibitive under normal conditions. However, at Wairakei, where large quantities of geothermal steam are available, production of heavy water would be quite feasible. Plans were

[8] Deuterium or heavy hydrogen (atomic weight 2) is an isotope of hydrogen. Its natural occurrence is one part of deuterium in 6700 parts of ordinary hydrogen. In water its compound with oxygen is known as "heavy water" (D_2O). Heavy water is used to slow the speed of neutrons in nuclear investigations.

made to establish a plant at Wairakei to produce heavy water in conjunction with the generation of electricity. Later, the heavy-water-plant
project was abandoned and the installations were confined to the production of electric power. By 1954 eighteen wells, ranging from 574
to 3,200 feet in depth, were producing enough steam to generate 20,000
kilowatts of electric power. By 1958, 65,000 kilowatts were being produced from thirty-nine wells. A total of eighty-eight wells have been
drilled in the Wairakei area, of which fifty-seven are rated as commercial, with a power potential of 226,000 kilowatts. Power installations
are now (1961) being increased to bring the capacity of the area up to
91,400 kilowatts.[9]

The extensive natural steam resources of North Island, which even
now are not fully explored, will unquestionably play an important role
in the future development of New Zealand.

Developments in Iceland

A general description of Iceland has already been given in Chapter 11
in connection with the Icelandic type of eruption. It may be well, however, to point out again that Iceland consists entirely of volcanic material, chiefly successive outpourings of basaltic lava which have piled
up a mass that rises from the ocean floor to nearly seven thousand feet
above sea level. Following a long period of repose, the present volcanic
activity, which began in the Pleistocene (Ice Age) and has continued
uninterrupted to the present, is limited to a zone which crosses the central portion of the island in a northeast-southwest direction (Fig. 40).

Hot springs and geysers of Iceland

As defined by Allen and Day (1935), "Hot springs are circulating
ground water of surface origin heated and augmented by steam originally in a superheated state rising from an underlying magma through
deep cracks in the earth's crust." This statement so completely fits the
hot springs and geysers of Iceland that no additional comment is needed.

Hot springs and geysers are widely distributed in Iceland but the most
abundant and best known are in the southwestern part in the vicinity of

[9] Furnished by the Department of Scientific and Industrial Research, Wellington, New Zealand, April 13, 1961.

Reykjavík. A geyser is a special type of hot spring which at intervals erupts a column of steam and boiling water. There are about thirty true geysers in Iceland, which represent only 1 percent or less of the total number of hot springs. This compares with two hundred geysers in Yellowstone National Park, which is about 10 percent of the number of hot springs there. New Zealand, the only other area in the world in which geysers are found, has fewer than Iceland, but its chief claim to geologic fame is based on the world's largest geyser, Waimanga, which was active from 1890 until 1904.

The most famous spouting hot spring in the world, which has given the name *geyser* to such phenomenon, is Big Geysir in Iceland. The name, an Icelandic word meaning "to gush," was first applied to this particular spring in 1647 by Bishop Sveinsson. Thus, in Iceland the word *Geysir* is a proper name and applies only to this particular boiling spring. In 1846 the German scientist Bunsen studied Geysir and proposed an explanation for its intermittent eruptions. Through his work the word was introduced as a technical term for all hot springs which show intermittent fountain action. For unknown reasons the English spelling was modified to *geyser*.

Big Geysir, known long before the Yellowstone or New Zealand geysers, is owned and carefully supervised by the Icelandic government. Its eruptions, which range from one hundred to two hundred feet in height, occur at irregular intervals varying from a few hours to a few days, or even weeks. From 1915 to 1935 it was absolutely inactive, but was reactivated by the cutting of a notch in the lip surrounding the basin, which lowered the water level about three feet. Immediately it became active again, and although the gap was subsequently closed, with the return of the water level to its previous mark, the activity continued.

The nature of geyser action

Geysers have much in common with volcanoes, in addition to occurrence in the same regions, in areas where recently active volcanoes exist. Geyser activity is quite similar to volcanic eruption in its intermittent nature and in the part played by steam. In fact, the eruption of Big Geysir has been compared to a volcanic eruption (Sonder, 1937). The German chemist R. Bunsen proposed the commonly accepted explanation of geyser action, a theory based on studies of Big Geysir more than one hundred years ago. Bunsen's explanation takes into account the increase in the boiling point of water due to increase in pressure in the geyser tube. If the tube is too restricted to allow convection currents to operate, much of the water in the geyser tube will be heated to a temperature above the surface boiling point but will not boil because of the increased pressure. Finally, some of the water in the tube reaches its boiling point, even at the increased pressure, and some steam forms. The expanding steam pushes up the column of water sufficiently to cause some of it to overflow. This may happen several times, reducing the pressure in the tube until the water is above its boiling point and it flashes into steam. This is the eruption, which continues until the tube is emptied. The tube refills and the process is repeated, sometimes at regular intervals, as in the case of Old Faithful geyser in Yellowstone National Park, but more often irregularly.

While the above explanation is the one still commonly given in textbooks, it has long been known that it does not fit all types of geysers. It is beyond the scope of the present work to review all the theories which have been proposed, but it is appropriate to call attention to the work of Thorkelsson (1940) on the geysers of Iceland. His theory, published in Icelandic and Danish journals, is not widely known in the United States. It is based on the entrance of "spring" gas (derived from magmatic water and from normal ground water) into the geyser tube. As the gas rises it produces a gentle ebullition (boilinglike action), which carries the heat upward in the geyser tube, and also reduces the density of the water in the tube. The gases, being in contact with hot water, will become saturated with steam. Thorkelsson calculated that if the temperature is $2°$ C. below the boiling point the spring gases make up 6.9 percent by volume against 93.1 percent steam. The gases, however, in spite of their small quantity, are necessary for the existence of the "steam bubbles," which many investigators have observed rising in the geyser tube. Barth (1950, p. 60) cites an example of a geyser in Iceland which boils slowly for a period, then increases to violent boiling, which empties the basin. It then fills again with slowly boiling water, gradually becomes violently boiling, and again is emptied. This cycle takes about one hour. However, the maximum temperature in the spring is $97°$ C.,

showing that ebullition by rising gases rather than steam is responsible
for the "boiling." Such "cold"-water geysers have forced a re-examination of Bunsen's theory. Barth (1950, p. 82) summarizes Thorkelsson's
theory as follows: "The influx of gas will produce violent ebullition;
heat will be carried rapidly upward by the gas bubbles and the ebullition will spread downward; great quantities of gas and water become
engaged in the eruption. It is like opening the stopper of a bottle of
soda water: gas bubbles form in the bottle and the contents erupt."
Thus the striking similarity between geysers and volcanoes, in both of
which gas is the prime agent in the eruption, is apparent.

Utilization of geothermal heat

It has long been the custom of the Icelanders to use the hot springs
near Reykjavík as a free public bath and wash-house. Many also cook
their food either in the hot ground or in the hot springs. For example,
bread was cooked by placing it in tin molds and covering it with hot
earth or lowering it into the spring. About the middle of the nineteenth
century the hot water from the springs was used to evaporate sea water
which had been pumped into shallow pans in order to recover salt.
The average temperature of Iceland (37° F.) is too cold for many types
of plants, but in the vicinity of the hot springs mild temperatures permit
the growing of many plants not possible elsewhere. In some cases the
warm areas are extended by carrying the hot water in pipes through
the soil. Natural hot water is also used to heat extensive greenhouses
in which many vegetables, flowers, and even tropical fruits such as
bananas are grown.

Initially, in 1928, hot water from the nearby springs was pumped
to Reykjavík and used to heat the hospital, a school, and a swimming
pool. The results were so satisfactory that it was decided to expand the
system to a city-wide basis. Since a larger source of water was needed,
a spring at Reykir, ten miles east of Reykjavík was selected for development. This spring had a flow of 1,320 gallons per minute at a temperature of 80° C. In order to increase the amount of water, wells were
drilled to depths ranging from 450 feet to 1,200 feet. Work was begun
in 1939 but was stopped by World War II before completion of the

PLATE 35. Steam well at Hveragerdi, Iceland. A natural steam power plant with a capacity of 15,000 kw. is to be completed in 1963.

project. The wells, ranging from four inches to eight inches in diameter, are concentrated in an area of 160 acres. The water temperature from the wells is 87° C., as compared to 80° C. in the surface spring. Work was renewed on the project by Danish engineers and the first houses heated by the new works were connected in December, 1943. Now 90 percent of the houses in Reykjavík, a city of 55,000 population, are heated by the municipally owned water system under the supervision of the Hot Water Board. The main problem in piping the hot water is insulation, since the source is ten miles from the city and the low winter temperatures in Iceland would soon cool the water. For the main supply pipes the insulation is lava slag and peat; for the urban system, lava slag; and for the individual houses, glass wool sealed with tar paper. The heat loss from the wells to the outlet in the homes is held to between 5° C. and 6° C. (Illingworth, 1949). Recent borings (Bodvärsson, 1960) within the city of Reykjavík are providing per second about 100 liters of water with a temperature of up to 138° C., while the springs and wells at Reykir furnish per second about 320 liters of water at 87° C.

The water is piped from the wells to insulated holding tanks from which pumps deliver it through fourteen-inch insulated lines to the main reservoir tanks above the city. From these reservoir tanks there is gravity feed to the outlets in the city, with booster pumps helping out when the load is heavy. In the schools the water serves a double function: after it has run through the radiators it is used in swimming pools. Charges for the water, which is metered, are based on the amount used. The average cost is about 10 percent below the cost of hot-water heating which utilizes conventional fuels. The upkeep is low and the city realizes a substantial profit on the investment. It is estimated that the total cost of the installation is about 1,000,000 pounds and that the yearly profit is around 50,000 pounds, an average return of 5 percent.

The town of Sellfoss, Iceland, also has a municipal hot-water system similar to that at Reykjavík. The utilization of natural heat for domestic heating and for greenhouse heating is being expanded and as of now (1960) about one-fourth of the population of Iceland live in houses heated by natural heat. It seems likely that this ratio may be increased to one-half in the near future.

Developments in Sonoma County, California

General geologic characteristics

The best known of the numerous hydrothermal areas in California is "The Geysers," eighteen miles east of Cloverdale and about ninety-five miles north of San Francisco (Fig. 59). It is on the western edge of the Mayacmas Range, in the Coast Range, which trends in a north-westerly direction, parallel to the Pacific coast. The highest peak in the range is Mount St. Helena (4,344 ft.), whose name is sometimes applied to the Range. The Mayacmas Range is composed of sharply folded, faulted, and metamorphosed rocks of the Franciscan group of Jurassic Age. These rocks form the "basement" in this area. They consist of sandstones and shales which have been intruded by diabases and gabbros, now largely altered to serpentine and related schists. Cretaceous rocks are present in the region but they are preserved largely in synclinal areas and are not present in the immediate vicinity of The Geysers. The backbone of the Mayacmas Range is doubtless volcanic, for the high peaks, such as Mount St. Helena, are composed of lavas and tuffs and are typical volcanic edifices.

The Sonoma group, a series of lava flows, tuffs, and nonmarine conglomerates and alluvial sediments of Pliocene and Pleistocene ages, occur in scattered patches overlying the Franciscan rocks. The first volcanic activity represented by the Sonoma consisted of lava flows, followed by pyroclastics, which are now chiefly pumiceous tuffs. Simultaneously the streams were actively eroding the slopes of the volcanic cones and spreading over the area large quantities of gravel and sand as alluvial aprons, which are interbedded with the volcanics. This heterogeneous mixture is the Sonoma group.

Structure

In general the Mayacmas Range is an anticlinorium of Franciscan rocks with the adjacent synclines containing younger Mesozoic sediments. The whole region has been intricately fragmented by a system of northwest trending faults, which control the drainage and the topography. The faulting, which began in late Tertiary (pre-Sonoma), has continued to the present. The latest faulting, which is doubtless still in progress, consists predominantly of strike-slip (lateral) movements in which the southwestern segment is moving northward with respect to the northeastern segment (Fig. 59). The southwestern side, in many cases, has been uplifted as well as moved laterally. Along the Healdsburg Fault, which extends northwest through Healdsburg, lateral displacement of three miles can be recognized. Interestingly, this same type of movement occurred along the famous San Andreas Fault in the 1906 San Francisco earthquake. The San Andreas Fault is about twenty miles to the west, along the Pacific coast. The Healdsburg Fault, projected southward, is lost under recent alluvium near San Pablo Bay. The Hayward Fault (along which horizontal displacement occurred in the earthquake of 1868) is an approximate continuation of the trend of the Healdsburg zone of faulting to the south of San Pablo Bay.

The Geysers is located in a zone of faulting about eight miles to the east of the Healdsburg Fault. The fault on which The Geysers is located follows Sulphur Creek, a narrow canyon along the southwestern side of the Mayacmas Range. The belt containing the steam vents and the hot springs is parallel to the strike of the rocks of the Franciscan and also closely related to the band of serpentine intrusions. The western side of the Mayacmas Range has been an important producer of quicksilver since 1862. The cinnabar is found, like the steam vents, along fault zones in the Franciscan, and much of the ore is associated with hydrothermally altered serpentine.

The Geysers is said to have been discovered in 1846. A hotel-health resort was established at the site in 1852. When it is recalled that Yellowstone was not discovered until 1870, it is rather surprising that the name *Geysers* was applied to an area devoid of geysers. Today the area is a recreational and health resort. The fumarole and hot-springs area is about fifty yards from the mouth of Geyser Creek, a small tributary which enters Sulphur Creek from the north. The hot springs are generally along the creek bed, while the fumaroles are higher on the banks. The most active area comprises about fifty acres. The fumarole which discharges the greatest volume of steam is known as The Smokestack; others are Steamboat and Safety Valve. The temperature, as recorded

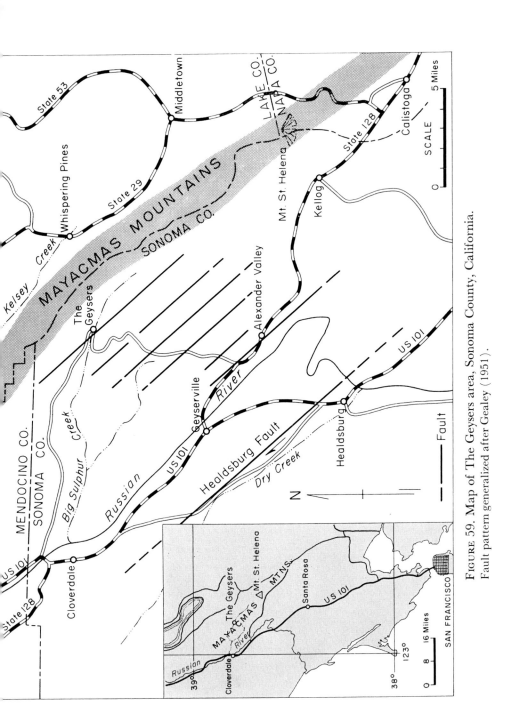

FIGURE 59. Map of The Geysers area, Sonoma County, California. Fault pattern generalized after Gealey (1951).

by Allen and Day (1927), at a depth of three feet was 101.5° C. at Steamboat Fumarole and 98° C. at Safety Valve Fumarole.

The first drilling was done in 1921 by Mr. J. D. Grant in the hope of using the steam to generate electric power. At a depth of 203 feet a steam pressure of 62 psi was encountered. In 1922, when a second well was drilled, using steam from the first for power, a pressure of 61 psi was found at a depth of 318 feet. By 1925 a total of eight wells had been drilled to depths ranging from 320 to 636 feet. The pressure was greater in deeper wells but did not increase in proportion to depth. Closed-in pressures varied from 60 to 275 psi. Each well was calculated to deliver about one thousand kilowatts. Drilling of new wells did not affect the pressure.

Ground temperature measurements by Allen and Day (1927) at depths of 1.5 to 4 feet varied between 98° C. and 99° C., which is a little higher than the boiling temperature at the prevailing pressure. Temperatures for two of the wells, with valves wide open, were as follows:

Well No. 2, 165.6° C. at the top and 168.6° C. at the depth of 320 ft.

Well No. 4, 163.4° C. at the top and 172.6° C. at a depth of 420 ft. The temperatures varied with the pressure but approximated that of saturated steam.

Composition of water and steam

The composition of the water and steam is influenced by the fact that it comes through a considerable body of serpentine, giving it a high magnesia content. Representative analyses of the steam and other gases, as given by Allen and Day, are as follows:

	Total H_2O	CO_2	H_2	CH_4	N_2A	H_2S	NH_3
		Other gases recalculated to 100%					
Well No. 2	98.68	59.1	16.4	15.8	3.7	3.2	1.8
Well No. 6	98.94	62.7	14.1	14.8	3.2	3.5	1.7
Steamboat Fumarole	99.20	65.2	12.3	13.8	2.7	3.6	2.4

The unusual feature of these gases, other than steam, is the relative high methane and hydrogen and low carbon dioxide content. A number of unusual minerals (Vonsen, 1946, p. 287) have been identified in

PLATE 36. Natural steam development at The Geysers, Sonoma County, California, 1960.   Courtesy Pacific Gas and Electric Company.

the deposits around the hot springs and fumaroles, chiefly sulphates of magnesium, ammonium, aluminum, and iron. Allen and Day concluded that the steam is of magmatic origin, although unquestionably ground water is admixed with it. Their reasons for a magmatic origin are: The steam at The Geysers rises in a region where there should be a meager supply of ground water; it is accompanied by volcanic gases; and the steam is superheated. The temperature and pressure of the steam at The Geysers is equal to and in some cases higher than that at Larderello in

Italy. Furthermore, the gas content is lower, a desirable feature for power development.

In 1955 an experimental well was drilled at The Geysers to a depth of 603 feet. This well, according to reports, penetrated the fault zone, thus making it possible to determine the dip of the fault along which the steam is rising. A bottom rock temperature of 600° F. at a depth of 590 feet, with a measured steam flow equivalent to 1,450 kilowatts, was reported. An increase of 100° F. in bottom-rock temperature was obtained in the 100 feet of additional depth, as compared to an adjoining well. It is anticipated that the volume and temperature of the steam will increase with deeper drilling along the fault plane. It should be noted, however, that in New Zealand deeper drilling has not resulted in temperature increases proportional to depth. However, if the wells are located so that they penetrate the fault zone at a greater depth, the situation may be quite different. The Thermal Power Company of San Francisco has a lease on a belt extending for about five miles along the fault zone in The Geyser area, and plans are under way to drill additional wells and to install steam turbines for generating electric power.[10]

A small power plant using the natural steam in a reciprocating engine has produced electricity for the small community at The Geysers for the past thirty years. The steam has also been used to heat the buildings and a swimming pool.

Other Steam Areas in the World

No complete list of the areas in which natural steam prospects are being considered or developed is available, but some of those which have come to the writer's attention are listed below.

The West Indies

A geothermal survey has been made on the island of St. Lucia, first island south of Martinique in the Lesser Antilles. Since the study

[10] The Pacific Gas and Electric Company opened the first commercial geothermal power plant in the United States at The Geysers in 1960. The initial installation was a 12,500 kw. power plant but plans are under way to expand this capacity.

PLATE 37. Geothermal power plant at The Geysers, Sonoma County, California. This plant, which was placed in operation in 1960, is the first commercial installation of this type in the United States. Courtesy Pacific Gas and Electric Company.

revealed that the total heat of the steam exceeds that of saturated steam, it is presumed to be of magmatic origin. No drilling has been done.

El Salvador

Preliminary studies have been carried on by the Servicio Geologico Nacional de El Salvador for several years. The area which appears to be the most promising is the hot springs, mud pots, and fumaroles near Ahuachapan in western El Salvador. On the basis of a survey of the surface-heat loss, McBirney (1956) concluded that the area had possibilities for power production. His study also indicated that the steam was in all probability of magmatic origin, a fact which would imply that high-pressure and high-temperature steam might be obtained by drilling. Only shallow test drilling has been carried out so far (1960), but plans for a thorough exploration of the area are under way.

Nicaragua

In Nicaragua are numerous hot-spring and fumarole areas which may be potential sources of geothermal energy. The area which has received the most attention is about eighteen miles north of León, at the northeastern base of San Jacinto Volcano. San Jacinto Volcano is one of a cluster of volcanic cones of which Telica has been intermittently active since the time of the earliest Spanish occupation of the area in the sixteenth century. San Jacinto itself has had no eruptions in historic time. The most active part of the San Jacinto fumarole area covers about twenty acres and consists of many boiling springs, mud pots, and steam vents. A few kilometers to the northeast, apparently aligned along a fracture, is another area known as "Tisate." Recent studies (McBirney, 1955) indicate that at least part of the steam is of magmatic origin and that the area has economic possibilities.

Japan

It is reported that electric power is now being generated at Naruko from natural steam and that additional installations are being made.

Russia

It is reported that electric power is being developed from natural steam in the volcanic region of Kamchatka. No details have been released.

Not all the frontiers of the future are in outer space. The heat and power from within the earth are still largely an unexplored dimension of our universe. The developments described in the preceding pages provide examples of how the power resources from within the earth may be utilized. New and inexpensive sources of power must be developed for the future, since the conventional sources of energy—oil, gas, and coal—all have foreseeable ends of supply. Water power is necessarily limited and while millions of dollars are being spent on the development of atomic solar and tidal power, these are still largely in the experimental stage.

The consumption of electric energy is increasing at a phenomenal rate. In many areas the consumption of power has doubled in the last decade and this pattern may continue for some time into the future. To meet this tremendous increase all sources of energy must be tapped. Atomic energy is certainly on the horizon, but in areas where geothermal steam is available its low cost will make it a competitor with all other sources of energy which may be developed in the relatively near future.

Italy, lacking the more conventional sources of energy, was more or less forced to utilize its natural steam resources, which now have been developed to the point where they are an important national asset. The first geothermal power installation in the United States was put into operation late in 1960. Installations are either under way or in the planning stage in Iceland, New Zealand, and perhaps elsewhere. The engineering problems of utilizing geothermal steam have been solved—all that is required is an adequate source of steam. We are also discovering that deposits of natural steam are far more widely distributed than was formerly suspected. The low cost of power from natural steam and the almost inexhaustible supply which a deposit will yield is an incentive to explore all possible areas without delay.

Come wander with me, she said,
Into regions yet untrod;
And read what is still unread
In the manuscripts of God.

LONGFELLOW

15. VOLCANOES IN GEOLOGIC PERSPECTIVE

ALTHOUGH THE NUMBER OF VOLCANOES known in the world runs into the thousands, only about five hundred have been active in historic times and are considered, therefore, to be "active volcanoes." A recent list (Bull. Volcanologique, 1947) of the active volcanoes of the world contains 476 entries, of which 60 are submarine eruptions. In this list any volcano which has erupted in historic times is considered to be active. Actually, this is somewhat misleading, because some of the volcanoes which are included in the list have not erupted for centuries and today appear to be extinct or dormant. A listing which included only those that show some signs of activity would be most helpful, especially to a person who wished to seek an active volcano in order to observe an eruption. However, for our immediate purpose, that is, to consider the distribution of volcanoes as a clue to their origin, the present listing is quite satisfactory. Any eruption in historic time, regardless of how remote, is certainly in the "present" if considered as a part of geologic time.

Distribution of Active Volcanoes
General distribution

The great majority of the active volcanoes, as well as the recently active, are concentrated in a belt bordering the Pacific Ocean (Fig. 60). So marked is the concentration of active volcanoes in this belt that it is known as the "fire girdle of the Pacific." The volcanoes in these encircling areas are associated with geologically young or still growing mountains which are arranged as a series of festoons or arcs around the margin of the Pacific Ocean. The convex side of the arc is always toward the Pacific Ocean. A second belt of recent mountain building which contains active volcanoes is the Alpine-Himalayan zone, extending from southeastern Europe through the Mediterranean and southern Asia and into the East Indies Archipelago. In addition, more or less isolated volcanoes occur within each of the three great oceanic regions of the world, the Pacific, the Atlantic, and the Indian oceans.

In the circum-Pacific belt the volcanoes are either near the margin of the bordering continent or in island arcs which lie along the continental margin. In striking contrast, the lands bordering the Atlantic Ocean are relatively free of volcanoes, earthquakes, and growing mountains. In only two places do the Pacific type of island arcs encroach on the Atlantic: in the volcanic loop of the Lesser Antilles at the eastern border of the Caribbean Sea and in a similar loop of the Southern Antilles which links Patagonia with Grahamland in the far South Atlantic. Otherwise, volcanic activity in the Atlantic is limited largely to islands on the mid-Atlantic Ridge, such as the Azores and Iceland, and to the Canary and Cape Verde islands off the west coast of Africa.

The following tabulation of the world's active volcanoes, though necessarily incomplete, is inclusive enough to show the pattern of distribution. The information on which the compilation is based is the most reliable obtainable, but in some cases it can be only an estimate.

ACTIVE VOLCANOES OF THE WORLD[1]

	Partial Total	Subtotal	Total
Circum-Pacific belt			283
Asia and the southwestern Pacific		163	
*Kamchatka	20		
*Kurile Islands	33		
Japan	49		
*Philippines	11		
*Melanesia (New Guinea, New Britain, Admiralty Islands, Solomon Islands, Santa Cruz Islands, and New Hebrides)	29		
New Zealand, Kermadec Islands, Tonga Islands, and Samoa Islands	21		
North America		48	
Alaska and Aleutian Islands	36		
Western United States	1		
*Mexico	11		
*Central America		31	
Costa Rica	6		
Nicaragua	11		
El Salvador	7		
Guatemala	7		
South America		41	
Southern Andes	22		
Central Andes	8		
Northern Andes	11		

(Continued on p. 369)

[1] Information on areas marked with an asterisk (*) is based on Catalogue of the Active Volcanoes of the World (1951–1959). Other figures compiled from miscellaneous sources.

	Partial Total	Subtotal	Total
Alpine-Himalayan belt			98
Canary Islands		3	
Mediterranean area (Italy, Sicily, and			
Aegean Sea)		17	
Barren Island (Bay of Bengal)		1	
*Indonesia		77	
Sumatra	12		
Java	20		
Lesser Sunda Islands	20		
Banda Sea	8		
Celebes	6		
Sangihe Islands	5		
Moluccas	6		
Pacific Ocean			7
Hawaiian Islands		4	
Galapagos Islands		3	
Atlantic Ocean			46
Iceland	26		
Azores		9	
Lesser Antilles (West Indies)		9	
St. Paul Rocks		1	
Cape Verde Islands		1	
Indian Ocean			2
Reunion Island		1	
Heard Island		1	
*Africa			16
Ethiopia and Red Sea		6	
East Africa		7	
Central Africa		2	
West Africa		1	
Antarctic			2
Grand Total			454

Perhaps the most significant fact revealed by the accompanying distribution list is that almost two-thirds of the active volcanoes are in the Pacific region. If the Lesser Antilles and the Indonesian arcs are included with the Pacific, as is suggested later, the dominance of the Pacific becomes even more striking. This concentration of volcanoes in a belt surrounding the Pacific Ocean suggests that in this zone must exist some unusual conditions which have a direct relation to the origin of volcanoes. When it is discovered that most of the earthquakes of the world are also centered in this same belt and that it also includes the youngest mountains, some of which are still growing, the connection seems unmistakable. A brief survey of the two major volcanic belts will be helpful in speculating on these relationships.

Volcanic belts

CIRCUM-PACIFIC VOLCANIC BELT. In a survey of the circum-Pacific volcanic belt (Fig. 60) it will be convenient to begin with the Alaska Peninsula and its continuation, the Aleutian Islands, which contain 36 volcanoes (Coats, 1950) that have erupted in historic time. The Kamchatka Peninsula and the Kurile Islands, with fifty-three active volcanoes, are the Asiatic counterpart of the Alaskan-Aleutian arc. Farther southward the next area is the Japan arc, then through the Ryukyu Islands to the Philippines, the latter with eleven active volcanoes. Then the belt continues through New Guinea, New Hebrides, and the Solomon Islands, where numerous active volcanoes occur, and to New Zealand. From New Zealand the belt is continued to the northeast through the Kermadec Islands, the Tongas, and Samoa. Significantly, an extension of this trend would include the Hawaiian Islands.

From Alaska southward down the Pacific coast of North America no active volcanoes occur until Mount Lassen in northern California is reached, although a number of peaks in the Cascade Mountains were certainly active in very recent geologic time. A wide gap exists in the volcanic belt, from California to southern Mexico, where active volcanoes are again found. With some minor gaps the belt is then continuous through Central America and the Andes of South America.

ALPINE-HIMALAYAN BELT. Along the Alpine-Himalayan belt—apart from Indonesia—volcanoes are distributed more sporadically. The volcanic belt can be traced from the Canary and Madeira islands through the Mediterranean region, where it includes Vesuvius, Stromboli, Vulcano, and Etna in Italy and Sicily, thence to the Aegean volcanoes, the best known being Santorin, and eastward to Mount Ararat on the Turkey-Armenian border, and Mount Demavend in Iran, near the southern end of the Caspian Sea. Mount Ararat and Mount Demavend, although prominent volcanic cones, have not been active in historic time. Mount Ararat, according to tradition, was the resting place of Noah's ark. Beyond the Himalayas the volcanic belt reappears in Burma and continues southward through Barren Island, in the Bay of Bengal, where historic eruptions are known to have occurred. The belt then continues through Sumatra, with twelve active volcanoes, Java, with twenty vents, and the Lesser Sunda Islands, with twenty centers of activity. The Indonesian section (Sumatra, Java, etc.) is a typical island arc such as those characteristic of the circum-Pacific belt.

With the uneven spacing of volcanoes in this belt long gaps occur, especially in the main section of the Alps and Himalayas. It has been suggested that in these regions, where the crust has been greatly thickened by folding and overthrusting, the magma has not been able to penetrate to the surface. Volcanoes are present around the margins of such areas, but the central portion of both the Alps and the Himalayas, as well as the highly compressed core of other fold-mountain ranges exhibit no recent volcanic activity.

Significance of distribution pattern

From the above survey we may conclude that the active volcanoes of the world are concentrated in a belt encircling the Pacific Ocean, and that they are aligned in a series of arcuate chains, or island arcs. Only three island arcs, each surmounted by a row of active volcanoes, are known outside the Pacific Ocean. These are Indonesia, the Lesser Antilles, and the Southern Antilles arcs, and each borders the Pacific Ocean in such a way that the structures may belong to the Pacific belt. The volcanoes in the Atlantic Ocean are, for the most part, related to the mid-Atlantic ridge. This ridge, throughout its entire extent from Iceland on the north to Tristan de Cunha in the far South Atlantic, conforms so closely with the configuration of the continents as to suggest some fundamental relationship.

It is apparent, then, that volcanoes, island arcs, and new mountains are all interrelated and that it is impossible to explain one without taking the others into account. Accordingly, in a discussion of island arcs and mountain making the relation of volcanoes to each of these will become apparent. In this way volcanoes will be placed in their proper perspective, that is, they will be understood as one manifestation of the complex process of the birth of a mountain range.

Linear spacing of volcanoes

A particularly striking feature of the linear arrangement of volcanoes is the tendency for the interval between members of a group to be nearly constant. For example, the volcanoes of the Galapagos Islands are roughly twenty miles apart (Fig. 61). A similar spacing is indicated in Hawaii, Fiji, and Tahiti. In the Canary Islands, as well as in the Lesser Antilles, the distance is roughly doubled; and in the northern Andes it is halved. In the Phlegraean Fields the volcanoes are situated at the corners of a triangular network in which the cones are only from one to two miles apart. The question which naturally arises is whether the spacing is significant and what inferences, if any, can be drawn from it. It has been repeatedly stressed that volcanic vents are located at the intersection of two sets of fractures. If this is true, then the spacing may be a clue to the thickness of the earth's crust. To illustrate this point, Shand (1938, p. 83) suggests that a slab of chocolate be used to represent the earth's crust. It can be broken by bending, and the pieces in turn, can be broken in the same way, but with greater and greater difficulty as the length and the width of the pieces approach their thickness, after which they cannot be broken anymore by bending. In the same way, the interval between neighboring volcanoes, assuming that they are along fractures which divide the earth's crust into blocks, should be roughly equal to the thickness of the earth's crust at each place.

Admittedly the interval is only suggestive, but it is a point worthy of

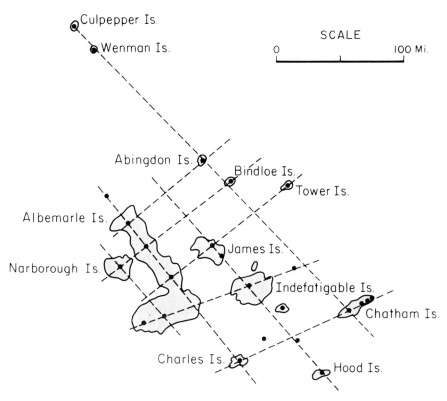

FIGURE 61. Spacing of the volcanoes in the Galapagos Islands.
After Shand (1938).

consideration. One cannot fail to be impressed by the frequency of an interval of about twenty miles between the larger volcanoes, and by the further coincidence that earthquakes accompanying many volcanic eruptions come from a depth of about twenty miles. The shallowness of the magma at Vesuvius (adjacent to the Phlegraean Fields), perhaps about three miles in depth, although not, of course, as shallow as indicated by the spacing in the Phlegraean Fields, still suggests a general area of agreement and gives support to this theory of relationship between thickness of the earth's crust and the distance between volcanoes.

Island Arcs

Location and Structure

Island arcs are a very conspicuous feature of the earth's surface but they are not uniformly distributed. They are common features around the borders of the Pacific Ocean, especially along the eastern border of Asia (Fig. 3). They do not occur in the Atlantic Ocean, except for the two which have already been mentioned. Island arcs are usually surmounted by active volcanoes and they are also zones of strong seismic (earthquake) activity. They are so situated that a deep furrow in the ocean floor (known as a marginal deep) lies on their convex, or ocean-basin, side and a relatively shallow platform attaching the shoal to the continental mass lies on their concave, or landward, side. In some cases deep sea basins separate the island arc from the mainland, and the island arcs, such as the Marianas, Yap, and Palau arcs off the China coast, stand more or less isolated in front of the continental mass. Others continue into the continent and have a counterpart on the mainland. Such are the East Indies arc, which continues into the Asiatic continent at Burma, and the Aleutian arc, which continues into the North American continent at Alaska. The Aleutian Islands, with a front of 1,450 miles, are bordered on the Pacific side by the Aleutian Trench, a long narrow trough more than 2,000 miles long and 50 to 100 miles wide with a maximum depth of slightly over 25,000 feet. Back of it is the Bering Sea, a relatively shallow body of water, much of which is less than 100 fathoms in depth. The Aleutian arc fits a radius of 760 miles (Fig. 50).

The main island of Japan is defined by an arc with a radius of 650 miles. Offshore from the northern part of the arc lies the Tuscarora deep, a part of the Japan Trench.

Island arcs are structural features and must have a marginal deep on the ocean side; they must also give evidence of volcanic activity. Hence, a row of islands more or less arc-shape, such as those off the coast of British Columbia, are not typical island arcs, since they are not associated with deep sea troughs and are not the site of active volcanoes. The association of active volcanoes with typical island arcs is so striking that they become an important factor in considering the origin of volcanoes.

It was the great Austrian geologist, Edward Suess (1904), who early in the twentieth century, in his classic work *The Face of The Earth,* focused attention on the arcuate structure of the great mountain systems of the earth. It was early noted that the arcuate belts are arranged around the ancient nucleus (of each continent), spreading in an ever-widening arc, the younger the arc the greater its distance from the nucleus. Many ancient mountain systems were the site of active volcanoes when they were being formed. We may infer, then, that the present island arcs, with their associated volcanoes, are mountain ranges in the process of being formed.

Island arcs, to the geologist, are one of the most challenging features of the earth's surface. Many theories have been offered to explain them but none is entirely satisfactory. Nevertheless, much can be learned by considering some of the theories which have been proposed, realizing that the final answer is yet to come.

Island arcs occur as single arcs and as double arcs. Where the arc is double, as in the Sumatra-Java arc of the East Indies (Fig. 70), the active volcanoes are always associated with the inner arc. Some arcs are strongly arcuate while others have only a slight curvature. It was early pointed out that many mountains and island arcs are truly circular if traced on a large-scale globe. If one slices deeply into an orange, the trace of the slice on the peel is circular, but if the peel is flattened out, as in the case of a flat map of the earth, it becomes arcuate. Further, the radius of the arc is dependent on the angle of the slice. It appears, then, that a slice (or shear zone) at the base of each island arc would account for its shape. No other explanation is so simple or complete. If a shear zone, or "thrust plane" in geologic terminology, is present, the dip or slope can be determined because it is equal to the angle subtended at the center of the earth by the radius of the arc. This explanation of island arcs appears to hinge on evidence of a deep shear zone associated with each island arc. Such evidence is obtained from a study of earthquakes associated with island arcs.

Relationship to Earthquakes

Earthquakes, which are due primarily to the jar given the earth by slippage along a fault or shear zone, are shaking the earth constantly.

The great majority of earthquakes originate in the crust of the earth at depths not exceeding thirty-five kilometers. In fact, it was long held that no earthquakes could originate below this depth. Such reasoning was based on the idea that because of great heat and pressure the rocks below this depth could not rupture and would yield to stresses by flowage. Thus originated the concept of a zone of fracture, the surface crust down to a depth of ten to fifteen miles, and below this a zone of flowage. In 1928 Harold Jeffreys, a distinguished English scientist, made an exhaustive survey of earthshocks and concluded that the great majority originated in the outer layers of the earth's crust at depths not exceeding thirty-five kilometers, apparently confirming the zone-of-flowage–and–zone-of-fracture concept. In the same year workers in Japan produced clear evidence that aside from the normal shocks with which Jeffreys was dealing, there were other earthquakes in the area around Japan with a focal depth of several hundred kilometers. This was verified.

Later studies divided earthquakes into three classes: (1) normal shocks, at depths not exceeding 60 kilometers, (2) intermediate shocks, at depths from 60 to 250 kilometers, and (3) deep shocks, at depths from 250 to 700 kilometers. No earthquakes have been positively identified with foci exceeding 700 kilometers (435 mi.) in depth. The discovery that earthquakes occur at great depths in the earth does not mean that the earlier idea of a zone of fracture and a zone of flowage is entirely erroneous. A re-examination of the effect of stresses on plastic material has revealed that such material will respond to sudden shocks of short duration, just as a piece of wax may be fashioned into a tuning fork which will respond, as a brittle substance, to a sudden blow, but will be deformed as a plastic when subjected to slow-acting stresses. Seismologists agree that deep-focus earthquakes are in no essential respect different from normal shocks and are caused by slippage along shear zones. This conclusion is basic if deep-focus earthquakes are to be used in the interpretation of island arcs.

Deep-focus earthquakes are known mostly in the island-arc areas around the margin of the Pacific Ocean. In the Japanese area deep-focus earthquakes occur at depths from 300 to 650 kilometers. The important feature concerning these shocks is that the foci increase in depth toward the continent and away from the ocean basin. Similar results are obtained from many other island-arc areas. In island arcs normal seismic activity is concentrated in the marginal trough lying on the convex side of the arc. Shocks with foci of intermediate depth occur continentward, followed in turn by deep-focus shocks sometimes situated well under the continental margin. This establishes the presence of a shear zone extending from the island arc under the continent, and, further, makes possible the determination of the angle of slope (or dip) of the zone. Interestingly, deep-focus earthquakes are not known on the Pacific coast of the United States, but no marginal deeps are present in this area either!

Along the Pacific coast of South America the situation is different. Off the coast of Peru and northern Chile is a marginal trough. In this area deep-focus earthquakes occur continentward, finally attaining a depth of more than six hundred kilometers to the east of the Andes. Further, the area contains many active and recently active volcanoes. Thus, the Andean Cordillera has all the characteristics of an island arc. It seems clear, then, that shear zones (as defined by deep-focus earthquakes) are associated with island arcs and that they dip inward beneath the continents, implying that the continents are overriding the ocean basins, or that the ocean basins are underthrusting the continents. The slope of the shear zone, as determined from the depth of earthquake foci varies considerably from that determined by the curvature of the arc. In most cases the curvature of the arc is rather arbitrarily established, and there is also the possibility of crustal deformation of the arc by later movements. More probable, however, is the possibility of a change in the slope of the shear plane as it extends deeper into the earth. Having established the fact that island arcs are at intersections of shear zones with the earth's surface, the geologist still must answer the problem of origin. Before he can intelligently consider this question he must give some attention to the composition of the outer part of the crust of the earth, which is basic to a solution.

The Earth's Crust

The outer shell, or crust, of the earth is made up of rocks in great variety, which on land areas of the globe are commonly covered by a

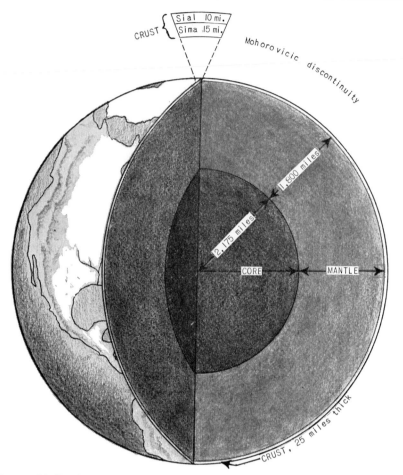

FIGURE 62. Section of the earth showing the various zones.

layer of soil or loose debris. From a study of the rate of transmission of earthquake waves it is known that the crustal zone has a thickness of from eighteen to twenty-seven miles, a density of under 3.0, and a structure which consists of two relatively distinct layers. Below the crust and extending to a depth of about eighteen hundred miles is a zone known as the "mantle" (Fig. 62). The velocity of earthquake waves in this zone indicates that it is solid and of somewhat greater density than the crust. Below the mantle and extending to the center of the earth is the core. The core is believed to be composed of nickel-iron alloys and to have a central density of around 15. The fact that the S-wave of an earthquake is not transmitted through the core leads to the conclusion that it is, at least in part, liquid.

Volcanoes are not related in any way to the liquid core of the earth, but have their origin in the crust and upper mantle layers, and at a depth probably not exceeding twenty miles. These layers, therefore, are the only part of the earth directly relevant to a consideration of volcanoes.

From thousands of analyses of the rocks of the earth's crust the average composition has been established. The remarkable fact is that eight elements make up more than 98 percent of the rocks of the earth's crust. These eight elements in the order of their abundance are: oxygen, silica, aluminum, iron, calcium, sodium, potassium, and magnesium. These elements rarely occur in the native state, but in combination, usually with oxygen to form oxides. Some of these oxides are minerals, like hematite (Fe_2O_3), but more commonly several of the oxides combine to form a mineral. In this process the oxide of silica (SiO_2) is especially important because it not only forms quartz, a very common mineral, but also enters into chemical combination with the other oxides to form a group of rock minerals known as the silicates, which are an important constituent of many rocks. The classification of rocks into igneous, sedimentary, and metamorphic is well known and need not be reviewed here. We are primarily concerned with the igneous rocks (those which cooled from a molten state) and are regarded as primary rocks. Granitized rocks, when they reach the stage of transfusion by through-passage of hot gases, pour out on the surface as lavas known as "rhyolites" or, more commonly, as tuff-flows known as "ignimbrites."

In general the rocks of the earth's crust fall into two contrasted groups, arranged in separate layers.

(1) Light-colored rocks, including granite and related types, having an average specific gravity of about 2.7. Chemically these rocks contain a high percentage of *silica*, up to 70 percent, while *alumina* is the most abundant of the remaining constituents. These rocks are referred to as the "sial," a word coined from the chemical symbols for silicon and aluminum.

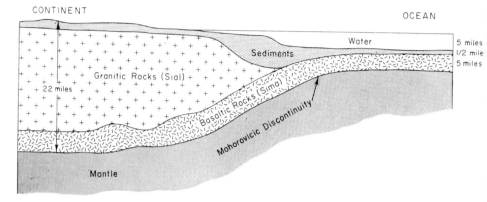

FIGURE 63. Section of continental area and ocean basin showing relationship of sial and sima.   After Stokes (1960).

(2) Dark-colored rocks, including basalt and related types, having a density ranging from 2.9 to 3.4. In these also silica (40–50 percent) is the most abundant constituent, although in considerably lower proportion than in the sialic rocks, while *magnesia* is the most abundant of the remaining constituents. This layer is known as the "sima."

The sial and sima, constituting the crust of the earth, together have a thickness of eighteen to twenty-seven miles, although beneath some of the mountain ranges, such as the Alps, the thickness is much greater. The sial, or upper layer, varies from five to fifteen miles in thickness; the sima or under layer, from ten to twenty miles. The continents consist of sial resting on sima; the ocean floors are composed of sima with little or no sialic cover. It is believed that a few local patches of sial may be present on the floor of the Atlantic and Indian oceans, but sial is entirely absent from the Pacific floor, except possibly in the vicinity of Easter Island (Fig. 63). The absence of sial in the Pacific basin is another indication that the Pacific Ocean is different from the other oceans. The sial, being lighter, would of course float on the sima. Whether the continents stand at a higher level *because* they are composed of sial and must stand higher to balance the heavier sima of the ocean basins is one of the unsolved problems of geology. Volcanoes which erupt from the floor of the Pacific Ocean yield basaltic lavas with the composition of the sima, but volcanic products corresponding to the sial (or some form of reaction with sial) in composition, such as rhyolite and ignimbrite, are confined to volcanoes on continents and islands underlain by sial. The Andesite Line, which marks the border between the continental mass and the ocean basin may be some distance from the present edge of the continent, as is strikingly shown in the southwest Pacific (Fig. 3).

Mountains and Geosynclines

Deposition of sediments

The great mountain systems of the earth, such as the Appalachians, the Alps, and the Rockies, invariably consist dominantly of sedimentary rocks and volcanic material, frequently highly metamorphosed by earth movements. It has taken many years and the work of many geologists to firmly establish the concept that the great mountain systems are born out of downwarps in the earth's crust in which tremendous thicknesses of sediments had accumulated. It was near the middle of the last century when the Rogers brothers discovered from their studies in the Appalachian Mountains that the folded sediments, out of which the mountains were formed, were shallow-water types, largely marine, which at places attain a thickness of forty thousand feet. In the nonfolded region in the interior of North America rocks of the same age are only a fraction of this thickness. Thus it came to be recognized that all the great mountain systems of the earth invariably consist of thick accumulations of sediments mixed with volcanic material. It is true that these rocks have been profoundly metamorphosed by earth movements until now they may be slates, marbles, or similar rocks, but the original sedimentary nature is unmistakable.

The sediments making up the mountain chain are usually shallow-water deposits with ripple marks, mud cracks, and other shallow-water features, in some cases coal beds, indicating that at times swampy conditions existed. Basins receiving deposits of such material, accumulating over many millions of years and reaching a thickness of thirty thousand to forty thousand feet or more, are the birthplace of mountain chains. The evidence of shallow-water deposition indicates that such deposits do not represent the filling of ocean deeps, although they are thick enough to overflow any existing deep. Only one conclusion seems possible: the crust of the earth was slowly sinking as the sediments accumulated, and the depth of the water was never very great at any time. As the sediments were deposited the basin warped slowly downward, making possible the accumulation of tremendous thicknesses of sediments. Such a trough is known as a "geosyncline." The Appalachian geosyncline, out of which the Appalachian Mountains were born, extends more than fifteen hundred miles from Newfoundland to Alabama in a belt three hundred to four hundred miles in width. The sediments which filled the geosyncline came largely from the east.

Origin of geosynclinal belts

The origin of geosynclinal belts is another one of the puzzles of geology. It might be inferred that the weight of the accumulated sediments would cause the trough to sink, but, while this may be a factor, it cannot account for such great thicknesses as thirty thousand to forty thousand feet. The accumulating material is surrounded by denser rocks, and their buoyancy would set a limit to the depth to which they can sink under their own weight, a situation similar to that of an iceberg, which floats with one-ninth its volume above water. Some other factors must be involved in the origin of the sinking trough. Since volcanism and igneous activity are commonly associated with geosynclines, it is appropriate that we inquire into the problem here. Perhaps it would be helpful to trace the development of a mountain chain from a geosyncline, or as some authors would describe it, the "orogenic cycle," and then speculate on the origin of the various features involved.

The orogenic cycle (history of a mountain chain)

Following the accumulation of tens of thousands of feet of sediments over hundreds of millions of years, the trough is filled and the orogenic (Greek, *oros* = "mountain"; genic = "origin" or "birth") stage begins. Lateral pressures[2] fold and crumple the rocks, often breaking and overthrusting the beds, resulting in an apparent shortening of

[2] A theory to account for the lateral pressure as well as the vertical uplift, mentioned later in this paragraph, is described on p. 387.

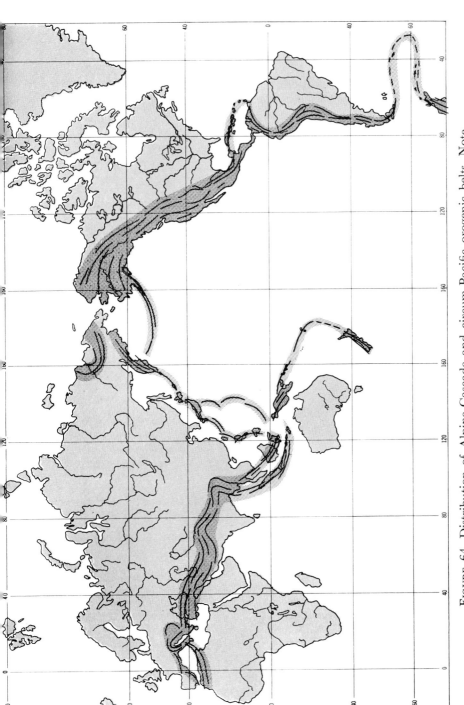

FIGURE 64. Distribution of Alpine-Cascade and circum-Pacific orogenic belts. Note that the West Indies, although in the Atlantic, appears to be a part of this system. Adapted from Umbgrove (1947).

the earth's crust by tens of miles. It is as though the crustal blocks of the foreland had acted as the jaws of a giant vise, irresistibly closing on the geosynclinal sediments and mashing them into folds. The actual orogeny probably extended over a few tens of millions of years and in geologic terminology is referred to as a "revolution." Erosion, of course, begins to operate on the rocks as soon as they are uplifted above sea level. In the final stage of the orogenic cycle there is widespread, more or less vertical uplift without folding, which may raise the area thousands of feet, permitting erosion effectually to carve the rocks into the shapes which are the actual mountains as they appear today.

The last great mountain-making revolution to disturb the earth is the Alpine orogeny of Europe and the equivalent Coast Range orogeny of western North America. Starting in mid-Tertiary time (about 20 million years ago) in the Alps and in late Tertiary time (about 10 million years ago) in North America, the movements are still in progress in some areas, notably in the East and the West Indies. The results of this orogeny were a fold belt of mountains, a great ring encircling the Pacific Ocean, and a Mediterranean belt, which is a part of the Alpine-Himalayan system. It will be noted from Figure 64 that two corresponding mountain systems appear on each side of the Caribbean Sea: a northern one, which is in effect a continuation of a fold belt from North America, and a southern one, which swings eastward from the Andes through northern Venezuela and Trinidad. The two systems are now being joined by the actively growing volcanic arc of the Lesser Antilles. A somewhat similar situation exists in the western Mediterranean, where the Sierra Nevada Mountains of Spain and the Atlas Mountains of northern Africa are linked by an inner arc through Gibraltar. The main ranges, however, remain separated and are cut off abruptly on the western end by the Atlantic Ocean.

A polar view of the Northern Hemisphere clearly presents the essential features of this orogeny (Fig. 65). This shows that the land masses are rimmed by an orogenic belt where they border the Pacific Ocean or Tethys.[3]

---

[3] *Tethys* is the name applied to a great seaway which existed between Europe and Africa and in which geosynclinal sediments which formed the Alps-Himalayas, as well as the Atlas Mountains of North Africa, were deposited. The Alpine-

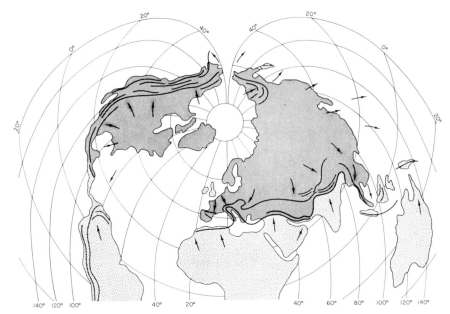

Figure 65. Polar projection showing ring of mountain chains (orogenic belts) bordering the Pacific Ocean. The same belt continues through the Himalaya-Alpine chain in the Mediterranean region. A similar relationship exists in the Southern Hemisphere, where growing mountain chains border the Pacific Ocean. The probable direction of continental movement is shown by arrows.   Adapted from Holmes (1945).

The direction of movement of the continent (i.e., overriding of the ocean basin by the continent) is shown by arrows. The complications in the Alps and the Himalayas, of Europe and Asia respectively, arise from the lateral pressures being derived from both Africa and Europe.

It becomes apparent from this discussion that the island arcs surrounding the Pacific Ocean are a part of the great orogenic belt of fold mountains and that the origin of the island arcs and their associated volcanoes is only a part of the larger problem involving geosynclines and mountain building.

Himalayan orogeny destroyed this sea, leaving only the present Mediterranean as the shrunken remnant.

Causes of mountain building

The problem resolves itself into a need for explanations of several elements: (1) the geosyncline, (2) the forces which cause the folding, (3) the uplift following the folding, and (4) the association of volcanoes with geosynclines and orogeny. Here again we are facing questions on which no uniformity of opinion prevails, but it will be helpful to speculate on these problems.

Many attempts have been made to find some mechanism competent to account for forces of sufficient magnitude to buckle and crumple the rocks of the earth's crust and to explain the sequence of events in the orogenic cycle. In a body like the earth, gravity tends to maintain equilibrium and stability, and the only agency believed to be capable of disturbing this equilibrium is heat. Increase of temperature causes expansion and fusion, and decrease in temperature results in contraction and consolidation. Thermal change, then, appears to be the most fruitful line of approach.

THE CONTRACTION THEORY. It seems reasonably certain that the earth was originally molten and that it attained its present state by cooling. A theory long held to account for mountains was the contraction hypothesis. It held that once a crust had developed and the interior of the earth continued to cool and shrink away from it, the rigid crust must accommodate itself to a smaller core by crumpling, much the same as the skin of an apple wrinkles when it dries. Although the simplicity of this explanation is appealing, there are so many objections from a geological point of view that it must be discarded. One of the principal objections is that the shrinkage would shorten every great circle, resulting in a decrease in diameter with a consequent increase in speed of rotation. No evidence of any such changes can be detected in the geologic record. Further, if one is to account in this manner for all the crumpling in the mountains of the earth, the surface area involved would be fantastic. The Alps alone, if smoothed out, thus removing all the folds, would be one hundred miles wider! When the Appalachian, Rocky, Sierra Nevada, and all the other mountain systems of the earth are added to this the total is staggering. Still further, the crustal wrinkles produced by uniform shrinkage should be in an allover pattern, like those on a drying apple, rather than concentrated or localized in restricted areas, as in orogenic belts. The most serious objection, however, and one which seems insuperable, is that from reasonable estimates of the distribution of radioactive minerals in the earth it is probable that all the heat now escaping from the earth is of radioactive origin. In fact, it is possible that the earth is getting hotter rather than cooler! Computations of heat transfer reveal that even in two billion years (a conservative estimate of the age of the earth) the earth cannot have lost any appreciable heat by conduction from a depth below seven hundred kilometers.

THE CONVECTION HYPOTHESIS. An explanation for geosynclines and mountains, based on subcrustal convection, has received serious attention by many reputable scientists. Convection is a process by which heat is transferred through bodily movement of hot material. In a pan of water on the stove, the water at the bottom is heated, causing it to expand and rise, and as it rises colder water sinks to the bottom to take its place. Thus a convection system is set up. Convection currents normally occur in pairs and are referred to as a "convection cell." In order for a convection system to operate it is necessary to have a source of heat which is continuously replenished. This heat source was found in 1906 when R. J. Strutt, later Lord Rayleigh, discovered the presence of radioactive materials in the rocks of the earth's crust. Of the hundreds of rock samples tested from all parts of the world not one was found to be without radioactive material. In fact, the rocks contain so much radioactive material that if it were present throughout the earth in amounts comparable to that present in the earth's crust, the earth would be in a molten state or have disappeared altogether! We must conclude, therefore, that such heat-generating material is concentrated in the earth's crust, but it need not be entirely absent from the mantle. Even minute quantities would suffice to keep convection going, and there is also the possibility that the mantle may receive some heat from the still liquid core. At any rate, the way seems open to explore some hypothesis based on subcrustal convection.

It may seem absurd, when evidence from seismic waves shows that the earth is rigid to a depth of at least two thousand miles, to think of the subcrustal part of the earth as a liquid subject to convection overturning. However, from the folded and contorted rocks exposed in

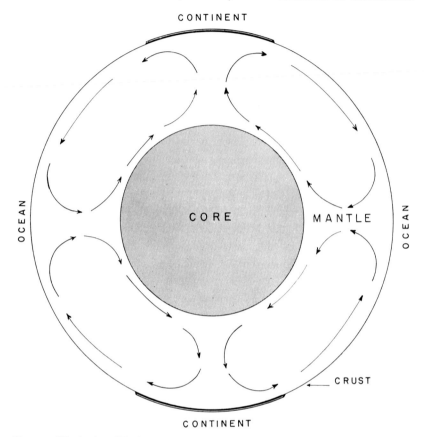

FIGURE 66. A simplified system of convection currents, with rising current beneath polar continents and descending current under equatorial oceans. After Gilluly, Waters, and Woodford (1959).

mountain ranges it is apparent that these rocks, although never molten, have been deformed as though they were in a viscous state. In addition, the sinking of the earth's crust in response to the great weight of the accumulated ice in northern Europe and northern North America during the last ice age is another proof of the yielding of the earth's crust. In fact, the rate of uplift of these regions in response to the melting of the glacial ice, a readjustment which is still in progress, has afforded a method of computing the viscosity of the mantle.

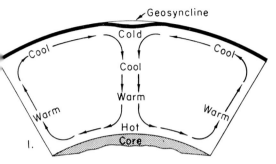

Stage 1. Initiation of convection currents. Cold material of the crust sinks to replace hot substratum material. The geosyncline slowly sinks as it is filled with sediment.

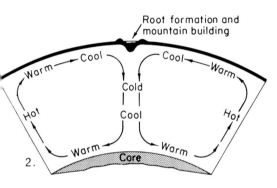

Stage 2. More rapid currents drag a root of sial into the sima. In the process of "root formation" the geosynclinal sediments are crushed by lateral pressure.

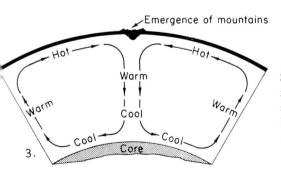

Stage 3. Currents slow down as hot material spreads out on the surface and cold material moves along the bottom. The root, because of buoyancy, is uplifted.

FIGURE 67. Possible correlation between the stages of an orogenic cycle and those of a hypothetical convection-current cycle.
Adapted from Holmes (1945).

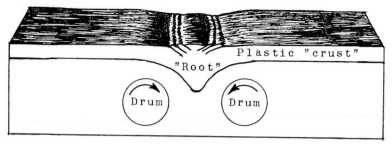

A.

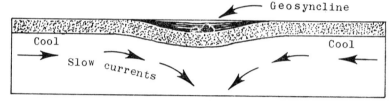

Model showing how convection currents can drag a plastic crust together and form a "root" projecting into the subcrustal layer. After Griggs (1934).

B.

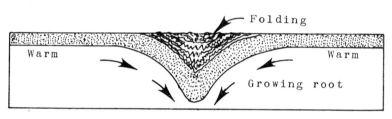

Stage 1

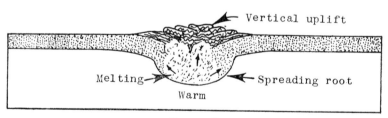

Stage 2

Stage 3

Three stages of mountain building according to the convection theory. The stages coincide with those listed for Figure 67. Adapted from Griggs (1934).

FIGURE 68. Diagrammatic illustration of how convection currents build mountains.

A simplified scheme of convection currents in an idealized earth with polar continents and equatorial oceans is shown in Figure 66. Here convection currents are rising beneath the continental masses and sinking beneath the oceans. Currents moving horizontally along the under surface of the crust exert a powerful "drag" on the crust, developing tension where they diverge and compression where they converge. Thus, orogenic belts would be expected where two opposing currents meet and turn downward. The descending currents would "drag" the sial deep into the sima resulting in a "root" of lighter material pulled into the denser sima. This, in geologic terminology is known as "root formation," that is, the root of a mountain chain.

At the beginning of a convection cycle the rate of flow must be extremely slow. The subcrust, not being a true liquid, has a certain resistance to flow, which must be overcome before convection can begin. As hotter and lighter materials from the base rise to become ascending currents, and heavier and denser materials from the top form descending columns, the velocity is increased (Fig. 68). It is during this accelerated stage that the drag of the descending currents pulls the sial (crust) down into a root. When the hotter material reaches the top and begins to spread out and the cooler material begins to flow along the bottom, the currents slow down and eventually come to rest. Thus a cycle of convection begins slowly, speeds up to a maximum, and then slows down and stops. The cooler material at the bottom is again heated by radioactive material, or by conduction from the core of the earth, until a new cycle is initiated, possibly at another location.

The crustal effects brought about by the stages in the convection cycle correspond closely with the stages in the simplest type of orogenic cycle. Griggs (1939), an American geophysicist who has been chiefly responsible for the development of the convection hypothesis, made a very effective series of experiments with scaled-down and speeded-up models simulating earth conditions. In one model, designed so that earth processes requiring one million years could be reproduced in one minute, the crust was made of a mixture of oil and fine sawdust and the mantle of glycerine. Physical analysis showed that these substances have the same properties in relation to the scale of the model as rocks do to the earth. The currents were obtained by rotating drums (Fig. 68A).

When the drums are rotated slowly the crust is gently downwarped (Fig. 68B, Stage 1). As the rotation is speeded up the greater part of the crust is dragged downward to form a root and the material in the depression is folded and crumpled (Stage 2). When rotation is slowed down the currents stop and the buoyancy effect lifts the root well above its original level (Stage 3). Griggs made certain postulates and concluded that the time required for the several stages was as follows:

Stage 1.	Slowly accelerating currents	25 million years
Stage 2.	Rapid currents	5 to 10 million years
Stage 3.	Slowing down of currents	25 million years
Stage 4.	Period of quiescence—building up heat for new cycle	500 million years

Continents and the convection hypothesis

If the convection hypothesis, as postulated by Griggs, is valid, it offers an explanation for the origin of continents and ocean basins which hitherto have been one of the great puzzles of geology. Presumably the primordial crust, consisting of an upper layer of sial and a substratum of sima, was universal. In this case the origin of continents and ocean basins, which appear to have formed very early in earth history, becomes a problem. It has been pointed out that the sial is greatly thickened in the continents, and in the oceans is very thin (Atlantic) or absent (Pacific.) The root development in the convection hypothesis greatly thickens the sial in the orogenic belt by drawing it from the adjacent regions. The continents may have been formed as a result of repeated orogenies, each of which thickened the sial and thus added to the continental mass. The tendency of orogenic belts to migrate, as from east to west in the case of North America, would enlarge the continental mass each time a new orogeny added its root. Thus the sial has been concentrated in the continental masses at the expense of the ocean basins.

Island arcs and the convection hypothesis

On the basis of the convection hypothesis the island arcs and related features find a relatively simple explanation. The shear zone,

along which deep-focus earthquakes occur, is due to convection currents, although its exact location is probably controlled by the different
character of the rock of the ocean floor on either side of the shear zone.
On the continent side is a layer of sial, while on the ocean basin the
sialic layer is absent and the ocean floor consists of sima. This boundary
between the continental-type mass, with a cover of sial, and the ocean
basin, devoid of sial, is known as the Andesite Line, which has already
been mentioned. On the continentward side of the Andesite Line the
composition of volcanic material erupted implies the existence of a
sialic layer. On the oceanward side of the Andesite Line the material
ejected by volcanoes indicates a simatic crust devoid of a cover of sial.
The Andesite Line then marks the limits of the continental masses and
the beginning of the true ocean basin. The marginal deep, offshore from
an island arc, is the depression developed by the drag of the convection
currents and the resulting root formation. The concentration of earthquakes in the present marginal deeps attests to the fact that crustal
disturbances are still in progress in these zones.

A diagram of a simple island arc is shown in Figure 69. Here the sialic
crust is being pulled down into a root along a shear zone. The slope of
the shear zone is established by the depths of deep-focus earthquakes
occurring in this zone. The diagram shows the sial playing out on the
oceanward side, which would mark the position of the Andesite Line.
The upward arching of the crustal section on the left is due to underthrusting by the ocean basin. The direction of relative movement is
indicated by arrows. The arching of the crustal section causes a relief
of pressure on the substratum directly below and develops fractures
which allow the passage of hot gases from great depths, thereby supplying the latent heat, which in combination with the relief of pressure is
necessary to permit a reservoir of magma to form. It will be recalled
from the previous discussion that the rocks at this depth, because of the
pressure, are not molten, since a change from the solid to a liquid state
requires an increase in volume. The arching also causes fractures, which
provide avenues for the liquid and gaseous emanations from the magma
to reach the surface, and volcanoes develop at these points. The asymmetrical nature of the trough and the conclusion that the continental
segment is being arched upward and is overriding the ocean segment

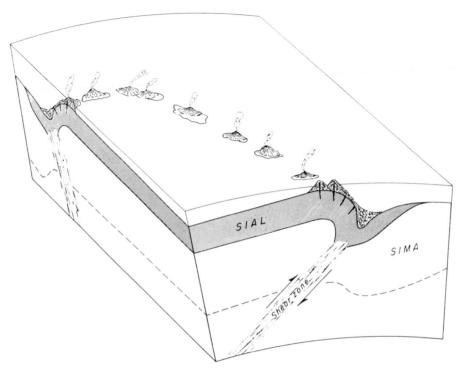

FIGURE 69. Diagram of a simple (single) island arc showing the belt of active volcanoes, the deep-sea trench, and the postulated underthrusting along the shear zone.   After Umbgrove (1947).

is based on gravity surveys which will be described in the following section.

The simple single island arc is the type shown in Figure 69. As indicated earlier, some of the arcs, such as the East Indies, consist of a double arc with two rows of islands, an inner volcanic belt, and an outer nonvolcanic belt with a marginal deep in front of it. It is unnecessary in this presentation to trace the complete history of the double arc. It may be helpful to point out the essential differences between the two and the reason why double arcs develop instead of the simpler single arcs. If the sialic layer is comparatively thin and hence situated below sea level, a deep sea trough will develop as it is pulled downward in a simple fold. On the other hand, if the sialic crust protrudes above sea level, or is of continental thickness, a different set of results is obtained. When the crust buckles to form a root of sial, because of its thickness it will crumple, and some of it will be squeezed out to form a ridge in the zone of buckling. It is comparable to forming a fold of a single layer of material, in which case a simple buckle will result, but if a number of layers of material are used some will crumple into a ridge in the middle of the fold instead of downfolding.

Volcanoes and earthquakes are, then, simply effects or accompaniments to the formation of an island arc, which in turn is one stage in the history of a mountain chain.

Gravity Measurements and Island Arcs

Every particle of the universe attracts every other particle by a force which is directly proportional to their respective masses and inversely proportional to the square of the distance between them. Thus is stated the universal Law of Gravitation, a law defining the force which draws all objects toward the center of the earth, and which was first recognized by the great English scientist Sir Isaac Newton (1642–1727). On the surface of the earth comparisons between two objects are made by weighing them, a procedure which actually compares the earth's attraction for one mass in relation to that for another. The weight of a body on the earth is a measure of the force that gravity exerts on it. The distance from the center of the earth and the density (as it determines mass) are factors affecting gravity (or weight).

To illustrate, if an object weighed 10 pounds at sea level, which is roughly four thousand miles from the center of the earth, it would weigh only 2.5 pounds if it were twice the distance from the earth's center (inversely as the square of the distance), or four thousand miles in the air above the earth's surface. Weight differs numerically from mass by a constant called the "acceleration of gravity" or "g"; thus mass × acceleration of gravity=weight ($mg=w$). Here g equals the number of feet per second by which a body falling freely in a vacuum increases its speed during each second of fall. In the above equation $g = 32.2$ feet per second.

For practical purposes the latitude and density of large rock bodies

near the earth's surface affect the force of attraction (gravity). The
unit of measure for differences in gravity is a "gal," named from Galileo.
By definition, a gal is an acceleration of one centimeter per second during each second of free fall. The acceleration of gravity at the earth's
surface is around 980 gals, but changes as small as a ten-millionth of
this may be significant. Consequently, the practical unit for expressing
gravity differences is the milligal, or one-thousandth of a gal. Changes
in the force of gravity will be reflected in changes in the weight of a body.

Very delicate instruments for measuring the force of gravity have
been perfected to aid in the search for hidden deposits of petroleum.
Such instruments are known as gravity meters. Actually, they measure
the force necessary to support a suspended mass, or the force of gravity.
The force of gravity at any given point is based on (1) distance of the
point from the center of the earth, (2) latitude (since centrifugal force
developed by the earth's rotation partially counterbalances the pull of
gravity, and such forces are greatest at the equator and zero at the
poles), and (3) density of the rocks in the immediate area. Factors 1
and 2 can be accurately computed for any point on the earth and a
correction factor applied to reduce the results to a common plane or to
sea level. Thus, a theoretical value for the force of gravity at any point
can be obtained. If the gravity meter shows the actual reading to be
different from the theoretical value, the difference must be due to Factor
3, the density of the surrounding material. Such differences are known
as "gravity anomalies."

The gravity meter was early used in the Gulf Coast area of Texas and
Louisiana to locate salt domes, with which oil is commonly associated.
One of the first large salt-dome oil fields was Spindletop, near Beau-
mont, Texas, which was discovered in 1901. A salt dome is a cylindrical
mass of salt which rises like a column for thousands of feet into the overlying sediments. Some salt domes actually reach the surface or come so
close to the surface that they form small hills, such as Spindletop, Barbers Hill, Damon Mounds, and others on the Texas Gulf Coast. These
were easily located, but those that lie several thousands of feet below the
surface could not be detected. This was where the gravity meter was
employed. The salt, having a lower density than the surrounding sediments, produces a gravity anomaly which can be measured. For ex-

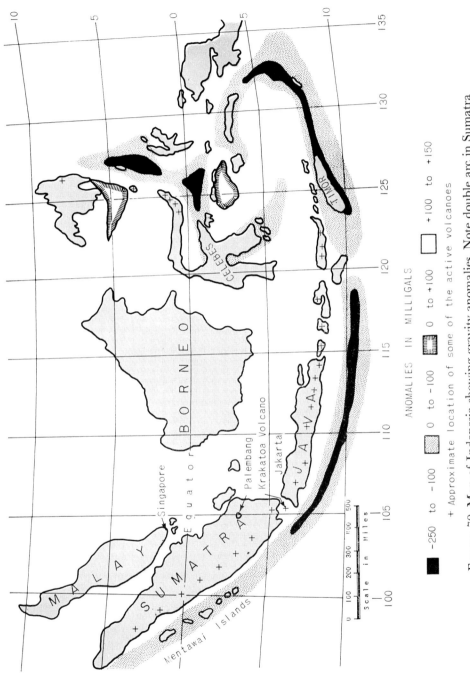

FIGURE 70. Map of Indonesia showing gravity anomalies. Note double arc in Sumatra (Mentawai Islands define the outer arc) with volcanoes limited to the inner arc. After Vening-Meinesz, et al. (1934).

ANOMALIES IN MILLIGALS

■ −250 to −100   ▨ 0 to −100   ▦ 0 to +100   □ +100 to +150

+ Approximate location of some of the active volcanoes

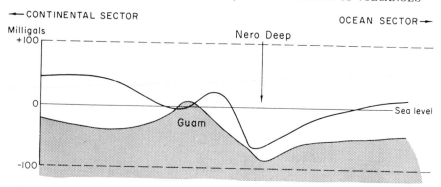

FIGURE 71. Gravity profile of Guam Island and Nero Deep.
After Vening-Meinesz (1934).

ample, a sphere of salt two thousand feet in radius, with its center four thousand feet below the surface and surrounded by sedimentary formations 10 percent denser than the salt, would cause the force of gravity directly above it to be about one milligal less than in the adjacent area. Thus, a gravity-meter survey of the region would detect the negative gravity anomalies, and, with the known presence of salt domes in the region, it would be reasonable to conclude that the anomalies are due to the presence of a buried salt dome. Only the drill can definitely locate the dome and determine whether oil is associated with it.

From the above discussion it is apparent that the gravity meter offers a means of comparing the density of the earth at various points. It has been used to produce some highly significant results in connection with the problem of island arcs. The distinguished Dutch geodesist, Dr. F. A. Vening-Meinesz (1934), using a submarine of the Royal Dutch Navy between the years 1923 and 1932, determined the value of gravity at many points on the sea floor. Since that date other workers have added similar observations from many parts of the globe. Interestingly, when Dr. Vening-Meinesz crossed the island-arc areas he found an elongate belt with a width of only sixty to seventy miles, characterized by a surprisingly great deficiency of gravity. Even after all corrections had been applied for various factors, such as the depth of the submarine below the surface and the topography of the underlying sea floor, a strong negative anomaly still existed. The belt is so narrow and the deficiency so strong that only a deep root of light rocks would account for it. Thus, as provided in the convection hypothesis, a deep root of sial extending into and displacing the denser sima is indicated. Much of Dr. Vening-Meinesz's studies were carried on in the East Indies, and a map showing the gravity anomalies of this region is reproduced in Figure 70. Numerous measurements were made at other points, where the results invariably indicated marked negative anomalies whenever the marginal deep of an island arc was crossed. The single-island-arc type, represented by the group of which Guam is a part, will serve as an example. Strong negative anomalies were found over the marginal deep (Nero Deep), implying that a root of light crustal material (sial) must have buckled downward replacing the heaver sima beneath it. The asymmetrical nature of the gravimetric profile (Fig. 71) suggests that the eastern part, or oceanic sector, is being thrust under the western or continental sector, causing this part to arch upward and fracture, thus accounting for the volcanoes which are associated with it.

Significance of the Convection Hypothesis

In the preceding pages the evidence in support of the convection hypothesis as applied to island arcs has been stressed. It would be unfair not to point out that not all geologists will agree (they never do) with the conclusions here presented. Most of the facts discussed here, as with every controversial issue, can be used to support other hypotheses. It does not seem pertinent to this discussion to review all the arguments, pro and con, for any hypothesis. It is the writer's aim to present a reasonable, logical explanation, which may not be the final word, but which gives the reader an over-all view of the complicated subject and a reasonably satisfactory explanation of the known facts. When other facts are uncovered it may be necessary to revise the explanation, or discard it altogether. Such has been the history of the progress of science. It seems appropriate here to review the problems in connection with volcanoes which find a suitable explanation through application of the convection hypothesis to the island-arc problem:

1) The location of island arcs at the margin of the continents, due

to an underthrusting of the continents by the denser Pacific Ocean basin.

2) The association of active volcanoes with island arcs due to the arching of the continentward segment by the underthrusting of the ocean segment. This relieves the pressure on the substratum directly beneath and develops fractures which allow the passage of hot gases from great depths, thereby supplying the latent heat, which in combination with the relief of pressure is necessary to permit a reservoir of magma to form. It further provides fractures along which the gases and molten material from the magma reservoir may reach the surface.

3) The absence of sial on the ocean floor and the concentration of it into continental masses.

4) The marked negative gravity anomalies associated with the marginal deeps of island arcs.

The Role of Water in Volcanic Activity

The fact that magma can contain water in solution in significant amounts and the importance of the water content in volcanic eruptions has already been discussed (see discussion of volcanic gases, pp. 37–43). In concluding this work on volcanic activity it seems permissible to speculate on the actual role of water in a volcanic eruption. Water present in a magma will migrate by diffusion, seeking to establish a uniform pressure. This does not mean, however, that the quantity of water is the same throughout, because the amount of water which can be contained in solution in the magma is determined by the confining pressure (weight of the overlying rocks) and the temperature. Water will diffuse and distribute itself in a magma so that the water-vapor pressure is the same throughout the magma chamber. This results in a concentration of water in the magma chamber in the regions of lowest pressures and temperatures. Although the effect of temperature on the solubility of water in the magma at a constant pressure is numerically small, roughly 0.5 percent by weight for each $100°$ C. decrease in temperature, it is highly important. Water will tend to diffuse toward the cooler, upper portion of the magma. To illustrate the effect of pressure on the water content of a magma, Kennedy (1955, p. 494), who reviews this problem in a thought-provoking article, uses the following example: ". . . let us assume that the top of a magma column extends to within 4½ miles of the surface of the earth. The confining pressure due to the weight of the rock load is approximately 2000 bars[4] at this depth, and if the magma is saturated with water, the top of the column will contain about 7.4 weight percent water. The equilibrium water content of the melt diminishes very rapidly with increasing depth. At a depth where the confining pressure has increased to 3000 bars the water content . . . will have diminished to less than 5.3 percent, and the melt will be far from saturated. At a depth where the confining pressure is approximately 4,000 bars, the water content will have decreased to about 2 percent. It appears, . . . that the deeper the burial of the magma chamber, the stronger the tendency of the water to be concentrated in the upper portion. Further, a magma chamber can be saturated with water vapor only at its very top."

Assuming the concentration of water in the upper portion of the magma, as outlined in the preceding paragraph, the stages in a volcanic eruption may be explained as follows: At the initial outbreak the magma will be gas-saturated and the explosive force of the expanding gases (largely steam) will shatter the material into ash and cinders. The mobility of the material, described by Reynolds (1954) as fluidization, is due to the fact that the particles are suspended in a gas. This is the period in which cone building is the most important process. Later, fluid, highly vesicular lavas rich in water but not sufficiently saturated to be disrupted by the escaping gases, will pour out. In the final phase of the eruption the lavas will have a higher viscosity (due to lower water content) and contain less volatiles. This pattern, observed at Parícutin Volcano, Mexico, and in other eruptions, is precisely what would be expected if the water is concentrated in the upper part of the magma column. It may also be reasoned that it is the decline in the volatiles that brings the eruption to an end. Indeed, as Kennedy (1955, p. 495) has pointed out, if the water was distributed uniformly with

[4] A *bar* is the pressure of the atmosphere at sea level, approximately 14.7 pounds per square inch, and equivalent to about twelve feet of rock load.

depth in the magma the eruption would be more catastrophic, coming to an end only when the magma chamber had been emptied, somewhat analogous to the emptying of a geyser tube.

Following an eruption, after the "wet" upper portion of the magma has been expelled, the equilibrium will have been disturbed and the water will now again diffuse into the zone of lower confining pressure and lower temperatures at the top of the magma column. In time the steadily accumulating pressure will be sufficient to blast aside the retaining rocks and renew the eruption. If the magma column is connected to a relatively large body of magma at depth, it seems possible that recurrent eruptions may occur at the same site over a long period of time, the cycle depending on the rate of diffusion of water in the magma.

It must not be overlooked that the sequence of events, as outlined above, is based on certain assumptions as to the distribution and diffusion of water in a magma chamber. Although these assumptions cannot at this time be proved, they are based on sound, scientific reasoning, and, if true, they do afford an explanation for a number of aspects of volcanic activity.

In this chapter an effort was made to present some of the problems which arise in seeking an explanation of volcanic activity and to indicate at least the direction in which possible solutions may be found. Science is not ready, at this time, to give complete answers to many of the problems of volcanism. The concentration of the active volcanoes of the world in belts in which mountain building is still in progress, or has only recently terminated, is significant. Further, throughout geologic time the major mountain-building episodes have been accompanied by active volcanism. Thus, volcanism must be viewed in proper perspective, that is, as one aspect of the larger process of mountain building. But mountain building is the process by which continents are reconstructed (by the concentration of the sial in huge cakes as a result of "root" formation); so it would be futile to attempt to explain volcanism except within the framework of a theory which will also include mountains and continents.

Since active volcanoes do offer an opportunity to observe one aspect of the complicated process of mountain building in operation it would seem unnecessary to urge scientists to avail themselves of this opportunity. Because of the length of time involved other aspects of the problem can only be studied by the results preserved in the geologic record. Permanent observatories are maintained at only a few of the world's active volcanoes today—the number being probably not more than half a dozen. The work which they are doing is highly significant, but no real approach to the problem can be made until continuous observations, with the most modern scientific equipment, are maintained at every active volcano on earth.

Tremendous strides are being made in our conquest of outer space and the time may be near when we will be studying the volcanoes (if they exist) on the moon or on some of our neighboring planets. It may seem trite to suggest that much work remains to be done on earth before we are qualified to solve the problems of outer space.

RETROSPECT

The reader who has reached this point may wish to take one last, fleeting backward glance over the way we have traveled—to glimpse in a parting view of broad outlines the main features of volcanoes.

The history of volcanology, like that of all our sciences, was interwoven with mythology and superstition in ancient times. With the acceptance of volcanoes as a natural phenomenon not related to the supernatural, volcanology began to be organized as a body of knowledge. No real progress was made, however, until the development of geology, with which volcanology is inseparable. In fact, the development of geology was to a large extent fostered by the controversies which surrounded volcanoes. As is true of most sciences, real progress is frequently the result of some outstanding event, a break-through in some aspect of the field, or some great catastrophe. The first artificial splitting of the atom revolutionized the field of physics, and gave it a stimulus which will carry it on—perhaps indefinitely. If a comparably significant event could be picked in volcanology it would doubtless be the eruption of Mount Pelée in 1902 with the tragic loss of life which accompanied the destruction of St. Pierre. This tragedy drew the wonder and sympathy of the civilized world, and scientists from many countries were dispatched to study the eruption. By common consent it was agreed that in some way information must be obtained which would prevent the reoccurrence of such a catastrophe, or at least give notice to the inhabitants so they could escape. The impetus given the study of volcanoes at that time is still felt in volcanology today.

After the eruption of Mount Pelée it was clear that volcanic eruptions were of different types and that with study the type of eruption might be anticipated. Accordingly, a classification of volcanoes based on the type of eruption was devised. This classification, with examples of the different types of eruptions, drawn from throughout the world, forms the "bulk" of this book. Only eruptions of volcanoes accepted as "types" are described, although in some cases examples could have been drawn from other volcanoes in which the eruption was more spectacular.

Developing along with the classification of volcanoes according to the type of eruption was the idea that the eruptions were often repeated at more or less regular intervals and that a volcanic cycle could be recognized. Information in sufficient detail to enable the eruptive cycle to be recognized was available on only a few volcanoes, but the fact that a cycle can be recognized has been an incentive for more detailed observations at many volcanoes. With the recognition of an eruptive cycle, the prediction of an eruption becomes a possibility; when this goal is reached the next step is to work out some means of control. This is a goal so far in the future that speculation on it at the present may be idle fancy, but some startlingly rapid advances have been made in science in recent years and it seems unwise to relegate anything to the "impossible."

One paying asset in the study of volcanoes is the utilization of volcanic energy for the development of power. The conventional basis for developing electric power is solar heat, stored as coal and oil in the earth crust. Even water power is based on solar heat since the sun's evaporation of the water results in the rainfall which keeps the streams flowing. It does not seem so remote, then, to utilize volcanic heat (also solar heat in that it was inherited from the sun when the earth was born) for the development of power. This phase of volcanology, which is one of the few immediate economic applications, is capable of tremendous expansion in many of the remote areas of the world where conventional sources of power are lacking or quite limited. It should be a great factor in the future development of all areas where geothermal energy is available.

The important relationship of volcanology to geology is underscored by speculation on the causes underlying volcanic activity. Since volcanic activity is intimately associated with mountain building and, in turn, with the origin of continents, it becomes one of the most fundamental problems of geology. The convection theory, described in some detail, cannot be claimed as a complete answer, but it is probably an important part of the answer, since it offers an attractive explanation for many of the problems involved in the origin of mountains and the causes of volcanism. The progress of science is marked by the alternate development and modification of theories—theories which explain a set of facts but which are modified when new facts are discovered. The convection theory may be in this category. When this proves to be the case, a new volume on volcanoes will be written.

APPENDIX

Geologic Time Scale*

			Approximate Number of Millions of Years Ago**
CENOZOIC ERA	Quaternary Period	Recent Epoch Pleistocene Epoch	0–1
	Tertiary Period	Pliocene Epoch Miocene Epoch Oligocene Epoch Eocene Epoch Paleocene Epoch	11–1 25–11 25–40 40–60 60–70
MESOZOIC ERA	Cretaceous Period Jurassic Period Triassic Period		135–70 180–135 225–180
PALEOZOIC ERA	Permian Period Pennsylvanian Period Mississippian Period Devonian Period Silurian Period Ordovician Period Cambrian Period		270–225 305–270 350–305 400–350 440–400 500–440 500–600
PRECAMBRIAN ERA			600–26000(?)

* *Age* when used to denote geologic time is a subdivision of an epoch, just as an epoch is the subdivision of a period.
** Post-Precambrian dates after Holmes (1959).

GLOSSARY

Aa. Lava with a surface composed of angular, jagged blocks.

Acidic. A descriptive term applied to those igneous rocks which contain more than 66 percent SiO_2, as contrasted with *intermediate* and *basic*.

Amygdaloid. An igneous rock (usually basalt or andesite) which contains numerous gas cavities filled with secondary minerals.

Andesite. A lava of intermediate composition, usually light gray in color.

Ash fall. A rain of ash from an eruption cloud.

Ash flow. An avalanche consisting of volcanic ash and gases, highly heated, traveling down the flanks of a volcano (SEE *Nuée ardente*).

Ash, volcanic. Uncemented pyroclastic material consisting of fragments mostly under 4 mm. in diameter; two grades are commonly distinguished: coarse ash, ¼ to 4 mm. in diameter; fine ash, less than ¼ mm. in diameter.

Atoll. A ringlike coral island or reef encircling or nearly encircling a lagoon.

Barrier reef. A coral reef which runs parallel to the coast but is separated from it by a lagoon.

Basalt. A dark-colored, fine-grained lava.

Basic. A general descriptive term for those igneous rocks that are comparatively low in silica, containing usually less than 50 percent.

Block lava. A term applied to lava flows which occur as a tumultuous mass of angular blocks.

Bombs, volcanic. Fragments of lava which were liquid or plastic at the time of ejection, but which acquired a distinctive shape or surface markings during flight through the air or at the time of landing.

Breached cone. A cinder cone from which a lava flow has carried away a sector, leaving an opening on one side.

Breadcrust bomb. A volcanic bomb in which the surface is cut with cracks (like a loaf of French bread).

Breccia. A rock composed of angular fragments.

Caldera. A large, more or less circular, more-than-1-mile-in-diameter depression formed either by collapse or explosion, usually at the summit of a volcano.

Cambrian Period. SEE Appendix.

Cenozoic Era. SEE Appendix.

Cone sheets. Thin sheets of intrusive material (dikelike) dipping concentrically inward toward the source of the magma. They are usually associated with ring dikes.

Convection currents. Movements of material due to differences in density, generally the result of heating.

Cored bomb. A volcanic bomb consisting of a nucleus of older lava coated on the outside with a layer of new lava.

Crater, volcanic. A steep-walled depression at the top or on the flanks of a volcanic cone, out of which the volcanic materials are ejected.

Cretaceous Period. SEE Appendix.

Crust (of the earth). That part of the earth lying above the Mohorovičić discontinuity.

Devonian Period. SEE Appendix.

Diastrophism. The process by which the rocks of the earth's crust are deformed, producing mountains, folds, faults, etc.

Dike. A tabular body of igneous rock that cuts across the structure of the adjacent rocks.

Dip. The angle at which a stratum or any tabular planar feature is inclined from the horizontal.

Eocene Epoch. SEE Appendix.

Fault. A fracture or fracture zone along which there has been displacement of the sides relative to one another.

Fluidization. A concept which accounts for the movement of some intrusive igneous bodies, tuff flows (ignimbrites) and certain types of lava flows as solid particles supported by gas.

Fringing reef. A coral reef which closely encircles or forms a fringe around the land; in contrast to a barrier reef which is separated from the shore by a lagoon.

Gal. A term used in gravity measurements equal to an acceleration of one centimeter per second. A milligal is 0.001 gal.

Geologic time. SEE Appendix.

Geosyncline. A surface of regional extent subsiding through a long time while contained sedimentary and volcanic rocks are accumulating.

Geyser. A hot spring from which a column of hot water and steam is explosively discharged at intervals.

Graben. A long relatively narrow block which has been downthrown along faults relative to the rocks on either side.

Horst. A block of the earth's crust, generally long in relation to its width, that has been uplifted along faults relative to the rocks on either side. Compare with graben.

Igneous. A rock formed as the result of the solidification of a molten mass.

Ignimbrite. A type of silicic volcanic rock formed by the eruption of dense clouds of incandescent ash. SEE *Nuée ardente*; ALSO welded tuff.

Isostasy. A condition of approximate equilibrium in the outer part of the earth, so that different segments of the crust, if of equal area, also have the same mass. The blocks thus balance one another. The less the mean specific gravity of a block, the higher it will stand.

Isostatic anomaly. The difference between the observed value of gravity at a point after applying to it the various corrections and the normal value of gravity at the point.

Isotopes. Elements having an identical number of protons in their nuclei but differing in the number of their neutrons.

Jökulhlaup. A destructive flood due to a volcanic eruption beneath a large glacier.

Jurassic Period. SEE Appendix.

Kipuka. A Hawaiian term for an islandlike area surrounded by lava flows.

Lahar. A torrential flow of water-saturated volcanic debris down the slope of a volcano in response to gravitative force. A type of landslide.

Lapilli. Volcanic ejecta ranging mostly from 4 mm. to 32 mm. in diameter, or about the size of a pea.

Lava fountain. A jetlike eruption of lava issuing vertically from a fissure or a central vent.

Lava plateau. A broad, elevated tableland underlain by a thick succession of lava flows.

Lithic tuff. An indurated deposit of volcanic ash in which the fragments are composed of previously formed rock.

Maar. A relatively shallow, flat-floored explosion crater, the walls of which consist largely of loose fragments of the country (surrounding) rock.

Magma. Molten rock together with its included gases as it exists underground.

Magmatic differentiation. The process by which different types of igneous rocks are derived from a single parent magma.

Magmatic stoping. A process of igneous intrusion whereby a magma gradually eats its way upward by breaking off blocks of the country rock.

Malpais. A term applied to any rather extensive area covered by recent lava flows; literally "bad land."

Mesozoic Era. SEE Appendix.

Meteoric water. Water derived from the atmosphere, that is rain water.

Metric equivalents: centimeter = 0.4 inch
                     kilometer = 0.6 mile
                     meter   = 39.3 inches
                     millimeter = 0.04 inch

Miocene Epoch. SEE Appendix.

Mississippian Period. SEE Appendix.

Mohorovičić discontinuity. The plane that marks the base of the crust of the earth.

Nested craters. A series of craters, one within the other.

Nuée ardente. A French term applied to a highly heated (incandescent) mass of gas-charged ash or lava which is expelled with explosive force and rushes down the mountain side with hurricane speed.

Obsidian. A volcanic glass.

Oligocene Epoch. SEE Appendix.

Ordovician Period. SEE Appendix.

Orogeny. The process of forming mountains, particularly by folding and faulting.

Pahoehoe. Lava with a ropy or billowy surface.

Paleocene Epoch. SEE Appendix.

Paleozoic Era. SEE Appendix.

Pennsylvanian Period. SEE Appendix.

Period. The fundamental unit of the standard geologic time scale during which a standard system of rocks was formed. Example, Cretaceous Period.

Permian Period. SEE Appendix.

Phreatic explosion. An explosion caused by the conversion of ground water to steam.

Pit crater. A circular, steep-walled depression sunk below the gently sloping surface of a volcano and not surrounded by a rim. Commonly located along the rift zone on the flanks of shield volcanoes, such as Kilauea.

Plateau basalt. Term applied to those basaltic lavas which occur in essentially horizontal position over vast areas, such as the Columbia River Plateau. They are believed to be the product of fissure eruptions. Also known as flood basalts.

Pleistocene Epoch. SEE Appendix.

Plinian. The term is now generally applied to the phase of an eruption in which there is a tremendous uprushing of gas, producing an eruption cloud which Pliny described as resembling a "Pino" or stone pine tree.

Pliocene Epoch. SEE Appendix.

Plutonic. A general term applied to igneous rocks which have crystallized at great depth and have assumed a granitoid texture.

Precambrian. SEE Appendix.

Pyroclastic. A general term applied to volcanic material (ash, cinders, etc.) which has been explosively ejected from a volcanic vent.

Pyrometer. An instrument for measuring temperatures, especially those beyond the range of mercurial thermometers.

Quaternary Period. SEE Appendix.

Radioactive element. An element capable of changing spontaneously into another element by the emission of charged particles from the nuclei of its atoms. Example, uranium.

Radioactive heat. The heat formed in rocks by the active disintegration of natural radioactive elements.

Recent Epoch. SEE Appendix.

Rift zones. Fissures along which repeated eruptions occur. They usually radiate from the summit of a volcano.

Ring dikes. Circular dikes which dip steeply outward, probably formed by the intrusion of magma along concentric fractures formed by the subsidence of a roughly circular mass of roof rock into a magma chamber.

Ropy lava. Same as pahoehoe lava.

Scoria. A basaltic type of volcanic ejecta, characterized by its vesicular nature; a volcanic slag.

Seismic. Pertaining to earthquakes or earth vibrations.

Shield volcano. A broad, gently sloping volcanic cone composed chiefly of overlapping flows of basaltic lava. Example, Mauna Loa, Hawaii.

Sial. A layer of rock underlying the continents largely granitic in composition. The thickness varies from 30 to 35 km.

Sillar. A Peruvian name for beds of consolidated rhyolitic tuff.

Silurian Period. SEE Appendix.

Sima. One of the layers of the crustal zone of the earth, largely basaltic in composition. In the continental areas it underlies the sial.

Solfatara. A volcanic vent from which only gases are emitted.

Somma. A ridge or rim representing the remnant of an ancient caldera wall.

Spatter cone. A mound or cone formed by lava fragments (spatters) accumulating around a vent.

Tectogene. A large downfold of the granitic crust (sial) beneath a mountain belt.

Tectonics. Study of the broader structural features of the earth and their causes.

Tephra. A collective term for all clastic volcanic material, including ash, cinders, bombs, etc.

Tertiary Period. SEE Appendix.

Tholoid. A volcanic dome, usually composed of viscous lava filling a crater.

Tiltmeter. An instrument used to measure the displacement of the ground from the horizontal. Used in volcanology to measure the doming-up of a volcano by magmatic pressure.

Trap rock. A term applied to dark-colored rocks of dikes, sills, and lava flows.

Triassic Period. SEE Appendix.

Tuff. A rock composed of compacted volcanic fragments, generally smaller than 4 mm. in diameter.

Tumescence. In volcanology, the swelling of a volcano during periods of rising magma preceding an eruption.

Volcanic bombs. Detached masses of lava erupted by volcanoes, which as they fall, assume rounded forms.

Volcanic dome. A steep-sided mass of viscous lava forming a more or less dome-shaped mass over the volcanic vent. SEE Tholoid.

Xenolith. Rock fragments that are foreign to the igneous rock in which they occur. An inclusion.

BIBLIOGRAPHY

Agostinho, J. (1936) The Volcanoes of the Azores Islands. Bull. Volcan-ologique, Nos. 27–30, 1931 (published in 1936).

Alfano, G. B., and Friedlander, I. (1928) La storia del Vesuvio. Naples, K. Holm.

Allen, E. T., and Day, A. L. (1935) Hot Springs of the Yellowstone National Park. Carnegie Inst. of Washington Publ. 466.

——— (1927) Steam Wells and Other Thermal Activity at The Geysers, California. Carnegie Inst. of Washington Publ. 378.

Anderson, Tempest. (1903) Volcanic Studies in Many Lands. London, John Murray.

Anderson, Tempest, and Flett, J. S. (1902) Royal Soc. of London, Vol. 70, pp. 423–445.

——— (1903–1908) Report on the Eruption of the Soufrière, in St. Vincent, in 1902, and on a visit to Montagne Pelée in Martinique. Phil. Trans. Royal Soc. of London, Ser. A, Vol. 200, pp. 353–553; Vol. 208, pp. 275–332.

Arduino, Giovanni. (1759) Fisico-mineralogico di Lythogomia e orognosia. Atti dell' Accademia delle Scienze di Siena, T. V.

Atwood, W. W., Jr. (1935) The Glacial History of an Extinct Volcano, Crater Lake National Park. Jour. Geology, Vol. 43, pp. 142–168.

Barth, Tom F. W. (1950) Volcanic Geology, Hot Springs and Geysers of Iceland. Carnegie Inst. of Washington Publ. 587.

——— (1952) Theoretical Petrology. New York, John Wiley & Sons.

Bemmelen, R. W., van. (1929) Het Caldera Probleem. De Mijningenieur, No. 4.

Bodvärsson, Gunnar. (1960) Hot Springs and the Exploration of Natural Heat Resources. International Geological Congress, XXI Session, Guide to Excursion A-2, pp. 46–55.

Bosanquet, F. C. T., ed. (1907) Pliny's Letters. London, George Bell & Sons, Ltd.

Bowen, N. L. (1928) The Evolution of Igneous Rocks. Princeton, Princeton University Press.

Bruce, J. A., and Shorland, F. B. (1932) Utilization of Natural Heat Resources in Thermal Regions. New Zealand Jour. of Agri., Vol. 45, pp. 272–279; also Vol. 47, pp. 29–33, 1933.

Brun, A. (1911) Recherches sur l'exhalaison volcanique. Kündig, Geneva.

Bullard, Fred M. (1956) Resumen de la historia del Volcán Parícutin, Michoacán, Mexico. Twentieth International Geologic Congress Guide Book, Excursion A-15.

———— (1954) Volcanic Activity in Costa Rica and Nicaragua in 1954. Trans. Am. Geophysical Union, Vol. 37, pp. 75–82.

———— (1954a) A Volcanic Cycle as Exhibited by Italian Volcanoes. Tulsa Geol. Soc. Digest, Vol. 22, pp. 101–110.

———— (1954b) Activity of Stromboli in June and December, 1952. Bull. Volcanologique, Ser. 2, Vol. XV, pp. 91–98.

———— (1947) Studies on Parícutin Volcano. Geol. Soc. America Bull., Vol. 58, pp. 433–449.

———— (1947a) The Story of Parícutin. Scientific Monthly, Vol. 65, pp. 357–371.

Burnett, Thomas. (1681–1689) Telluris theoria sacra. London, R. N. Impensis Gault, Kettilby. Later (1734) published in English with the title, Sacred History of the Earth, London, H. Lintot.

Butler, Samuel. (1897) Authoress of the Odyssey. London, A. C. Fifield.

Cassius, Dio Cocceianus. (1914) Dio's Roman History; with English translation by E. Carey on the basis of the version of Herbert Bladwin Foster. In nine volumes. London, W. Heinemann.

Catalogue of Active Volcanoes of the World, pts. 1–9. (1951–1959) International Volcanological Association, Naples, Italy.

Church, Alfred, and Brodribb, W. J. (1872) Pliny's Letters. London, William Blackwood and Sons.

Coats, R. R. (1950) Volcanic Activity in the Aleutian Arc. U.S. Geol. Survey Bull. 974B.

Corti, E. C. C. (1951) The Destruction and Resurrection of Pompeii and Herculaneum. Translated from the German by K. and R. Gregor Smith. London, Routledge and K. Paul.

Daly, R. A. (1933) Igneous Rocks and the Depths of the Earth. New York. McGraw-Hill Book Company.

Daubeny, Charles. (1848) A Description of Active and Extinct Volcanoes. London, Richard and John E. Taylor, 2nd ed. 1st ed. (1826) London. W. Phillips.

Day, A. L., and Shepherd, E. S. (1913) Water and Volcanic Activity. Bull. Geol. Soc. America, Vol. 24, pp. 573–606.

DeFiore, O. (1922) Vulcano. Supp. N. III della Revista Vulcanologica, Pt. 1, 380 pp.

De Lorenzo, G. (1906) The Eruption of Vesuvius in April, 1906. Quart. Jour. Geol. Soc. of London, Vol. 62, pp. 476–483.

Decker, Robert. (1959) Renewed Activity of Anak Krakatau. Inst. Tech. Bandung, Contributions Dept. of Geol. No. 34.

Diller, J. S., and Patton, H. B. (1902) The Geology and Petrography of Crater Lake National Park. U. S. Geol. Survey Prof. Paper 3.

Diodorus, Siculus. (1913) Diodorus of Sicily; with an English translation by C. H. Oldfather. London, W. Heinemann.

Dryden, John. (1910) Plutarch's Lives, revised by Arthur H. Clough. New York, E. P. Dutton & Company.

Escher, B. G. (1919) De Krakatau groep als vulkaan. Handel van bet. le. Ned.-Ind. Natuurwet. Cong. Welteverden, pp. 28–35.

Fenner, C. N. (1936) Bore Hole Investigations in Yellowstone Park. Jour. of Geology, Vol. 44, pp. 225–315.

Fouqué, Ferdinand André. (1879) Santorin et ses eruptions. Paris, G. Masson.

Frazer, James B. (1930) Myths of the Origin of Fire. London, The Macmillan Company.

Fries, C., Jr. (1953) Volumes and Weights of Pyroclastic Material, Lava, and Water Erupted by Parícutin Volcano, Michoacán, Mexico. Am. Geophys. Union Trans., Vol. 34, pp. 603–616.

Fries, C., Jr., and Gutiérrez, C. (1950) Activity of Parícutin Volcano from August 1, 1948, to June 30, 1949. Am. Geophys. Union Trans., Vol. 31, pp. 406–418.

——— (1950a) Activity of Parícutin Volcano from July 1 to December 31, 1949. Am. Geophys. Union Trans., Vol. 31, pp. 732–740.

——— (1951) Activity of Parícutin Volcano from January 1 to June 30, 1950. Am. Geophys. Union Trans., Vol. 32, pp. 212–221.

——— (1951a) Activity of Parícutin Volcano from July 1 to December 31, 1950. Am. Geophys. Union Trans., Vol. 32, pp. 572–581.

——— (1952) Activity of Parícutin Volcano from January 1 to June 30, 1951. Am. Geophys. Union Trans., Vol. 33, pp. 91–100.

———— (1952a) Activity of Parícutin Volcano from July 1 to December 31, 1951. Am. Geophys. Union Trans., Vol. 33, pp. 725–733.

———— (1954) Activity of Parícutin Volcano in 1952. Am. Geophys. Union Trans., Vol. 35, pp. 486–494.

Gadow, Hans. (1930) Jorullo. Cambridge, The University Press.

Gealey, W. K. (1951) Geology of the Healdsburg Quadrangle. Calif. Div. of Mines, Bull. 161.

Geikie, A. (1903) Textbook of Geology, 4th ed., Vol. 1. London, The Macmillan Company.

Gilluly, James, Waters, A. C., and Woodford, A. O. (1959) Principles of Geology. San Francisco, W. H. Freeman & Co.

González, R., Jenaro, and Foshag, William F. (1947) The Birth of Parícutin. Smithsonian Inst., Ann. Report for 1946, pp. 223–234.

Goranson, R. (1931) The solubility of water in granitic magmas. Am. Jour. of Sci., 5th ser., Vol. 22, pp. 483–502.

Griggs, D. (1939) A Theory of Mountain Building. American Journal of Science, Vol. 237, pp. 611–650.

Hamilton, W. M. (1954) Geothermal Energy. Cawthorn Lecture Series No. 27, Cawthorn Institute, New Zealand.

Hamilton, William. (1774) Observations on Mt. Vesuvius, Mt. Etna, and Other Volcanoes. London, T. Cadell.

Hazen, Henry A. (1884) Sun Glows. Am. Jour. Sci., Vol. 27, pp. 201–212.

Heilprin, A. (1903) Mount Pelée and the Tragedy of Martinique. Philadelphia, J. B. Lippincott.

———— (1904) The Tower of Pelée. Philadelphia, J. B. Lippincott Company.

Hill, R. T. (1902) National Geographic Magazine, Vol. 13, pp. 224–269.

Holmes, Arthur. (1945) Principles of Physical Geology. New York, Ronald Press.

———— (1950) Petrogenesis of katungite. Am. Mineralogists, Vol. 35, pp. 772–792.

———— (1959) A Revised Geologic Time-scale. Trans. Edinburgh Geological Society, Vol. 17, Pt. 3, pp. 183–216.

Hovey, E. O. (1902) Martinique and St. Vincent, a Preliminary Report upon the Eruption of 1902. Bull. Am. Mus. of Nat. Hist., Vol. 16, pp. 333–373; also, Nat. Geog. Magazine, Vol. 13, pp. 444–459.

Humboldt, Alexander von. (1866) The Cosmos, translated from the German by E. C. Otté. New York, Harper & Brothers.

———— (1811) Essai politique sur le royaume de la Nouvelle-Espagne.

Paris, F. Schoell. Also, Essai geognostique sur le gisement des roches dans le deux hemispheres. Paris, F. G. Levrault, 1823.

Hutton, James. (1795) Theory of the Earth with Proofs and Illustrations (2 vols.). London, Cadell, Junior, and Davies.

——— (1788) Theory of the Earth. Trans. Royal Soc. of Edinburgh, Vol. 1.

Illingworth, Frank. (1949) Iceland's Municipal Water System. Water and Water Engineering, Vol. 52, pp. 437–444.

Imbo, G. (1951) L'attivita eruttiva vesuviana e relative osservazioni nel corso dell'intervallo intereuttivo 1906–1944 ed in particolare del parossimo del marzo, 1944. Annali dell'Osservatorio Vesuviano, 5th ser., Vol. 1, Pt. 1.

——— (1928) Variazioni cicliche nella successione dei periodi di riposo etnei. Bull. Volcanology, Nos. 15 to 18.

Jaggar, T. A. (1949) Steam Blast Volcanic Eruptions. Hawaiian Volcano Observatory, 4th Special Report.

——— (1945) Volcanoes Declare War. Honolulu, Paradise of the Pacific Ltd.

——— (1931) Volcanic Cycles and Sunspots. Volcano Letter No. 326.

Johnston-Lavis, H. J. (1918) Bibliography of the Geology and Eruptive Phenomena of the More Important Volcanoes of Southern Italy. London, The Univ. of London Press, 2nd ed.

——— (1888) Recent Eruption of Vulcano. Nature, Vol. 38, p. 173; also, Vol. 30, 1889, pp. 109–111; Vol. 42, 1890, pp. 78–79.

Judd, John W. (1881) Volcanoes. New York, D. Appleton & Company.

——— (1875) Lipari Islands. Geol. Magazine for 1875. This journal contains a series of articles by Professor Judd dealing with the Lipari Islands beginning with Jan. 1875, pp. 1–16, 99–115, 146–152, 206–214.

Keller, W. D., and Valduga, A. (1946) The Natural Steam at Larderello, Italy. Jour. Geol., Vol. 54, pp. 327–334.

Kennan, George. (1902) The Tragedy of Pelée, pt. V. Outlook, Vol. 71, pp. 769–777.

Kennedy, George C. (1955) Some aspects of the Role of Water in Rock Melts. Geol. Soc. of America, Special Paper 62, pp. 489–504.

Lacroix, A. (1908) La Montagne Pelée après ses eruptions. Acad. Sci. Paris, pp. 79–93.

——— (1904) La Montagne Pelée et ses eruptions. Paris, Masson.

Leet, L. Don. (1948) Causes of Catastrophe. New York, Whittlesey House.

Leet, L. Don, and Judson, S. (1954) Physical Geology. Englewood Cliffs, New Jersey, Prentice-Hall, Inc.

Lobeck, A. K. (1939) Geomorphology. New York, McGraw-Hill Book Company.

Lobley, J. L. (1889) Mount Vesuvius. London, Roper and Drowley.

Lyell, C. (1875) Principles of Geology, Vol. 2, 12th ed., London, John Murray.

———— (1830) Principles of Geology. London, John Murray.

Macdonald, Gordon A. (1952) The 1952 Eruption of Kilauea. Volcano Letter No. 518.

Macdonald, G. A., and Eaton, J. R. (1955) The 1955 Eruption of Kilauea Volcano. Volcano Letter Nos. 529–530.

———— (1954) The Eruption of Kilauea Volcano in May 1954. Volcano Letter, No. 524.

Macdonald, G. A., and Finch, R. H. (1950) The June 1950 Eruption of Mauna Loa. Volcano Letter No. 509.

———— (1949) The Mauna Loa Eruption of January, 1949. Volcano Letter No. 503.

MacGregor, A. G. (1939) The Royal Society Expedition to Montserrat, B. W. I. The Volcanic History and Petrology of Montserrat with Observations on Mt. Pelée in Martinique. Phil. Trans. Royal Society of London, Ser. B, Vol. 229, pp. 1–90.

———— (1951) Eruptive Mechanisms: Mt. Pelée, the Soufrière of St. Vincent and the Valley of Ten Thousand Smokes. Bull. Volcanologique, Vol. 12, pp. 49–74.

McBirney, A. (1956) An Appraisal of the Fumarolic Activity near Ahuachapán, El Salvador. Anales del Servicio Geológico de El Salvador, Bol. 2, pp. 19–32.

———— (1955) Chemical Aspects of the Fumarolic Activity in Nicaragua and El Salvador. Comunicaciones Instituto Tropical de Investigaciones Científicas, Universidad de El Salvador, Vol. 5, pp. 95–101.

Mason, Arnold C., and Foster, Helen L. (1953) Diversion of Lava Flows at O'Shima, Japan. Am. Jour. Sci., Vol. 251, pp. 249–258.

Melmoth, William. (1763) The Letters of Pliny the Consul. 5th ed. London, R. and J. Dodsley.

Mercalli, G. (1907) I vulcani activi della terra. Milan, Hoepli.

———— (1891) La eruzione dell'Isola de Vulcano. Annali dell'Ufficio centrale del meterologicae geodinamica, parte 4, Vol. 10. A review and summary of the conclusions is given in English by G. M. Butler, Eruption of Vulcano, August 3, 1888 to March 22, 1890, in Nature, Vol. 46, pp. 117–119, London, 1892.

Minakami, Takeshi. (1956) Report on Volcanic Activities and Volcanological Studies in Japan for the Period from 1951 to 1954. Bull. Volcanologique, Ser. 2, Vol. 18, pp. 39–55.

Ordóñez, Ezequiel. (1943) The New Volcano of Parícutin. Univ. of Texas, Inst. Latin Am. Studies, pp. 62–78.

———— (1906) Excursion du Jorullo. Guide des excursions du X Congres Geologique International, XI, Mexico.

Palmieri, L. (1873) Relazione del grande incendio del 26 April del 1872. Ann. del Royal Oss. Met. Vesuvius (Nunva) 1, Napoli.

Parks, James. (1910) Geology of New Zealand. London, Whitcombe and Tombs, Ltd.

Parsons, Willard H. (1960) Kilauea Speaks. Inside Wayne, Vol. 21, April 6.

Parsons, Willard H., and Mulford, John W. (1958) Capelinhos Volcano, Fayal Island, Azores. Cranbrook Institute of Science Newsletter, Vol. 28, No. 2, pp. 10–22.

Perret, F. A. (1935) Eruption of Mt. Pelée 1929–32. Carnegie Inst. of Washington, Publ. 458.

———— (1924) The Vesuvius Eruption of 1906. Carnegie Institute of Washington, Publ. 339.

Phillips, John. (1869) Vesuvius. Oxford, The Clarendon Press.

Playfair's Works. (1822) Collected Works of John Playfair, Esq., with a Memoir of the Author, 4 vols. Edinburgh, Arnold Constable.

Plinius Caecilius Secundus, C. (1763) The Letters; with an English translation by William Melmoth. London, R. and J. Dodsley.

Plutarchus. (1910) Plutarch's Lives. Dryden ed., revised by Arthur Clough. New York, E. P. Dutton & Company.

Popcock, L. G. (1955) The Landfalls of Odysseus. Christchurch, Whitcombe and Tombs, Ltd.

Preller, C. S. DuRiche. (1924) Italian Mountain Geology. Northern Italy and Tuscany. London, Wheldon and Wesley, Ltd.

Reclus, E. (1891) Nouvelle Geographic Universelle, Vol. 17, pp. 488–489. Paris.

Reck, Hans, et al. (1936) Santorin, der Werdegang eines Inselvulkans und sein Ausbruck 1925–1928. Berlin, D. Reimer, Andrews and Steiner.

Reynolds, Doris L. (1954) Fluidization as a Geological Process, and Its

Bearing on the Problem of Intrusive Granites. Am. Jour. of Sci., Vol. 252, pp. 577–614.

———— (1956) Calderas and Ring-Complexes. Nederlandsch Geologisch-Mijnbouwkundig Genootschap, Verhandelingen, Geol. Ser. Vol. 16 (Brouwer Jubilee Volume) pp. 355–379.

Richey, J. E. (1957) Birth of Volcanoes: Recent Eruption in the Azores. The Times [London] Science Review, Winter, 1957.

Rittmann, A. (1944) Vulcani attivita e genesi. Napoli, Edetrice Politecnica.

———— (1939) Threngslaborgir-line isländische Eruptions-Spalte am Myvatn. Natur u. Volk, Vol. 69, pp. 275–289.

———— (1933) Die geologische dedingte Evolution and Differentiation des Somma-Vesuvmagmas. Napoli, Zeitsch. f. Vulkanologie Vol. 15, pp. 8–95.

———— (1929) Der Atna und Seine Laven. Naturwissen-schaften, Vol. 17, pp. 94–100.

Rubey, William. (1951) Geologic History of the Sea. Bull. Geol. Soc. America, Vol. 62, pp. 1111–1148.

Sapper, Karl. (1931) Volcanology, Physics of the Earth. National Research Council Bull. 77.

———— (1927) Vulkankunde. Stuttgart, Englehorn.

———— (1925) Los volcanes de la América Central. Max Niemeyer, Halle (Saale).

Schuchert, C. (1935) Historical Geology of the Antillean-Caribbean Region. New York, John Wiley and Sons.

Scofield, John. (1958) A New Volcano Bursts from the Atlantic. The National Geographic Magazine, Vol. 63, June, pp. 735–757.

Scrope, G. Paulett. (1872) Volcanoes, the Character of Their Phenomena, Their Share in the Structure and Composition of the Surface of the Globe, and Their Relation to Its Internal Forces with a Descriptive Catalogue of All Known Volcanoes and Volcanic Formations. 2nd ed. London, Longmans, Green, Reader and Dyer. 1st ed., London, W. Phillips, 1825.

Segerstrom, Kenneth. (1950) Erosion Studies at Parícutin, State of Michoacán, Mexico. U.S. Geol. Survey Bull. 965-A, pp. 1–164.

Shand, S. J. (1938) Earth Lore. New York, E. P. Dutton & Co.

Sicardi, L. (1940) Il recente cielo dell'attiva fumarolica del Isola di Vulcano. Bull. Volcanologique, Ser. II, Vol. 7, pp. 86–140.

Signore, F. (1937) La deficienza gravimetrica nella zona di Boscoreale. Bull. Volcanologique, Vol. 2, pp. 173–182.

BIBLIOGRAPHY

Smith, William. (1816) Strata identified by Organized Fossils. London.

Sonder, R. A. (1937) Zur Theorie und Klassifikation der eruptiven vulkanischen Vorgange. Geol. Rundschau, Vol. 28, pp. 499–549.

Squier, E. G. (1859) Volcanoes of Central America. Harper's New Monthly Magazine, Vol. 19, pp. 739–763.

———— (1852) Nicaragua, Its People, Scenery, Monuments. New York, D. Appleton & Co.

———— (1850) On the Volcanoes of Central America. Proc. Am. Assoc. for Adv. of Sci., New Haven meeting.

Stearns, Harold T. (1946) Geology of the Hawaiian Islands. Bull. 8, Div. of Hydrography, Terr. of Hawaii.

Stearns, H. T., and Macdonald, G. A. (1946) Geology and Ground Water Resources of the Island of Hawaii. Hawaii Div. of Hydrography, Bull. 9.

Stehn, O. E. (1929) The Geology and Volcanism of the Krakatoa Group. 4th Pacific Sci. Cong. Guidebook: Batavia.

Stokes, W. L. (1960) Essentials of Earth History. Englewood Cliffs, New Jersey, Prentice-Hall.

Stoppanni, A. (1900) Corso di geologia. Milano, L. F. Cogliati [?].

Strabo. (1854–57) The Geography of Strabo; literally translated with notes. The first six books by H. C. Hamilton; remainder by W. Falconer. London, H. G. Bohn.

Suess, Eduard. (1904) The Face of the Earth. Translated by H. B. C. Sollas, Oxford, Clarendon Press.

Thorarinsson, S (1950) The Eruption of Mt. Hekla, 1947–1948. Bull. Volcanologique, Vol. 10, pp. 157–168.

———— (1956) Hekla on Fire. Munich, Hanns Reich Verlag.

Thorkelsson, Th. (1940) On Thermal Activity in Iceland and Geyser Action. Isafoldarprentsmidja, Rekyjavík.

Trask, Parker. (1943) The Mexican Volcano Parícutin. Science, Vol. 98, pp. 501–505.

Umbgrove, J. H. F. (1950) Symphony of the Earth. The Hague, Martinus Nijhoff.

———— (1947) The Pulse of the Earth. The Hague, Martinus Nijhoff.

Vening-Meinesz, F. A., Umbgrove, J. H. F., and Kuenen, P. H. (1934) Gravity Expeditions at Sea, 1923–1932, Vol. 2 Publication of the Netherlands Geodetic Commission, Delft.

Verbeek, R. D. M. (1886) Krakatau. Batavia, Imprimerie de l'état. Pub. by order of the Gov.-General of the Netherlands-Indies.

Vonsen, M. (1946) Minerals at The Geysers, Sonoma County, California. California Jour. of Mines and Geology, Vol. 42.

Washington, H. S. (1917) Persistence of Vents at Stromboli. Bull. Geol. Soc. America, Vol. 28, pp. 249–278.

Wilcox, Ray E. (1954) Petrology of Parícutin Volcano, Mexico. U.S. Geol. Survey Bull. 965-C, pp. 281–349.

———— (1947) Activity of Parícutin Volcano from December 1, 1946, to March 31, 1947. Am. Geophys. Union Trans., Vol. 28, pp. 725–731.

Williams, Howel. (1952) The Great Eruption of Coseguina, Nicaragua, in 1835. Univ. California Publ. Geol. Sci., Vol. 29, No. 2, pp. 21–46.

———— (1950) Volcanoes of the Parícutin Region, Mexico. U.S. Geol. Survey Bull. 965-B, pp. 165–279.

———— (1945) Geologic Setting of Parícutin Volcano. Am. Geophys. Union Trans., Vol. 26, pp. 255–256.

———— (1941) Calderas and Their Origin. Univ. California Publ. Bull., Dept. Geol. Sci., Vol. 25, pp. 239–346.

Wolff, F. von (1914, 1923, 1929, and 1931) Der Vulkanismus. Stuttgart, Von Ferdinand Enke.

INDEX

aa: 55–56

Abano Volcano, Italy: 337

Acqui Volcano, Italy: 337

active volcanoes. SEE volcanoes, active

Aeolian Islands: description of, 173–175; in mythology, 174; structural relations of, 176–178; cones and craters of, 178; active volcanoes of, 178; as setting of *Odyssey,* 182

Alban Hills, Italy: eruption in, 330; mentioned, 329

Aleutian island arc: marginal deep of, 374; radius of, 374; mentioned, 316

Aleutian Islands: Bogoslof Volcano in, 316; island arc of, 316; volcanoes of, 316; Aleutian Trench and, 316

Aleutian Trench: depth of, 316; description of, 374

Alicudi, Aeolian Islands: cone of, 178

Alpine Fault: location of, 342

Alpine-Himalayan zone: of active volcanoes, 367, 370

Alpine orogeny: 384

Andean Cordillera: as island arc, 377; deep focus earthquakes in, 377

Anderson, Dr. Tempest: volcanic studies by, 25–26; on advantages of volcanology, 26

andesite: defined, 52

Andesite Line: in Pacific Ocean, 60; in relation to continents, 381; sial and sima in relation to, 393

Apennine Mountains, Italy: in relation to volcanic centers, 175; mentioned, 329, 330

Arduino, Giovanni: 19

Aristotle: on nature of volcanic activity, 14

ash: defined, 45; shard structure in, 48; tuff type of, 48; from Parícutin Volcano, 278; falls in Mexico City, 278; distribution of, at Jorullo, 297; mentioned, 9

Atlantic-type lava: 173

Atlas Mountains, Africa: in relation to Italian structure, 175

atoll: 211

atomic energy: 365

Auvergne district, France: studies by Desmarest in, 19; von Buch in, 23; Puy de Dome of, 23

Azores Islands: location of, 310; structural trends in, 310; Mid-Atlantic ridge and the, 310; shield-type cones of, 310; calderas of, 310; historic eruptions in, 311

Aztecs of Mexico: fire god of, 12

426

bar: 400, 401 n

barrier reef: 211

basalt: defined, 52

Bay of Naples: structure of, 168–169

Bermuda Islands: 99–100

Big Geysir, Iceland: meaning of name of, 352; **eruptions of, 352**; studies of geyser action at, 352–353

Bláfjall-Leirhnúk fissure system, Iceland: eruption of, 250; volume of lava from, 250; sequence of events in eruption of, 250

blocks: defined, 44. SEE ALSO pyroclastics

bocas: of Parícutin lava flows, 278; of 1944 Parícutin flows, 282–286 *passim*; mentioned, 162

—of San Juan flow: description of, 284; whirlpool of, 284; convection in, 284; graben of, 284; ferrous chloride deposits at, 286; of Juatito, 288; of Ahuan, 288

Bogoslof Volcano, Alaska: disappearing island of, 316; location of, 316; lava domes of, 316, 319; eruptions of, 318

bombs: breadcrust, 34, 45, 185; defined, 44; size of, 44. SEE ALSO pyroclastics

boric acid: from Larderello, 331, 335; method of recovery of, 336

Bowen, N. L.: on magmatic differentiation, 58

breccia, volcanic: 48

Bringhenti process: 333

Brownson trough: 97

Brun, A.: on composition of vapor cloud, 38

Buch, Leopold von. SEE von Buch, Leopold

Bunsen, R.: on geyser action, 352–353

Caldeira Volcano, Fayal Island, Azores: and origin of term, 311 n

caldera: defined, 71–72; distinguished from "crater," 72, 75; theory of origin of, 72; of Krakatoa, 79, 84;

Krakatoa-type of, 84; of Coseguina, 87; of Vulcano, 188; of Mauna Loa, 217; of Kilauea, 229–242 *passim*; in the Azores, 310; origin of term, 311 n; and Italian lakes, 329

Campiglia Marittima, Italy: description of, 339; mentioned, 338

Campo Bianco Volcano, Lipari: description of, 178; and Roche Rosse, obsidian flow from, 180; pumice of, 180; lava dome of, 180; Judd's description of, 180

Canary Islands: spacing of volcanoes of, 372

Capelinhos Volcano, Fayal Island, Azores: location and description of, 311–312; earthquakes preceding birth of, 312; birth of, 312–313; destroyed by waves, 313; subsequent history of, 313–314; phreatic cone of, 314; Strombolian-type eruptions of, 314

Capps, S. R.: 4

Capri Island, Italy: structural setting of, 168–169

carbon dioxide: in relation to declining volcanic activity, 43

carbonatite magma. SEE magma, carbonate-rich

Casamicciola earthquake: 130

casita: at Parícutin, 282, 286

Cassius, Dion: description of A.D. 203 eruption of Vesuvius by, 157; mentioned, 146

Castle Rock. SEE Bogoslof Volcano, Alaska

Catania, Sicily: destruction of, 64–65; diversion of lava flow at, 64, 67; in 1669 eruption of Etna, 264

Cerro Negro Volcano, Nicaragua: 85

Cimini Volcano, Italy: 329

cinders: defined, 45. SEE ALSO pyroclastics

Ciparis, Auguste: 108–109

circum-Pacific belt: of active volcanoes, 367, 370. SEE ALSO fire girdle of Pacific

Civita, Italy: as Pompeii, 154; mentioned, 150, 152

classification of volcanoes: early classifications of, 32; by Lacroix, 32–33. SEE ALSO Hawaiian type of eruption; Icelandic type of eruption; Peléan type of eruption; Strombolian type of eruption; solfataric stage; Vulcanian type of eruption

Coast Range orogeny: 384

Columbia River lava plateau: basalt of, 55; volume of 244

Compere-Leandre, Leon: 109–110

Concepción Volcano, Nicaragua: 85, 87

cones: cinder, 70–71; composite, 71

Conte, Prince Piero Ginori: 332

contraction theory: of mountain building, 386–387

convection: in ground water, 326; in mountain building, 387

convection hypothesis: and origin of continents and oceans, 392; root development in, 392; and island arcs, 392–400; confirmation of, by gravity, 399; as applied to island arcs and volcanoes, 399–400; role of gravity anomalies in, 400

—and mountain building: source of heat in, 387; and viscosity of mantle, 387–388; root formation in, 391; outline of cycle of, 391; experimental model of, 391–392; stages in cycle of, 392; time estimates of, 392

coral reefs: types of, 211

core of earth: heat of, 387; physical state of, 379

Coseguina Volcano, Nicaragua: description of, 87; caldera of, 87; 1835 eruption of, 87–90; volume of ejecta from, 90–91

crater: defined, 70; distinguished from caldera, 72, 75

crater-accumulation theory: Lyell and, 24; Werner and, 24

crater-elevation theory: described, 23; von Buch and, 23; applied to La Palma Volcano, 72; Jorullo as example of, 292, 299, 300; and Monte Nuovo, 303–304, 307; mentioned, 24, 25

Crater Lake, Oregon: caldera of, 76; description of, 76; ancestral cone of, 76. SEE ALSO Mount Mazama

creation: Mosaic account of, 16

crust of earth: and spacing of volcanoes, 372; and zone of fracture, 376; and zone of flowage, 376; thickness of, 378, 380; layers of, 378; density of, 378; composition of, 379; importance of silicon dioxide in, 379; sial layer of, 379–380; sima layer of, 380; yielding of, under pressure, 388

curtain of fire: 214, 220. SEE ALSO lava fountains

Cuicuilco Pyramid, Mexico: 12

cycles: of natural phenomena, 258; of climate, 258; of sunspots, 258. SEE ALSO volcanic cycles

Daubeny, Charles: on source of water, 38

da Vinci, Leonardo: 16

Day, A. L.: 28, 39

Deccan lava plateau, India: 244

de Dolomieu, Gratet. SEE Dolomieu, Gratet de

De Fiore, O.: 35

delli Falconi, Antonio Marco: on eruption of Monte Nuovo, 305–306

del Nero, Francesco: on eruption of Monte Nuovo, 307

de Riaño, Antonio. SEE Riaño, Antonio de

deuterium: 350 n

di Toledo, Pietro Giacomo: on eruption of Monte Nuovo, 306–307

Dolomieu, Gratet de: 17

earthquakes: transmission of waves of, 24; of Casamicciola, 130; in eruption of Kilauea, 240; in eruption of Kilauea Iki, 241; depth of lava from records of, 242; in eruption of Vesuvius, 267; at birth of Monte Nuovo, 302; at birth of Capelinhos Volcano, 312; and faulting in California, 358; depth of, in volcanic eruptions, 373; depth of origin of, 376; classes of, 376; and shear zone, 377; concentration of, in marginal deeps, 393; island arcs and, 395

—deep-focus type of: in White Island Trench, 345; response of, to stresses in zone of flowage, 376; location of, 376; depth of, 376; depth of, in relation to continent, 377; in Andean Cordillera, 377; mentioned, 393

East Indies Arc. SEE Indonesian Arc

East Indies Archipelago: active volcanoes of, 367

Edgecumbe Volcano, New Zealand: 342

Eldgjá fissure, Iceland: eruption of, 252; volume of, 252

El Salvador: Ahuachapán steam area of, 364

energy. SEE geothermal energy

engulfment theory: applied to Krakatoa and Santorin volcanoes, 72. SEE ALSO explosion-collapse theory

Ente Nazionale Idrocarburi: 336

enthalpy: 327

epimagma: 229, 231

explosion-collapse theory: 75. SEE ALSO engulfment theory

Falconi, Antonio Marco delli. SEE delli Falconi, Antonio Marco

Falcon Island, Tonga Islands: submarine eruption of, 314

Fiji Islands: spacing of volcanoes of, 372

Filicudi, Aeolian Islands: cone of, 178

fire: gods of, 11, 181; myths of, in Polynesia, in Tonga, in Samoa, 12; Aztec god of, 12; Hawaiian goddess of, 12

fire girdle of the Pacific: active volcanoes of, 367; mentioned, 85. SEE ALSO circum-Pacific belt

fissure eruptions: character of, 244–245; of Iceland, 245, 250–252; of Bláfjall-Leirhnúk, 250; volume of,

250, 251, 252, 253; sequence of events in, 250; of Laki, 250–251; of Eldgjá, 252; Hekla type of, 252–254

fluidization: 116, 401

fringing reef: 211

Fujiyama, Japan: worship of, 13

fumaroles: of Ahuachapán, El Salvador, 364; of San Jacinto, Nicaragua, 364; of Tisate, Nicaragua, 364; mentioned, 323

—at The Geysers, California, 358; sublimates of, 361

Funicolare Vesuviana: 166

gal: definition of, 396

Galapagos Islands: spacing of volcanoes of, 372

gas blow-off: of 1906 Vesuvius eruption, 164; of 1944 Vesuvius eruption, 166–168

gases: importance of, in volcanic eruptions, 8–9; water vapor as eruptive force, 37; composition of, 39–40; sampling of, 39; juvenile, 39; as source of heat, 39; volume of, 41; as source of oceanic waters and earth's atmosphere, 41–42; composition of, at Vulcano, 188; in eruption of Hekla, 254; volume of water vapor at Parícutin, 290; and geyser action, 353; as explosive forces in eruptions, 401

—sublimates of: sulphur, 41; ferrous chloride, 41; ammonium chloride, 41; metallic oxides, 41

gas-fluxing hypothesis: of Daly, 198–199

Geological Society of America: 273

geosynclines: type and thickness of sediments in, 381–382; and mountains, 381–382; description of Appalachian, 382; sinking of, 382

geothermal energy: surface heat losses and, 326; from geothermal gradient, 328; power installations of, in United States, 365; as economic application of volcanology, 405–406. SEE ALSO natural steam, heat

—development of: in St. Lucia Island, 362; in El Salvador, 364; in Nicaragua, 364; in Japan, 364; in Russia, 364

—from natural steam. SEE Iceland; Italy; natural steam; natural steam wells; New Zealand; The Geysers, California

geothermal gradient: normal value of, 326, 328; as source of heat, 328

geysers: of Yellowstone National Park, 323; of Iceland, 351–354; definition of, 352; origin of name of, 352; theories of action of, 352–353; "cold-water" type of, 354

Geysers, California, The. SEE The Geysers, California

Geysir, Big, Iceland. SEE Big Geysir, Iceland

glaciers: of Iceland, 247, 248

god of wind: 174–175

gods of fire: 11, 181. SEE ALSO fire

Goranson, R.: experiments by, 40, 325; on water content of magma, 40

Graham Island, Mediterranean: location of, 309; birth of, 309; history of, 309–310; destruction of, by waves, 310

gravity: measurement of, 395, 396; island arcs and, 395; law of, 395; example of law of, 395; gravity anomalies, 396–398; submarine measurements of, 398; gravimetric profile of island arcs, 399; in support of convection hypothesis, 400

Great Crack, Kilauea: rift zone of, 228

Grenada Trough: 96

Grimsvötn Volcano, Iceland: subglacial eruption of, 249

Grosseto Volcano, Italy: 337

ground water: role in steam-blast explosions, 28–30; in Yellowstone, heated by magma, 324; steam contamination of, 325; convection circulation of, 326; in natural steam, 337; effect of pressure on boiling of, 347

Halemaumau, Kilauea: fire pit of, 229; lava lake of, 229, 232, 234; temperature measurements of, 231; convection circulation in, 236; variations in level of lava in, 236; convection in, 284

Hamilton, Sir William: 17, 150 n, 160

Hawaii, Hawaiian Islands: description of, 213; lava domes of, 213, 217

Hawaiian Archipelago: composition of, 207; rift of, 219; mentioned, 211

Hawaiian Islands: discovery of, 209; history of, 209; geology of, 209–211; age of, 213; stages in development of volcanoes of, 214–216; submarine eruptions of, 308; spacing of volcanoes of, 372. SEE ALSO Oahu, Hawaiian Islands; Hawaii, Hawaiian Islands; Kauai, Hawaiian Islands

Hawaiian type of eruption: defined, 33; examples of, 213; characteristics of, 213–214; shield volcano and, 214

Hawaiian Volcano Observatory: establishment of, 27–28; Jaggar, Thomas A. and, 27–30; 1949 eruption from, 224; mentioned, 4, 39, 228

Hawaii National Park: Bird Park in, 221; mentioned, 217, 228

Hayward Fault: 358

Healdsburg Fault: 358

heat: radioactive materials as source of, 326; magma as source of, 326; faulting as source of, 326; geothermal, 328; as agent in mountain building, 386; source of, in convection hypothesis, 387; from radioactive material, 387; solar source of, 405. SEE ALSO geothermal energy

heavy water: use of, 345; steam in production of, 350; content of, in water, 350

Hephaestus: 11

Herculaneum, Italy: burial of, by mud flow, 149–150; discovery of, 152–153; excavations of, 152–156 *passim*; mentioned, 135

Hilo, Hawaii: protection from lava flows at, 66; lava flows in, 222

Hobbs, W. H.: 4

Hookena postoffice, Hawaii: destruction of, 226

hornitos: 300

hot springs: distinction between magmatic and meteoric, 43; indications of origin of, 43; of Yellowstone National Park, 323; in New Zealand, 344; of Iceland, 351–352, 354–356; of Ahuachapán, El Salvador, 364; of San Jacinto, Nicaragua, 364. SEE ALSO The Geysers, California

Hot Springs, Arkansas: 326, 326 n

Hot Water Board, Iceland: 356

Hualalai Volcano, Hawaii: lava dome of, 213

Humboldt, Alexander von. SEE von Humboldt, Alexander

Hutton, James: theories of, 20–21; recognition of igneous rocks by, 20–21

Huzi Volcano, Japan: 322

Ice Age: in Iceland, 247, 248

Iceland: fissure eruptions of, 244; location of, 246; history of, 247; glaciers of, 247; volcanic history of, 247; zone of modern volcanism in, 248; palagonite deposits of, 249; historic fissure eruptions of, 250–252; Mount Hekla in, 252–254; volcanism in, 351; hot springs and geysers of, 351–354; municipal hot water systems of, 356. SEE ALSO Reykjavík; Sellfoss

Icelandic type of eruption: character of, 245; compared to Hawaiian type, 245; under water, 249; historic examples of, 250–254. SEE ALSO palagonite

ignimbrite: mentioned, 347
—in New Zealand: occurrence of, 342; volume of, 342; as steam trap, 348

index of explosiveness: formula for, 85; as calculated by Sapper, 87

Indonesian island arc: as example of double type, 375; mentioned, 371, 374. SEE ALSO island arcs

Ischia Island, Italy: last eruption on, 130; Casamicciola earthquake on, 130; structural setting of, 170; mentioned, 133, 337

island arcs: of Aleutians, 316, 374; in Atlantic Ocean, 367; outside Pacific Ocean, 370; characteristics of, 374; distribution of, 374; in relation to volcanoes and earthquakes, 374; marginal deep of, 374; structural features of, 374; of Indonesia, 374; of Japan, 374; of Marianas, 374; of Palau, 374; of Yap, 374; age of, in relation to continents, 375; and mountains, 375; single type of, 375; double type of, 375; theory of origin of, 375; shear zone in, 375–377; and seismic activity, 377; Andean Cordillera as, 377; and orogenic belts, 385; underthrusting in, 393, 399, 400; arching of crust in, 393, 399, 400; formation of magma in, 393, 400; differences between single and double types of, 394; gravity anomalies in, 398–399; gravimetric profile of, 399; explanation of, by convection hypothesis, 399–400; association of volcanoes with, 393, 395, 400

Italy: geologic history of, 329

—natural steam of: utilization of, 330–335; electric energy output of, 334; composition of, 335–336; prospective areas of, 337; evidence of magmatic source of, 337. SEE ALSO Larderello, Italy; natural steam

—volcanoes of: distribution of, 329; structure relations of, 329; Vulsini, 329; Cimini, 329; Sabatini, 329; Alban Hills, 329; Roccamonfina, 329; Vesuvius, 329; Phlegraean Fields, 329; caldera lakes of, 329; trend of activity of, 329–330

Jaggar, Thomas A.: life of, 27–30; establishment of Hawaiian Volcano Observatory by, 27–28; ideas of, 28–30; and steam-blast eruptions, 28–30; and bombing lava flow, 28; control of lava flows by bombing, 66–67;

lava flow predicted by, 66; on eruptive cycle of Kilauea, 260–262; mentioned, 4

Japan: natural steam in, 364

Japan island arc: radius of, 374; trench of, 374

Japan Trench: 374

jökulhlaup: of Volcano Grimsvötn, 249; volume of, 249; of Katla Volcano, 249; compared to Amazon River, 249. SEE ALSO Iceland

Jorullo Volcano, Mexico: cooling of lava flows from, 63; crater-elevation theory and, 292; location of, 292; eruptive history of, 293–298; Humboldt's visit to, 294; birth of, 294–298; floods of water in eruption of, 296; eye-witness accounts of eruption of, 296–297 *passim*; distribution of ash at, 297; duration of eruptive activity of, 298; thirty years after eruption of, 298–299; von Humboldt's description of, 299; hornitos of, 300; dimension of cone and crater of, 301; fumaroles in crater of, 301; vegetation on cone of, 301

"juvenile" water: 38

Kalapana, Hawaii: black sand beach of, 214

Kapoho, Hawaii: 237–242 *passim*

Karapiti blowhole, New Zealand: 344

Katla Volcano, Iceland: subglacial eruption of, 249

Kauai, Hawaiian Islands: garden island of, 213

Kermadec Islands: structural alignment of, 342

Kermadec Ridge: location of, 345

Kermadec-Tonga Trench: location of, 342; formation of, 342; depth of, 345

Ketetahi, New Zealand: steam area of, 344

Koolau Volcano, Oahu: lava dome of, 213

Kilauea Iki crater, Hawaii: eruption of, 241; lava lake of, 241; lava fountains of, 241; seismic activity in eruption of, 241; mentioned, 242

Kilauea Volcano, Hawaii: lava dome of, 213; 228; example of Hawaiian type of eruption, 213; description of, 228; rift zones of, 228; 1823 lava flow of, 228; lava lake of, 228–229; caldera of, 229; Halemaumau, 229; typical eruption of, 231; phreatic eruptions of, 232; 1924 eruption of, 232; eruptive cycle of, 234, 242; table of eruptions of, 235; percent of time in eruption, 235; 1952 eruption of, 235–236; 1954 eruption of, 236–237; 1955 eruption of, 237–241; flank eruption of, 237; earthquakes in eruption of, 240; subsidence in 1955 eruption of, 240; basis for predicting end of eruption of, 240–241; 1959–1960 eruption of, 241–242; eruptive cycle of, 259–262; correlation of eruptions of, with sunspots, 261

kipuka: 221

Krakatoa Volcano, Indonesia: distribution of ash by, 49–50; sun glows produced by, 49–50; caldera of, 71, 79–80, 84; engulfment theory and, 72; description of, 78; history of, 79–80, 84; 1883 eruption of, 80

Lacroix, A.: classification of volcanoes by, 33

lagoni: 331

Lake Avernus, Italy: in Phlegraean Fields, 302; in mythology, 302; mentioned, 132, 133

Lake Bolsena, Italy: 329, 338

Lake Bracciano, Italy: 329

Lake Lucrine, Italy: 302, 303

Lake Myvatn, Iceland: craters of, 250

Lake Vico, Italy: 329

Laki Fissure, Iceland: 1883 eruption of, 251; volume of, 251; damage by 1883 eruption of, 251

432

VOLCANOES

La Palma Volcano, Canary Islands:
caldera of, 72; as example of crater-
elevation theory, 72

lapilli: defined, 45. SEE ALSO pyroclastics

Larderel, Count Francesco: 331

Larderello, Tuscany: natural steam resources of, 330; location of, 330;
steam wells of, 333–334; power production of, 334–335; composition of
steam of, 335–336; chemical production at, 336; geologic conditions
at, 336–337; presence of magma at,
339; travel to, 339; steam traps at,
347–348

Las Pilas Volcano, Nicaragua: 85

Lassen Peak, California: as example of
Vulcanian type of eruption, 190

La Soufrière, St. Vincent Island: description of, 120; history of, 120–
123; mentioned, 97, 99

—1902 eruption of: preliminary activity in, 123; mud flows of, 123; nuée
ardente of, 124; ash falls from, 125;
destruction by, 125–126

Latial Volcano, Italy: 337

lava: defined, 51; origin of name of,
51; composition of, 52–53; acid type
of, 52; basic type of, 52; intermediate type of, 52; temperature of, 54;
crystallization of, 56; variation in
composition of, 57–58; Atlantic type
of, 60; Pacific type of, 60; Mediterranean type of, 60, 329; temperature
of, at Halemaumau, 231; mentioned,
9. SEE ALSO andesite; basalt; rhyolite

—of Hekla: temperature of, 253; composition of, 253; carbon dioxide in
eruption of, 254

lava domes: at Mount Pelée, 117, 120;
formation of, 118; significance of,
118–120; at Mount Vesuvius, 163;
of Campo Bianco, 180; of Oahu,
213; of Hawaii, 213; shield-volcano
type of, 214; of Mauna Loa, 217; of
Bogoslof, 316, 318–319

lava flows: extents of, 55; mobility of,
55; surfaces of, 55; rate of cooling
of, 62; and entrance to sea, 214, 241;
volume of, on Mauna Loa, 222, 228;

rate of flow of, 226; of Kaapuna,
227, 228; temperature of, 231; attempts to stop, 239, 241; velocity of,
at Kilauea, 240; volume of, at Kilauea, 240; flank flows at Kilauea,
260; Carthaginian army stopped by,
264; Catania destroyed by, 264;
bocas of, at Parícutin, 278; of Parícutin in 1944, 282; village of Parícutin covered by, 282, 286; San
Juan de Parangaricutiro covered by,
282; of San Juan, 284–286; of Parícutin 1945–1952, 286–289; area
covered by, at Parícutin, 290; volume of, at Parícutin, 290; of Jorullo,
298; from Capelinhos Volcano,
Azores, 313. SEE ALSO aa; pahoehoe;
scoria

—control of: by bombing, 66; Jaggar
on, 66–67

—cooling of: in Yellowstone National
Park, 62; at Parícutin Volcano, 63;
at Mount Etna, 63; at Mount Vesuvius, 63; at Jorullo, 63

—destruction by: at Torre Annunziata,
63; at Torre del Greco, 63; at San
Juan de Parangaricutiro, 64, 68; at
Catania, 64; at Hilo, 65

—diversion of: at Catania, 64, 67; on
Mauna Loa by bombing, 66–67; at
Torre Annunziata, 68; at O'Shima
Volcano, 68–69

—stopping of: at Mount Etna, 64; at
Mauna Loa, 65

lava fountains: causes of, 214; of
Mauna Loa, 225; at Kilauea, 236–
237; at Kilauea Iki, 241

lava plateaus: of Columbia and Snake
Rivers, 243; of Deccan, 244; of
Paraná, 244

lava tunnel: 56

law of gravity: illustration of, 395

Lesser Antilles: description of, 96;
geology of, 96–97, 99; spacing of
volcanoes of, 372; island arc of, 384;
mentioned, 367, 371

Lighthouse of the Mediterranean: 194,
201

limestone-assimilation hypothesis: Rittmann on, 171; Holmes on, 173

Limestone Caribbees, Lesser Antilles: 96, 99

Lipari Islands: volcanoes of, 178. SEE ALSO Aeolian Islands

liparite: 180

Lyell, Sir Charles: and beginnings of modern geology, 22; on source of water, 38

McCulloch Peak. SEE Bogoslof Volcano, Alaska.

Madam Pele. SEE Pele, Madam

magma: definition of, 8; solubility as basis for order of crystallization of, 21; water content of, 40, 42, 325, 338; development of pressure in, 40; carbonate-rich, 173; gases of, 323; rate of cooling of, 324; steam from, 324–326; cooling needed for Larderello steam, 337; rate of solidification of, 338; at Larderello, 339; in island arcs, 393, 400; solubility of water in, 400; distribution of water in, 400–401; pressure control of water in, 401; water diffusion in, 402

magmatic differentiation: Bowen on, 58; by fractional crystallization, 58; Palisade sill, New Jersey, and, 58; Barth on, 59; mentioned, 170

magmatic-sclerosis: 171

magmatic springs: composition of, 43; as compared to meteoric, 43; examples of, 43

magmatic storms: 258

Maiuri, A.: 156

malpais: of Jorullo, 298, 299, 300

mantle of the earth: thickness of, 378; physical state of, 378; heat from, 387; viscosity of, 388

Marianas island arc: 374

Massa, Italy: destruction of, in 1872, 163; destruction of, in 1944, 165–166; destroyed by lava flow, 268

Mauna Loa Volcano, Hawaii: description of, 65, 217; lava dome of, 213, 217; as example of Hawaiian type of eruption, 213; shield volcano of, 217; volume of, 217; rift zone of, 219; typical eruption of, 219–221; 1859 flow of, 221–222; longest flow of, 221–222; 1881 flow of, 222; volume of lava flows from, 222, 228; age of, 222; eruptive cycle of, 223; duration of eruptions of, 223; January, 1949, eruption of, 224–225; summit eruption of, 224–225; June, 1950, eruption of, 225–228; flank eruption of, 225–228; correlation of eruption of, with sunspots, 261

Maungakakaramea Volcano, New Zealand: 342

Mayacmas Range, California: structure of, 357–358; quicksilver in, 358

Mediterranean type of lava: 173, 329

Mercalli, G.: classification of volcanoes by, 33; definition of Vulcanian type by, 190

mercury: at Mount Amiata, Italy, 338; in Mayacmas Range, California, 358

Mesa de los Hornitos: 282

Metcalf cone. SEE Bogoslof Volcano, Alaska

meteoric springs: composition of, 42–43; as compared to magmatic springs, 43

mid-Atlantic Ridge: and Iceland, 246; and Azores, 246, 310; and Ascension, 246; and Tristan de Cunha, 246; depth of, 247; volcanoes on, 367; shape of, 371

milligal: 398

mineralizers: 337

Mokuaweoweo Caldera, Mauna Loa: eruption on floor of, 224; mentioned, 217, 220, 225

Momotombo Volcano, Nicaragua: 85

Monte Chirica Volcano, Lipari: 178

Monte Nuovo Volcano, Italy: birth of, 302–303; earthquakes at birth of, 302; description of, 303; in crater-elevation controversy, 303–304; eyewitness accounts of eruption of, 305–308; mentioned, 130

Monte Pelato, Lipari. SEE Campo Bianco

Mont Sant'Angelo Volcano, Lipari: 178

Mount Amiata, Italy: description of, 338; mentioned, 337, 339

Mount Ararat, Turkey: as resting place of Noah's ark, 371

Mount Demavend, Iran: 371

Mount Etna, Sicily: myths of, 10; Virgil on, 10; cooling of lava flows from, 63; lava flow of 1669 from, 64, 67; secondary vents of, 71; parasitic cones of, 262, 271; history of, 263–264; in classical literature, 263–264; dates of early eruptions of, 264; 1669 eruption of, 264; eruptive cycle of, 264; typical eruption of, 264; lateral eruption of, 264; future eruptions of, 265; mentioned, 4. SEE ALSO Catania, Sicily

Mount Hekla, Iceland: description of, 252; as strata or shield type, 252; eruptive history of, 252–253

—1947 eruption of: description of, 253–254; Plinian phase of, 253; volume of lava in, 253; composition of lava, 253–254; temperature of lava, 253

Mount Lassen, California: hot springs of, 324; mentioned, 370

Mount Mazama, Oregon: glaciers on, 76–77; *nuées ardentes* from, 78; volume of ejecta, 78. SEE ALSO Crater Lake, Oregon

Mount Misery, St. Kitts: 97, 99

Mount Pelée, Martinique: tholoid of, 23; Perret at, 27; as stimulus to volcanology, 95–96; description of, 100, 102; history of, 100; significance of, in volcanology, 404–405. SEE ALSO Ciparis, Auguste; Compere-Leandre, Leon; lava domes

—1902 eruption of: mudflows, 104, 105; destruction of St. Pierre, 105–106, 110–111; eye-witness accounts of, 107–108, 114; survivors of, 108–110; *nuées ardentes* from, 114–116; spine of, 117–118

—1929 eruption of: *nuées ardentes* of, 119; lava dome of, 120

Mount St. Helena, California: 357

Mount Shasta, California: volume of, 217

Mount Somma, Italy: blocks in debris of, 170; mentioned, 157, 267

Mount Vesuvius, Italy: cooling of lava flows from, 63; destruction by lava flows from, 63; lava from, at Torre Annunziata, 68; importance of, 129; cyclic pattern of, 130; geologic setting of, 130; early history of, 133–134; as described by Diodorus Siculus, 133; as described by Strabo, 134; Spartacus and, 134; not recognized as volcano, 135; earthquakes of A.D. 63 at, 135; 1906 eruption of, 148; 1631 eruption of, 152, 156, 158–159; A.D. 203 eruption of, 157; A.D. 472 eruption of, 157; early history of, 157; 1036 eruption of, 157–158; rejuvenation of, 158, 170–173; 1139 eruption of, 158; eruptive cycle of, 159–168 *passim*, 265–268; 1767 eruption of, 160; 1779 eruption of, 161–162; Ottaiano in 1779 eruption of, 162; 1793 eruption of, 162; 1872 eruption of, 163; lava domes of, 163; 1906 eruption of, 163; gas blow-off of, 164; 1944 eruption of, 165; changes in crater of, 168; depth of magma at, 168, 170; structural setting, 168–170; length of cycles at, 268; current status of, 268; depth of magma at, 372; and theory of crustal thickness, 372

—A.D. 79 eruption of: Pliny's account of, in letters to Tacitus, 138–144; mentioned, 9, 135

mountain building: role of heat in, 386; contraction theory of, 386; convection hypothesis of, 387–395; root formation in, 391; association of volcanoes and earthquakes with, 395

mountain systems: arcuate structure of, 375; relation of, to island arcs, 375; and geosynclines, 381–382; history of, 382–384; Spanish Sierra Nevada, 384; African Atlas, 384

—development of: circum-Pacific, 384; Alpine-Himalayan, 384; Mediterranean, 384

—as orogenic belts: direction of movement of, 385; relation of island arcs to, 385; and association of volcanoes, 385 mudflows: in 1902 eruption of Mount Pelée, 104; at Herculaneum, 149–150; in 1631 eruption of Vesuvius, 159; in 1906 eruption of Vesuvius, 164

municipal hot water system. SEE Reykjavík, Iceland, municipal hot water system of. SEE ALSO Sellfoss, Iceland

Myozin-syo Volcano, Japan: location of, 319; eruptions of, 319; vessel and crew lost in eruption of, 319–321; end of activity of, 321; volcanic belt of, 321–322

Myrdalsjökull, Iceland: 249

mythology: gods of fire in, 11; legend of Pele, 12; forge of Vulcan in, 11; Aeolian Islands in, 174–175; Vulcano in, 181

Naples, Italy: University of, 4

National University of Mexico: 273

natural steam: types of, 324; from magma, 324–326; primary type of, 324–326; soffioni, 325; temperature and pressure of, 325; ground water contamination of, 325; quality of, 325–327; critical temperature of, 325; secondary type of, 326–327; heating of ground water by, 326; pressure control of, 327; drilling for, 327–328; utilization of, 330–335; chemicals from, 331–332, 336; power generation from, 332–334; evidence of magmatic source of, 337; magmatic cooling and volume of, 337; favorable localities for, 338; source of, at Larderello, 339; heavy water from, 350; Ahuachapán, El Salvador, area of, 364; San Jacinto, Nicaragua, area of, 364; as explosive force in eruptions, 401. SEE ALSO natural steam wells

—in New Zealand: areas of, 344; exploration for, 345; relation to structure, 347; drilling for, 348; relation to depth and temperature of, 347; pressure and volume of wells, 349; composition of, 349; removal of water from, 349; power resources of areas of, 350

natural steam wells: depths of, 333–335; pressures of, 333–334; volumes of, 334; drilling of, 335; composition of, 335–336. SEE ALSO natural steam

—in New Zealand: at Wairakei, 342; depth of, 345; drilling of, 348; volume and pressure of, 349

—at The Geysers, California: depth and pressure of, 360, 362; output of, 360; temperature of, 360; composition of, 360; influence of faults on, 362. SEE ALSO natural steam

Neptunists: theory of, 18–19, 21; arguments by, against molten origin of granite, 21. SEE ALSO Werner, Abraham Gottlob

Nero, Emperor: on stage in Naples, 135

Nero, Francesco del. SEE del Nero, Francesco

Nero Deep: 399

new volcanoes: birth of, at Jorullo, Mexico, 294–298; as distinguished from parasitic cone, 271–272; birth of, in North America, 272; of Parícutin, 272; of Monte Nuovo, 302–303

—by submarine eruptions: Graham Island, 309–310; in the Azores, 310–311; of Capelinhos, Fayal Island, 311–314; Sabrina Island, Azores, 311; Falcon Island, 314; of Noyöe, Iceland, 314, 316; of Myozin-syo, Japan, 319–322

New Zealand: geography of, 340; physical features of, 340; thermal regions of, 344; drilling steam wells in, 348; power resources from steam areas of, 350; power installations at Wairakei, 351; geysers of, 352

Ngauruhoe Volcano, New Zealand: dates of eruptions, 344; mentioned, 340, 342

Nicaragua: natural steam prospects of, 364; San Jacinto fumarole area of, 364; Tisate fumarole area of, 364

Noah's ark: and Mount Ararat, 371

Northern Lights: 258

Noyöe Volcano, Iceland: submarine eruption of, 314; destruction of, 314 *nuée ardente*: defined, 35; from Mount Mazama, 78; from Krakatoa, 84; temperature of, 113; in eruptions of Mount Pelée, 114–116; eyewitness description of, 114; Perret on mobility of, 116; mentioned, 129, 148, 342

Oahu, Hawaiian Islands: lava domes of, 213

obsidian: 57

Odyssey: locale of, 182

Oraeki-Korako, New Zealand: steam resources of, 350

orogenic belts: migration of, 392

orogenic cycle: outline of, 382–384; of Coast Ranges, 384; of Alps, 384

orogeny: SEE mountain building

O'Shima Volcano, Japan: diversion of lava flow from, 68–69

Ottaiano, Italy: destruction of, in 1779, 162; destruction of, in 1906, 164; destruction of, in 1944, 166

Pacific Gas and Electric Company, California: 362 n

Pacific type of lava: 173

Pahoa, Hawaii: 237, 240

pahoehoe lava: 55–56, 220, 231

palagonite: 249

Palau island arc: 374

Palisade sill, New Jersey: 58

Panarea, Aeolian Islands: 178

Pantelleria Island, Mediterranean: 309

Paraná lava plateau, South America: 244

Parícutin village, Mexico: covered by lava, 282

Parícutin Volcano, Mexico: cooling of lava flows from, 63; as example of cinder cone, 71; as example of Vulcanian type of eruption, 190; location of, 273; birth of, 273–275; first lava from, 276; first year's activity of, 276; at end of first week, 276; noise of explosions of, 277; bombs from, 277; Sapichu vent of, 278;

most violent activity of, 278; height of cone of, 280; 1944 lava flows from, 282–286; San Juan flow of, 284–286; outline of lava fields of, 286–288; *boca* of Juatito, 288; *boca* of Ahuan, 288; slumping of segment of cone of, 288; 1945–1952 lava flows from, 286–289; final activity of, 289–290; duration of eruptive activity of, 290; volume of eruptive products of, 290; composition of lavas of, 290–291; geologic setting of, 291–292; not a parasitic cone, 291; mentioned, 4

Pele, Madam: legend of, 13; mentioned, 229

Peléan type of eruption: defined, 35; Krakatoa as example of, 78–85; Coseguina as example of, 85–91; character of, 116; La Soufrière as example of, 120–127; significance of, 158; mentioned, 213

Pele's hair: 48

Perret, Frank A.: life of, 26–27; and observatory at Mount Pelée, 27; on mobility of *nuées ardentes*, 116

Perthshire, Scotland: 20

Phlegraean Fields, Italy: craters of, 132, 302; in classic literature, 132–133; crater lakes of, 133; structural setting of, 168–169; spacing of volcanoes of, 372–373; mentioned, 130, 329

Phreatic eruptions: of Kilauea, 28, 232; cones developed by, 314, 314 n

Pico Volcano, Azores: 310

pino: defined, 34; mentioned, 158, 159, 160, 163, 199

plateau basalts: 54–55

Pleistocene: 329

Pliny the Elder: life of, 136–137; death of, in Pliny's letters, 138; mentioned, 16

Pliny the Younger: life of, 135–136; letters of, to Tacitus, 138–144; comments on letters of, 144–145; mentioned, 16, 34, 35

Plinian phase: defined, 34–35; in eruption of Hekla, 253

Plutonists: 18, 21

Pocock, Professor L. G.: 182

Pompeii, Italy: A.D. 63 earthquake damage at, 135; nature of debris over, 147–148; excavations of, 148–156 *passim;* loss of life at, 149; discovery of, 150–152; discovery of first skeleton at, 154; Civita established as, 154; mentioned, 9

porphyry: texture of, 57

powers of ten: 251 n

Pulido, Dionisio: 275, 276

pumice: origin of, 45, 47; examples of eruption of, 47; in eruption of Noyöe Volcano, 314; mentioned, 9

Puna, Hawaii: 237, 240, 241

Puy de Dome, France: crater-elevation theory and, 23; observations of von Buch at, 23

pyroclastics: definition of, 8; classification of, 44

—distribution of: by Krakatoa, 48–49; by Parícutin, 50. SEE ALSO ash; blocks; bombs; cinders; lapilli

pyrometer: optical, 53; thermoelectric, 54

pyromagma: 231

radioactive materials: as source of heat, 326, 387

reefs. SEE atoll; barrier reef; fringing reef

Resina, Italy: 152, 156

Reykir, Iceland: hot springs of, 354, 356

Reykjavík, Iceland, municipal hot water system of: springs for, 354; wells for, 354–356; temperature of water of, 356; insulation of pipes of, 356; distribution methods of, 356; cost of, 356

rhyolite: defined, 52; mentioned, 379

Riaño, Antonio de: and description of Jorullo, 298–299

ring dikes: and caldera formation, 75

Rittman, A.: 35

Roccamonfina Volcano, Italy: 329

Roccastrada, Italy: 338, 339

root formation: in convection hypothesis, 392; and gravity anomalies, 399; mentioned, 391

Rotokaua, New Zealand: steam resources of, 350

Rotorua, New Zealand: steam area of, 344

Ruapehu Volcano, New Zealand: dates of eruptions of, 344; mentioned, 342

Russia: natural steam in, 364; Kamchatka region of, 364

Sabatini Volcano, Italy: 329

Sabrina Island, Azores: submarine eruption of, 311

St. Lucia Island, Lesser Antilles: natural steam prospects of, 362, 364

Salina, Aeolian Islands: cone of, 178

salt domes: and gravity meters, 396, 398; of Spindletop, 396; of Barbers Hill, 396; of Damon Mound, 396

Samoa Islands: submarine eruptions of, 308; structural alignment of, 342

San Andreas fault, California: 358

San Guiseppe, Italy: destruction of, in 1906, 164

San Jacinto Volcano, Nicaragua: 364

San Juan Parangaricutiro, Mexico: town of, 282; covered by lava, 282

San Sebastiano, Italy, destruction of: in 1872, 163; in 1944, 165–166; by lava flow, 268

Santa María Volcano, Guatemala: tholoid of, 23

Santiago Volcano, Nicaragua: 85

Santorin Volcano, Greece, engulfment theory and, 72; mentioned, 371

Sapichu, Parícutin Volcano, Mexico: *boca* of, 278, 288; breached cone of, 278–280

Sapper, Karl: 30

Sassoforte, Italy: 339

Sáyago, D. Manuel Roman: report on eruption of Jorullo, 293–297 *passim*

Sciacca, Sicily: 337

438 VOLCANOES

Sciara del Fuoco, Stromboli: origin of, 194

scoria: 55

Scrope, G. Paulett: classification of volcanoes by, 32

sector graben: 148

seger cones: temperature measurements with, 231; mentioned, 54

seismograph. 242

Sellfoss, Iceland: municipal hot-water system of, 356

Servicio Geológico Nacional de El Salvador: 364

Shakespeare, William: quotation from, 14

Shapley, Harlow: quotation from, 16

shard structure: 48

shear zone: and deep-focus earthquakes, 375–377; 393; and movements of continents, 377; slope of, from island arcs, 375; slope of, from earthquakes, 377

Shepard, E. S.: 28, 39

shield volcano: lava dome of, 214; of Mauna Loa, 217; of Kilauea, 228; Tancítaro, Mexico, an example of, 291; in the Azores, 310

Ship Rock. SEE Bogoslof Volcano, Alaska

sial: thickness of, 59, 380; composition of, 59, 379; origin of name, 379; and ocean basins, 380; and continental volcanoes, 381; root formation of, 391; absence of, in ocean, 392; thickening of, in continents, 392; in relation to Andesite Line, 393; in island arcs, 395; in gravity profile of island arc, 399

Siculus, Diodorus: description of Vesuvius, 133

sima: on ocean floor, 59; composition of, 380; thickness of, 380; and ocean basins, 380; and lava from Pacific volcanoes, 380; root formation in, 391; in relation to Andesite Line, 393; in gravity profile of island arc, 399

Skaptar Jökull. SEE Laki Fissure, Iceland

Smith, William ("Strata"): 21–22

Snake River lava plateau: 243–244

Societa Boracifera di Larderello: 330, 339

soffioni: mentioned, 325, 331, 332, 333, 336, 337

Solfatara Volcano, Italy: eruption of, 130; derivation of solfataric stage from, 132; mentioned, 302

solfataric stage: origin of name, 132; at Vulcano, 186

Somma: defined, 135; mentioned, 87 n. SEE ALSO Mount Somma, Italy

Sonoma County, California. SEE The Geysers, California

Sorrento Peninsula, Italy: structural setting, 168–170

Soufrière, Guadeloupe: 99

Soufrière Hill, Montserrat: 97

Southern Antilles island arc: 367, 371

spacing of volcanoes: in Galapagos Islands, 372; in Canary Islands, 372; in Tahiti, 372; in Fiji, 372; in Phlegraean Fields, 372; theory of, 372; in relation to thickness of crust, 372–373

Spallanzani, Lazzaro: 17

Spartacus, the gladiator: in history, 134 n; on Vesuvius, 134

spring gas: role in geyser action, 353

Stabiae, Italy: 135, 154, 154 n

Stazione Termale la Perla, Larderello, Italy: 339

steam: steam-blast eruptions of, at Kilauea, 28. SEE ALSO natural steam

Stoppanni, A.: classification of volcanoes, 32

Strabo: on nature of volcanic activity, 14; description of Mount Vesuvius by, 134

strato volcano: Mount Hekla, an example of, 252. SEE ALSO cones, composite

Stromboli Volcano, Aeolian Islands: as a weatherglass, 25, 175; typical eruption of, 33–34; description of, 192; Sciara del Fuoco of, 194; as Lighthouse of the Mediterranean, 194,

201; eruptive activity of, 194–198; crater of, 197; persistence of vents in crater of, 198; gas-fluxing hypothesis applied to, 198–199; more vigorous eruptions of, 199; Vulcanian-type eruptions of, 199; augite crystals at, 199–200; theories for constant activity of, 200; various eruptive types exhibited by, 200; a visit to, 201–206; mentioned, 4

Strombolian type of volcanic eruption: defined, 33; essential characteristics of, 191; Stromboli, type example of, 192; of Capelinhos Volcano, Azores, 314

structure: of Bay of Naples, 168–169; Italian volcanoes in relation to, 175; of Aeolian Islands, 176–178

subglacial eruptions: of Volcano Katla, 249; of Volcano Grimsvötn, 249; jökulhlaups of, 249

sublimates: 41, 361

submarine eruptions: extent of, 308; new volcanoes by, 308; of Graham Island, 309–310; in the Azores, 310–314; of Falcon Island, Tongas, 314; of Noyöe Volcano, Iceland, 314–316; of Myozin-syo, Japan, 319–322; loss of life in, 319–321

sulphur mining: at Vulcano, 184, 189

sun glows: of Krakatoa, 49; controversy about, 49–50

sunspots: cycles of, 258; daily number of, 258; as volcanoes of the sun, 258; in relation to magnetic storms, 258; years of maxima of, 259; correlation with eruptions of Kilauea, 261

Tacitus: letters to, from Pliny, 138–144; mentioned, 135

Tahiti Islands: spacing of volcanoes of, 372

Tancítaro, Volcano, Mexico: shield-type cone of, 291; age of, 291; Parícutin not a parasitic cone of, 291

Tarawera Volcano, New Zealand: date of eruptions of, 342, 346; mentioned, 340

Tarumai Volcano, Japan: tholoid of, 23

Tauhara Volcano, New Zealand: 342

tectogene: 342

Telica Volcano, Nicaragua: 85, 364

temperature: of lava, 54; color scale of, 53. SEE ALSO pyrometer; seger cones

Tennyson, Alfred: quotation from, 83

Tethys: 384 n–385 n

The Geysers, California: location of, 357; geology of, 357; relation to faulting of, 358; discovery of, 358; temperature of fumaroles of, 358, 360; steam wells of, 360; magmatic origin of steam at, 361; power production at, 362 n. SEE ALSO natural steam; natural steam wells

Thermal Power Company, California: 362

tholoids: of Santa María, Guatemala, 23; of Mount Pelée, Lesser Antilles, 23; of Tarumai, Japan, 23; Usu, Japan, 23; of Bogoslof, Alaska, 318. SEE ALSO lava dome

Thurston Lava Tube, Hawaii: 56

tilt: measurement of, 234; significance of, 234; value of, in predicting eruptions, 234; at Kilauea, 236, 237, 240; mentioned, 225. SEE ALSO tumescence; tilt meters

tilt meters: use of, in predicting eruptions, 240–241; mentioned, 260

Tobago Trough, Lesser Antilles: 97

Tokaanu, New Zealand: steam areas of, 344

Toledo, Pietro Giacomo di. SEE di Toledo, Pietro Giacomo

Tonga Islands: from submarine eruptions, 303; structural alignment of, 342

Tongariro Volcano, New Zealand: 342

Torre Annunziata, Italy: destruction of, by lava, 63; diversion of lava at, 68; destruction of, in 1906, 164

Torre del Greco, Italy: in 1631 eruption of Vesuvius, 159; in 1793 eruption of Vesuvius, 162

Tower of Mount Pelée: 117. SEE ALSO lava domes; Mount Pelée, Martinique; tholoids

Tristan de Cunha Island: 372

tsunami: 320. SEE ALSO earthquakes

tuff: defined, 48. SEE ALSO ignimbrite; pyroclastics

tumescence: measurement of, 234; at Kilauea, 234, 242; at Mauna Loa, 234. SEE ALSO tilt; tilt meters

Tuscarora deep: 374. SEE ALSO Japan Trench

Tyrrhenian basin: in relation to Italian volcanoes, 175

Tyrrhenian Sea: 329

uniformitarianism: doctrine of, 20; Hutton and, 20

University of Texas Research Institute: 273

Usu Volcano, Japan: tholoid of, 23

Vatnajökull, Iceland: 249

Vesuvian Volcano Observatory, Italy: Mercalli and, 30; mentioned, 4, 129

Vesuvius, Italy. SEE Mount Vesuvius, Italy

Vinci, Leonardo da. SEE da Vinci, Leonardo

Virgil: and myths of Mount Etna, 10; on giant Enceladus, 10

volcano: definition of, 8; derivation of name, 11

volcanoes, active: number of, 366; definition of, 366; and fire girdle of Pacific, 367; circum-Pacific belt of, 367, 370; of world, tabulation of, 368–369; concentration of, in Pacific belt, 370; Alpine-Himalayan belt of, 371; spacing of, 372–373

volcanic breccia: 48

Volcanic Caribbees, Lesser Antilles: volcanoes of, 97; geology of, 99

volcanic cycles: of Mauna Loa, 223; relation of sunspot cycles to, 259

—of Kilauea: stages in, 234; as illustrated by eruptions, 235–242 passim; characteristics of, 259–260; engulfment in, 260; periodicity of, 260–262; correlation of, with sunspots, 261

—of Mount Etna: length of, 264; pattern of, 264–265

—of Vesuvius: description of, 159–168 passim; stages in, 265; gas blow-off of, 267; length of, 268

volcanic edifice: definition of, 8

volcanic eruptions: Hawaiian type of, 33; Strombolian type of, 33; Vulcanian type of, 34; Plinian phase in, 34–35; Peléan type of, 35; Icelandic type of, 36; solfataric stage of, 36; water as force in, 401; diffusion of water and, 402; predictions of, 405

volcanic neck: of Graham Island, 310

volcanic observatories: need of, 403. SEE ALSO Hawaiian Volcano Observatory; Vesuvian Volcano Observatory; Perret, Frank A.

volcanic tuff: defined, 48. SEE ALSO ash

volcanic vent: opening of, at Kilauea, 239. SEE ALSO bocas

volcanology: definition of, 16; relation of Pliny the Younger to, 16; early history of, 16–25 passim; modern history of, 25–30 passim; significance of Mount Pelée in, 404–405; applied to geothermal energy, 405–406

von Buch, Leopold: crater-elevation theory of, 23; at Puy de Dome, 23; on Monte Nuovo as example of crater-elevation, 308

von Humboldt, Alexander: 24

von Wolff, F.: 30

Vulcan: forge of, 11, 181; as god of fire, 11, 12

Vulcanello, Vulcano, Aeolian Islands: birth of, 182; as landfall of Odysseus, 182; craters of, 189

Vulcanian type of eruption: defined, 34, 128–129; examples of, 173; Vulcano as example of, 189; characteristics of, 189–190; as used by Mercalli, 190; Parícutin Volcano, as example of, 190; Lassen Peak as example of, 190

Vulcanists. SEE Plutonists

Vulcano, Aeolian Islands: type of eruption of, 34; description of, 178; in mythology, 181; and origin of term *volcano*, 181; early history of, 181; and birth of Vulcanello, 182; in Dark Ages, 183; 1444 eruption of, 183; 18th century activity of, 183–184; sulphur mining in crater of, 184; 1888–1890 eruption of, 184–185, 190; cable breaks by eruption of, 185; cones of, 186; composition of gases from, 188; caldera of, 188; sulphur mining at, 189; mentioned, 337

Vulcanus: 11

Vulsini Volcano, Italy: 329, 338

Vulture Volcano, Italy: 337

Waianae Volcano, Oahu: lava dome of, 213

Waimanga, New Zealand: geyser of, 352

Waiotapu, New Zealand: steam area of, 344; steam resources of, 350

Wairakei, New Zealand: steam wells at, 342, 344; Karapiti blowhole at, 344; exploratory drilling at, 345; sequence of rocks at, 347; relation of steam to structure at, 347; steam traps at, 348; drilling steam wells at, 348; power resources of, 350; power installations at, 351

Warm Springs, Georgia: 326

water: of oceans and atmosphere from plutonic gases, 42; in volcanic activity, 400–401; as force in volcanic eruptions, 401

—in magma: solubility of, 400; distribution of, 400–401; pressure control of, 401; diffusion of, in control of eruptions, 402

water vapor: as eruptive force, 37

—sources of: according to Lyell, 38; according to Daubeny, 38; according to Brun, 38

welded tuff. SEE ignimbrite

Werner, Abraham Gottlob: students of, 18; and universal formation, 18; at Freiberg, 18; theory of, 18–19

Whakatane Fault, New Zealand: location of, 342; volcanic and thermal activity on, 342; alignment of, 342

White Island Trench, New Zealand: location of, 345; structure of, 345–346; earthquakes in, 345; volcanic eruptions in, 346; mentioned, 340

White Island Volcano, New Zealand: dates of eruptions of, 344; mentioned, 342

wind, god of: 174–175

Wolff, F. von. SEE von Wolff, F.

Yap island arc: 374

Yellowstone National Park, United States: cooling of lava beneath, 63; as example of hot springs and geysers, 324; primary steam content in, 326; geysers in, 352; Old Faithful, geyser of, 353

zone of flowage: 376

zone of fracture: 376

Zumpinito formation: 291